gargoyle

number 39/40
20th anniversary issue

editors
Richard Peabody & Lucinda Ebersole

london editor
Maja Prausnitz

staff
Jodi Bloom
Gretchen Sinclair
Joanne Sobieck-Lingg

publisher
Jane Lang

in memoriam
Chandler Brossard
Eva Cassidy
Larry Eigner
Shusaku Endo
Tina Fulker
Maurice Girodias
Essex Hemphill
Herbert E. Huncke
Jan Kerouac
Marvin Malone
Oscar Moore
Joyce Renwick
Edouard Roditi
Claudine Schafer-Legrand
Scott Sommer
Ralph Treitel

gargoyle magazine is published irregularly

by Paycock Press
c/o Atticus Books & Music
1508 U Street, NW
Washington, DC 20009
e-mail atticus@netrail.net
http://www.atticusbooks.com

In London: 152 Harringay Road,
Haringey, London N15 3HL, U.K.
e-mail maja@ursarum.demon.co.uk

Contributors are paid with one copy of the magazine in which their work appears. All rights revert to individual contributors upon publication though *Gargoyle* reserves the right to reprint material in a best of anthology. *Gargoyle* appears in the *Index of American Periodical Verse*.

Price per single issue varies.
Subscriptions are $20 for two issues to individuals;
$25 for institutions.

ISBN: 0-931181-04-6
ISSN: 0162-1149

Special Thanks to Herman Ayayo, Ron Baker, John Bowers, Greg Boyd, Grace Cavalieri, Kate Gale, Forrest Gander, Michael Horovitz, Jordan Jones, Kris & Casey Kane, Jamie Kowalski, Paul Lyalls, Simon Pettifar, David Sheridan, Zenon Slawinski, Liana Sperow, Patrick Tedd, David Trinidad, and Angela Weaser.

Nick Cave's "The Flesh Made Word" is reprinted from the forthcoming volume *King Ink II* (Black Spring Press, 1997). Lynn Crosbie's poems are reprinted from *Pearl,* publ. by House of Anansi Press in 1996. Inga Elsa Laird's poem is reprinted from *A Celebration/Of and For Frances Horovitz* (1938–1983) published by New Departures in 1984. Peggy Pfeiffer's "Harbinger" is reprinted from *WPFW89.3FM Poetry Anthology* (Bunny and the Crocodile Press, 1992).

Design and digital production for the interior of this issue was done by Jodi Bloom and the staff of Studio 405, Washington, DC. This issue was printed by McNaughton and Gunn, Inc., Saline, Michigan.

Gargoyle is distributed by
Bernhard DeBoer, Inc.
113 E. Centre Street
Nutley, NJ 07110.
USA
(201) 667-9300

Distributed in Europe by
Airlift Book Company
8 the Arena
Mollison Avenue
Enfield, Middlesex EN3 7NJ
UK
Phone: 0181-804-0400
Fax: 0181-804-0044

gargoyle

" The fault lines dividing the academic from the nonacademic, the capitalist from the anticapitalist, are not the only fractures that presently threaten the vitality of contemporary fiction. The most decisive issue concerns the rancorous split between the commercial presses and the independent presses. Since that blip on the screen which was the moment of the counterculture, when the American postmodern fiction canon—Barth, et al.—was established, the New York commercial publishing houses have, by keeping faith with their accountants only, jeopardized the meaningfulness of the literary past and the very possibility for a literary future. Marx once said that one of the principal products of capitalism was stupidity. The shit that has regularly cascaded from New York in the course of the last twenty years has performed admirably its task of keeping people stupid. What pride can be taken in a line which has given us Moral Fiction, Minimalism, the Literary Brat Pack, and now Generation X? Commercial publishing has, perhaps, not been as single-minded in this task as has television, but books have offered no one solace for, let alone an alternative to, the egregious cretinism of mass culture. "

— *Curtis White*

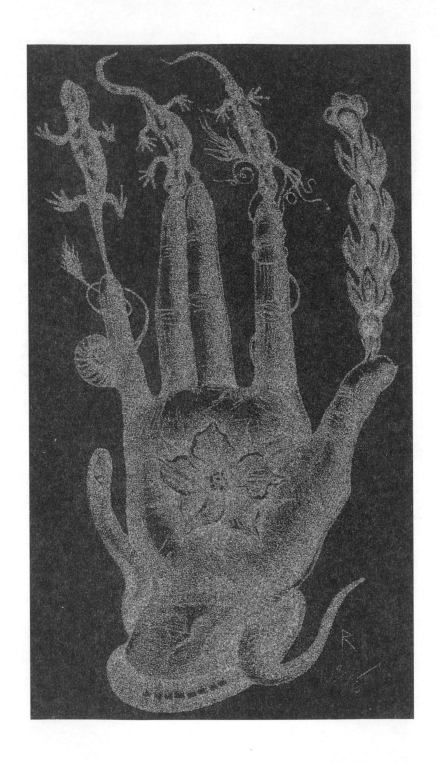

Rikki Ducornet

contents

Nick Cave

The Flesh Made Word
(For BBC Radio 3, July 1996)

Jesus said, "Wherever two or more are gathered together, I am in your midst." Jesus said this because wherever two or more are gathered there is a communion, there is language, there is imagination. There is God. God is a product of the creative imagination and God is that imagination taken flight.

As a child I believed that to use the imagination was wicked. I saw my imagination as a dark room with a large bolted door that housed all manner of shameful fantasies. I could almost hear my secret thoughts bumping and scratching behind the door, begging me in whispers to be let out. To be told. Back then I had no idea that those dark mutterings were coming from God. At eight years old I joined the choir in our local Anglican church and I attended services twice a week for the next four years but the God I heard preached about there seemed remote and alien and uncertain. So I sat in the stalls, in my crimson cassock, while rogue thoughts oozed beneath the bolted door of my imagination.

As I grew older and entered my teens, my now-deceased father decided it was time to pass on to his son certain information. Here I was thirteen years old and he would usher me into his study, lock the door and begin reciting great bloody slabs from Shakespeare's *Titus Andronicus,* or the murder scene from *Crime and Punishment,* or whole chapters from Nabokov's *Lolita.* My father would wave his arms about, then point at me and say, "This, my boy, is literature!" and I could tell by the way it empowered him that he felt he was passing on forbidden knowledge. I would sit and listen to all these mad words pouring from his mouth, happy to be invited into his strange, anomalous world. I would watch my father lose himself in the outpourings of his own creative energy and although he would have laughed at this notion, what my father was finding in his beloved literature was God. Literature elevated him, tore him from normality, lifted him out of the mediocre and brought him closer to the divine essence of things. I had no notion of that then, but I did see somewhere that art had the power to insulate me from the mundanity of the world, to protect me. So I set about writing some really bad poems.

At around fifteen years of age my friends and I formed a rock band and I gave up writing really bad poems and started writing really bad songs instead, and these songs were very much influenced by whatever the book was that I was reading at the time.

After I matriculated I went to Art School and it was there I began to be interested in religious art, largely, I think, because it irritated my instructors, who thought I should be more concerned with contemporary art forms. I had pictures by Grunewald, Fra Angelico, El Greco, Tintoretto and so on plastered around the walls of my work-space and I found, almost to my surprise, that I recognised the biblical scenes depicted in these pictures, knew the key players and their stories, so I went out and bought myself a pocket Bible, the King James Version, opened it up at the first page and began to read it. I found the stories of the Bible calling to me from somewhere in my subconscious, planted there in the choir-boy days of my childhood. I was still writing songs for the band I was in and I soon found in the tough prose of the Old Testament a perfect language, at once mysterious and familiar, that not only reflected the state of mind I was in at the time but actively informed my artistic endeavours. I found there the voice of God and it was brutal and jealous and merciless. For every bilious notion I harboured about myself and the world, and there were a lot of those, there in the Old Testament was its equivalent leaping off the pages with its teeth bared. The God of the Old Testament seemed a cruel and rancorous God and I loved the way He would wipe out entire nations at a whim. I loved to read the Book of Job and marvelled over the vain, distrustful God who turned the life of His "perfect and upright" servant into a living hell. Job's friend Eliphaz observed, "Man is born unto trouble, as the sparks fly upward," and those words seemed to my horrid little mind about right. And why wouldn't man be born into trouble, living under the tyranny of such a God? So it was the feeling I got from the Old Testament, of a pitiful humanity suffering beneath a despotic God, that began to leak into my lyric writing. As a consequence my words blossomed with a nasty, new energy. My band, which was called The Birthday Party, was all heavy bludgeoning rhythms and revved-up, whacked-out guitars and all I had to do was walk on stage and open my mouth and let the curse of God roar through me. Floods, fire and frogs leapt out of my throat. To loosely paraphrase William Blake, "I myself did nothing. I just pointed a damning finger and let the holy spirit do the rest." Though I had no notion of that then, God was talking not just to me but *through* me, and His breath stank. I was a conduit for a God that spoke in a language written in bile and puke. And for a while that suited me fine.

After a few years The Birthday Party fall apart and by this time I had grown weary and my writing too and it was an incredible struggle to squeeze out much at all. I was sick and I was disgusted and my God was in a similar condition. It was hard work loathing everything all the time. All that sustained hatred was a painful and tiring business. I would climb onto the stage and look down at the twisted faces that roared and shook their fists at me in the gloom and all I felt was sick and sad. I decided it was high time I started reading a different book, so I closed the Old Testament and I opened up the New.

There, in those four wonderful prose poems, Matthew, Mark, Luke and John, I slowly reacquainted myself with the Jesus of my childhood, that eerie figure that moves through the Gospels, the Man of Sorrows, and it was through Him that I was given a chance to redefine my relationship with the world. The voice that spoke through me now was softer, sadder, more introspective.

The more I read the Gospels, the more Christ called to my imagination, for His journey was, it seemed to me, just that, a flight of the imagination. Christ who called Himself both the Son of Man and the Son of God, as the occasion warranted, was exactly that—a man of flesh and blood, so in touch with the creative forces inside himself, so open to His brilliant, flame-like imagination, that He became the physical embodiment of that force, God. In Christ the spiritual blue-print was set so that we ourselves could become God-like.

There is that wonderful story in the Gospel of John where the scribes and Pharisees brought to Jesus a woman taken in adultery, and in an attempt to trap Him, asked if the woman should now be stoned under the law of Moses. Christ did not answer straight away but rather stooped down and with His finger wrote on the ground, as though He didn't hear them. The Pharisees persisted and after a time Christ lifted Himself up and answered, "He that is without sin among you, let him first cast a stone at her." And again He stooped down. For me, this seemingly distracted gesture, the stooping and the writing on the ground, is Christ accessing the God in Himself. Christ then delivers the line that disempowers His opponents—and what an extraordinary remark it is—then stoops again to recommune with God. What Christ shows us here is that the creative imagination has the power to combat all enemies, that we are protected by the flow of our own inspiration.

Clearly what Jesus most despised, what He really railed against time and time again, were the forces that represented the established order of things, symbolised by the scribes and Pharisees—those dull, small-minded scholars of religious law who dogged His every move. Christ saw them as enemies of the imagination, who actively blocked the spiritual flight of the people and kept them bogged down with theological nit-picking, intellectualism and law. What was Christ's great bugbear, and what has sat like dung in the doorway of the Christian Church ever since, was the Pharisees' preoccupation with the law, in preference to the *logos*. Said St Paul to the Corinthians, "The letter killeth, but the spirit giveth life." So how can one be elevated spiritually if they are loaded up with the chains of religious jurisprudence? How can the imagination be told how to behave? How can inspiration or for that matter God be moral?

"Woe unto you, scribes and Pharisees, hypocrites," berates Christ in Matthew, "for ye shut up the Kingdom of Heaven against men." And further on He says, "Ye are like unto whited sepulchres, which indeed appear beautiful outward, but are within full of dead men's bones." This was the language of the Lord and it was lines like these, that were at once compassionate and venomous, that I found reverberating through my own words. Christ was forgiving, merciful and loving but He was after all the Son of the Old Testament God and His Father's blood still boiled in His veins. In creating His son, God the Father had evolved. He had moved on. No longer was God's mercy reserved for elect nations and their kings, no longer were the divine rewards handed down to lords temporal and spiritual. Christ, the Son, came as an individual, the Word made flesh, to set right the misguided notions of His Father—or, as Paul wrote to the Corinthians, "God was in Christ reconciling the world to Himself." Christ came to right the wrongs of His Father. Christ, the man, who abhorred the concept of a spiritual elite, spoke to every man. He came with the gift of language, of love, of imagination. Said Jesus, in the Gospel of John, "The words that I speak unto you, they are spirit and they are life," and it is these words, His language, the *logos,* that sings so eloquently and mysteriously from the Gospels. Christ is the imagination, at times terrible, irrational, incendiary and beautiful—in short, God-like.

And so, like Jesus, there is the blood of my father in me, and it was from him that I inherited, among other things, a love of literature, of words. And just as Christ was to His Father, I am a generation further on, and, if you'll forgive me, Dad, in evolutionary terms, an advanced version. What my father always wanted to do was to write a book, and in that room where he used to take me and commune with me through the language of others, him giving and I receiving, was a desk which contained the beginnings of several aborted novels, all neatly, sadly, filed and titled. When I was about twelve my father asked me, weirdly, what I had done to assist humanity. I had no idea what he was talking about but turned the question around and asked him what he had done. He said he had written a couple of short stories that had been published in magazines and I shared in his pride as he showed them to me. But I noticed that the magazines were of an earlier decade and it was clear that these two short stories were tiny seeds planted in a garden that did not grow.

In 1985, I went to live in Berlin where I got it into my head to write a novel, and for the next three years I locked myself away in a room in Kreuzberg and wrote it. I called it *And the Ass Saw the Angel.* It was about a mad, hermetic mute boy called Euchrid Eucrow, who, having been denied the faculty of speech, eventually explodes in a catharsis of rage and brings to its knees the religious community in which he lives. The story, set in the American South and told through the voice or non-voice of Euchrid Eucrow, was written in a kind of a hyper-poetic thought-speak, not meant to be spoken—a mongrel language that was part-Biblical, part-Deep South dialect, part-gutter slang, at times obscenely reverent and at others reverently obscene. Throughout the story, God fills the mute boy with information, loads him up with bad ideas, "hate inspiration straight from God" as he calls it, but with no one to talk to and no way to talk, Euchrid, like a blocked pipe, bursts. For me, Euchrid is Jesus struck dumb, he is the blocked artist, he is internalised imagination become madness.

God is not found *in* Christ, but *through* Him. In the Gospel of Thomas, the Gnostic scripture discovered at Nag Hammadi in Egypt in 1945, Christ states that "the kingdom is inside of you and it is outside of you." This statement must have terrified early Christian ministry as it rendered them obsolete—why do we need the church to bring us close to God when He already lives within us?—and hence the Nicene Council's decision not to allow it into the New Testament canon. Apart from the sheer subversiveness of this statement, what is really so remarkable about it is the emphasis it places upon our individual selves. Rather than praising a personal and supernatural God as an all-mighty, all-knowing, all-seeing force existing somewhere in the great beyond, the emphasis is placed clearly on man, that without him as a channel God has nowhere to go.

"Wherever two or more are gathered together, I am in your midst," Jesus said. Just as we are divine creations, so must we in turn create. Divinity must be given its freedom to flow, through us, through language, through communication, through imagination. I believe this is our spiritual duty made clear to us through the example of Christ. Through us God finds His voice, for just as we need God, He in turn needs us. God found life through my father as he raved and flailed about his study reciting his favourite literature, but died in the desk drawer that contained those pages, the first painful contractions of his stillborn dreams. My father asked me what I had done to assist humanity and at twelve years old I could not answer. I now know. Like Christ, I too come in the name of my father, to keep God alive.

Reprinted from the forthcoming volume
King Ink II (Black Spring Press, 1997)

Joan Haverty Kerouac

from Nobody's Wife

Chapter 13

On Tuesday, November 14, we went to City Hall to get the license, and Jack found he was missing some important papers concerning the annulment of his first marriage to Frankie Edith Parker. He called the attorney who had handled the case, and then had to wait for a return call to confirm the fact that her father had indeed had the marriage annulled. The clerk's office stayed open 34 minutes beyond closing time to accommodate us.

So on Friday, November 17th, we were 34 minutes short of the required 72-hour waiting period, and City Hall was closing for the weekend. Jack was furious.

"Do you mean you can't stay open another 34 minutes?" he asked the clerk.

"The judges have all gone home," she explained. Jack walked ahead of me down the stairs, pouting.

"We can get married on Monday, Jack." I tried to be helpful.

"But the reception's tonight! You don't have a wedding *after* a reception. And there's the beer keg waiting. And all those people! Why does everything have to go wrong?" I smiled, amused at his outburst, as he threw his cigarette butt into the gutter angrily and scowled at me as though it were my fault. "And you laugh!" he shouted. "Why are you laughing?"

I composed myself and made a suggestion. "Why don't we just go back and *tell* them we got married? Then the beer can be drunk and everybody will be happy."

"You're not serious!" he said.

"I'm not? Okay, what'll we do?" We walked aimlessly, but in a general uptown direction, and I realized I had forgotten to get my new shoes. Just as well. These were comfortable, even if they didn't match my suit.

"I know!" Jack spun around. "We can go to a judge I know. Come on!" We ran to a subway entrance and in a few minutes we were in the Village, running up the exit stairs. "I'll just make a phone call and we'll be all set," he said, still running and steering me toward a Walgreen's. Once inside I stopped at a greeting card display and let him sprint ahead to the phones while I put on a browsing attitude and caught my breath.

Jack pulled the door to the phone booth closed, then opened it to look around for me.

"Come over here!" he ordered loudly, when he had located me. I bristled at his dictatorial tone, and took my time getting there.

"Now don't go away!" he said irritably.

"Did you think I was trying to escape?"

"Shhh!" He was dialing.

Arrangements made, we went to Horatio Street to be married by Judge Vincent Lupiano, a relative of Jack's by marriage.

"Do you want hearts and flowers?" he asked. "Or shall we just get it over with?"

"Any way you want to do it will be all right, Judge." Jack was easy to please now that his objective was in sight. The judge called in his wife and secretary as witnesses, and we got it over with. Jack's mother's ring, blessed by the Pope, was on my finger, and the judge poured each of us a shot. After the marriage certificate was signed, Jack took my arm and prepared to leave.

"Thanks a lot, Judge," he said.

"I'm still waiting for you to kiss your bride, Jack," the judge remarked.

"Oh yeah. That's right." He kissed me perfunctorily and said, "Now *that's* taken care of."

In the hallway I told him, "I'd like to get my shoes on the way back."

"Sure!" He was all smiles now. "There's a Thom McCan's just a coupla blocks from here."

✳

The reception was well underway when we arrived. Some two hundred people were packed into the loft, and they hadn't found it necessary to wait for us in order to celebrate. Nobody even noticed our arrival till we got to the kitchen. Lucien Carr, Allen Ginsberg, Bill Frankel and John Holmes were in there by the beer keg. Holmes introduced me to his wife, Marian, a vivaciously attractive girl with straight honey-colored hair and a scintillating smile full of perfect white teeth. We all piled into the breakfast nook where Jack and I, conspicuous in our sobriety, received best wishes and congratulations, delivered in varying degrees of sincerity. Marian stretched full length across three of our laps to give Jack an elaborate wedding kiss, and Holmes presented us with a bottle of champagne, saying over and over, "I believe in you, Jack and Joan. I believe in you."

Perhaps he felt we needed the support. We had so little understanding of the action we had just taken. Jack and I knew individually what we were doing but we had not discussed our motives, even with each other. The one concession I had asked of him was that he refrain from the meaningless declarations of love he thought were expected.

His requests of me had not been verbalized, but I knew even from the few days I had known him that he wanted me to listen to everything he had to say, without contribution or criticism. Beyond this we were playing it by ear. We had made a commitment to the marriage, but none to each other.

Halfway through his first drink Jack began to mimic the drunken state he aspired to. He assumed an expression of innocent glazed-eyed surprise with eyebrows raised and one finger in the air to command attention. His look said, "But wait!," as though he were performing a magic trick. I had witnessed this transformation of speech and gesture after as few as three swigs of beer, and would have believed he was actually drunk if I hadn't been monitoring his consumption. It was not an act—it was more like a conditioned response.

I wandered around the loft to see who was there that I knew. Our reception was typical of a well-advertised party, in that most of those present were uninvited. An unsmiling studious-looking girl intercepted me, possibly because of my corsage, to ask "Where is the bride?"

"Right here," I said.

"Oh dear!" Her eyes took in my conservative pin-checked suit. "I was expecting something more festive!"

There were wedding gifts to be unwrapped and more friends of Jack's to meet. It hadn't occurred to me to invite Sarah or anyone else I knew. The whole thing had been Jack's idea, and I had seen it as his party, and his wedding for that matter, and let him plan it. None of it seemed to have anything to do with the rest of my life. I felt that I had walked onto a stage set, and I half-expected to walk behind the beer keg and find that it was just a prop, real only from the vantage point of the audience. The room was full of extras I had never seen before, and in a short while they would leave the set and the main characters would resume their real identities.

It finally came to an end early Saturday morning. The last guests found their way noisily down the stairs and I was left with the star of the show. He sat on the bed, raving to himself, falling over from time to time and then righting himself.

"Donsha wanna wear diaphanous gowns?" he inquired, no longer focusing. He raised one finger in the air to explain, " 'S...," and then forgot what he was explaining.

"I know," I told him. "It's W.C. Fields."

" 'S right!" he said, hiccuping. " 'S doubla see feels. Wesher nightie?"

"I'll show you my nightie when you show me your pajamas."

"Sin err." He waved an arm in the direction of his suitcase. I got them out and threw them to him. He smiled vacantly at his pajama top as he held it up for my inspection and then fell over on it.

"No you don't!" I shook him. "Get your pajamas on!" If he woke up in his clothes, tomorrow would be disastrous. "I'll get your shoes off. You do the rest." I pulled off his shoes and went into the kitchen to put away the perishables. Hearing no sound from Jack, I called to him.

"Jack! Are you getting your pajamas on?"

"Uh," was the answer I got.

I found that he had taken his clothes off, at least. That was a good start. "Come on, Jack." I helped him. "First this arm. Then this leg. Now under the covers with you!"

"Wesher nightie?"

"I'm getting it on now." I turned out the bedside lamp on my way to the bathroom and put on the "diaphanous gown" Jack had insisted I buy for the occasion. By the time I got into bed he was completely out. So far, the marriage had lived up to my expectations.

✳

Daylight revealed muddy tracks from one end of the loft to the other. Hundreds of feet had walked through the beer from the dripping spigot. I got into my jeans and hung the fragile nightgown on the hook in the bathroom.

The kitchen had gotten the worst of it. I'd start there while the coffee perked. I filled a basin with suds and began sponging at one end of the room.

"Hey! What are you doing up so early?" Jack called from the bed. "Come back here!"

"Not till I get this floor washed."

"Floor washed? You have to wash the floor the morning after our wedding?"

"You should see it!" I said.

He got up, put on a plaid bathrobe and stood at the edge of the tiled floor.

"The black ones don't look too bad," he observed. "Just the white ones."

"Why don't you wash the black ones then, and I'll wash the white ones?"

"You can't be serious! I haven't even had my coffee!"

"After the floor," I said mercilessly.

"Then will you come back to bed? I didn't even see you in your nightgown last night. Too dark. Can we have our coffee in bed?"

"Sure."

"All right. Give me the other sponge. I'll start at this end."

I poured some suds into another pan and set it with the sponge at his end of the kitchen. We squatted opposite each other, working our way toward the middle.

"Jack! Your tail's in the water!" I laughed as he extracted his bathrobe tie from the suds and held up its dripping tassel, regarding it sadly.

"This is a terrible way to start married life," he said.

"It is?"

"How are you feeling this morning anyway?"

"What do you mean?"

"Well, last night...I mean, it was our wedding night. Was I...Was everything all right?" He looked at me shyly and then applied the sponge to the floor industriously. I scrutinized his face.

"Jack, I don't know how to say this, but you're..." It was my turn to look down at the floor in embarrassment. "Well...you're everything I could have wanted in a husband."

"Yeah? Let's get finished here and get back to bed. You'll put that pretty nightie back on?"

19

"Of course."

"You'll probably have to do this side over later." He was losing his balance, slipping and sliding around on the wet floor. Finally he reached the middle. "How's that coffee? Boy, I must have tied one on last night. What a head I've got!"

I tiptoed across the floor to get the coffee pot, and he got back under the covers with a groan. I brought our coffee to the bedside table and sat down.

"Thought you were going to put on your nightie," he reminded me.

"I don't want my coffee to get cold."

"It won't. Hurry so you'll be right back."

After a couple of sips, I went back to the bathroom to change. Approaching the bed, I was conscious of Jack's appraisal. There was something humiliating about being looked at like that, being judged like a horse. Was I high in the withers? How were my flanks? Oh well, I had brought it on myself. I walked awkwardly to minimize the effect of the nightgown and got into bed.

"Ah, lovely, lovely. Now you look like a bride."

"I should have worn it at the reception."

There was laughter in the hall as feet tramped up the stairs and fists pounded on the door.

"All right, you lovers! You've been in bed long enough!" It was Lucien's voice.

"Aw, wouldn't you know!" Jack said, getting up. "Why does everything have to go wrong?" He opened the door to admit Lucien and Allen.

"Rise and shine!" Allen said. "We came to help you drink that other bottle of champagne."

"Throw me my robe, will you, Jack?" I asked.

He brought it to me and apologized, "Sorry. We'll get back to this later."

While they popped the cork in the kitchen, I changed in the bathroom for what I hoped would be the last time, and I wondered how far I should go in dispelling Jack's fear that he might disappoint or deprive me. So far there was nothing in the marriage that could be destroyed by the knowledge that I was as uninterested as he was. But I couldn't predict his reaction, didn't know how it would affect the future. The wall was nothing more than a sheet of fiberboard, and I could hear Jack saying,

"Man, we wailed all night! Sweetest little girl in the world!"

"And the floor's clean!" Allen said. "What did you do, Jack? Make her wash the floor before she went to bed?"

"Ah, she's a real woman. I tell you, that little girl can do anything!"

I joined them and poured myself a glass of champagne, and I spoke to Allen. "Remember what Celine said? 'All women are housemaids at heart.'"

"Now!" said Jack. "The next order of business is to get my desk moved in here."

Richard McCann

A Late Moment, on the Phone

This is the vow I have made to her: I will phone my mother every day.

She is seventy-nine. She lives in a nursing home—a "life-care facility," as the staff calls it. Her third husband has died.

If I don't feel like calling, I hear a voice within me that accuses: "She is Seventy-nine. Why can't you call your mother once a day?"

But when I call, she says, "I thought the phone would never ring. The phone hasn't rung once today." Her collections of complaints and sorrows. Her brittle diabetes. Her inability to lift herself from a chair or to walk across a room unaided, since fracturing her hip four months ago. Her fear that the night nurse is stealing from her, since she can find neither her extra brassieres nor the five dollar bill she hid in her bureau. Her hair, which the nursing assistants who comb it have almost ruined, she says, since they don't respect its natural wave. I am her only friend, she says, now that her other friends and family have died.

As for her neighbors, the other "seniors" whose lives I glimpse each time I come down the corridor, since they're not supposed to close their doors: "They just talk small talk," she says. "You know how I hate small talk. You know how I am."

Her refrain, indirect, half-voiced: *You are the only one who remembers me when I was young. You're the only one who can see me now...*

"If you hadn't called," she says, "I would have been alone. If you hadn't called—"

It is my job to keep her from vanishing. "Do you remember the time I was photographed by *LIFE*?" she asks, although she was photographed by *LIFE* before I was born, when she still lived in what she called her "bachelorette apartment" in New York City. She says she dreams that her mother is sitting at the foot of her bed at night, wearing a silver fox coat. "You are an old woman," her mother whispers to her, while stroking her hand.

She says I know how to cheer her up, the way my father did. She calls me by the name of my brother who is dead.

Repetitions, aphasic fragments, memories that no one shares. The name of a Jewish girl who lived on her block. The color of a dress she wore to a school dance. A line from a poem her brother carried in his wallet. I am an ear pressed to the phone. I too am vanishing.

How long will we talk tonight? Thirty minutes? An hour? Now she is telling me what she was served for dinner—Chicken á la King on toast, followed by pineapple chunks. Now she is telling me the nurse jabs her with the lancet when she tests her blood sugar. Now she is telling me she has always had a few enemies, though she isn't sure why.

My friends advise me: "When you talk to your mother, you should do something else, like writing checks and paying bills."

And this is what my support group tells me: "You shouldn't talk to her at all, if you don't want to."

Someone in my support group volunteers his analysis: "She's always been a narcissist. You must learn to set limits. You don't owe her your life, you know."

Yes, of course, the others agree: I must learn to set limits. I must set limits now.

They know how it was; how it was back then, in the years after my father died, when my mother kept to her room, devoting herself to the lyrical mysteries of the big band music that issued from her bedside radio. Those nights, even the silence around her said *Save me.*

Sometimes she came downstairs, so I could set her hair. "Do you think I'd look all right with bangs?" she'd ask. If her hair was right, she thought, she'd get hired by a department store.

Her insomnious nights, stalking the house with sudden rages and accusations; or sitting on the edge of my bed, quietly discussing her dates: "His eyes looked haunted. Don't you think he looked like Glenn Ford?" Anxious nights, dense with yearning and recriminations; nights sitting on the front stoop, chain-smoking Parliaments. Sometimes, when she woke me in the morning, she said, "I'll tell you what I dreamed."

What now could relieve that mother and son? I have not released them. I must learn to set limits.

But each time I think this, something rises within me, wild and primitive: Why must I set limits now? Why now, so close to the end? Who would that be punishing?

It is true, what my mother told me: Because I will know her even after she dies, I will know her twice as long as she knew me. That's what it means to be the child, she said.

Should I draw a line in chalk on the hospital floor?—*Mother, you will not cross this line, you with your terrible old age and your terrible dying. Mother, I'm over here, alive…*No, better I should be like those I once read about in a book on middle ages, the ordinary ones, the ones who drew close to the bedsides of the dying, awaiting the mystery to be revealed.

"I'll tell you a secret," my mother whispers now into the phone.

What secrets could you have left? Who hurt you now? Whom do you blame? But all right, I will help you live a little longer. I will listen to what you want me to hear.

She says she's been dreaming of her father. Perhaps she is dreaming a memory she says, but she can't be sure. "I see myself sitting upstairs in my childhood room," she says. "It's early morning. It's the morning after my father left us, although I don't know that yet. I won't know that until I come downstairs. I'm just thinking how much I love my room. I am thinking I will love my room forever, no matter what."

Perhaps she is warning me of her death. She says she loved her father very much.

"When I came downstairs the whole world changed," she says. "But I can see that room so clearly. It is just as it was. The flocked wallpaper and the painted floor. The hand mirror. The beaded lamp shade."

Gregg Shapiro

Defending Karen Carpenter

In the basement of Bobby and Richie's parents' two-flat, after we'd finished our daily rehearsals to all-boy garage-staged shows where we'd lip-synch and pretend to strum guitars and run our fingers across keyboards that weren't plugged in to electric outlets (in much the same way The Partridge Family did) we'd huddle together, not touching like football players did (although I would have if someone had asked) and open our flies to expose ourselves and compare our individual and collective growth of a less obvious nature. I often thought about Karen Carpenter, how she wouldn't have passed judgment on us, how she wouldn't have screamed and yelled at us, the way Bobby and Richie's grandma did that time when we didn't hear her sneak up on us from behind.

At the onset of puberty, I found myself expending an awful lot of energy in defense of Karen Carpenter. With my voice cracking, and my legs still weak from the growing pains of the night before (pain so great, I imagined myself riding to Lincoln Junior High School on the school-bus-yellow Dodge van with the handicapped kids and playing wheelchair basketball in gym class), I was vocal in my opposition to anyone who dared to put down the dark-haired angel from Downey.

Like when Gary, the sexy, skinny, scary older guy who lived across the alley from Bobby and Richie with his creepy sisters and even creepier parents would invite us over and give us things just for the chance to run his sexy, skinny, scary fingers over our rapidly metamorphosing bodies. It was Gary who supplied me, the bookish one, with contraband copies of *The Exorcist* and *The Godfather,* two books that instilled a fear of Catholicism in me, a fear greater than that of the devil, the mafia or child molesters. Karen would have understood the small price I paid for knowledge and experience, a gnawing quest as persistent and bottomless as appetite.

I believe it was Karen Carpenter who saved me from thinking about how the white blonde hair I was born with darkened a quarter of a shade with every birthday. My only distinguishing mark in a family of mousy-haired dullards, taken away without my permission. How my younger brother continued to pummel me into submission in front of his friends as well as my own. I would listen to Karen complain beautifully about "Rainy Days & Mondays," while I rubbed the aching, just punched parts of my arms, chest and stomach, and know that if anyone could save me from the cruelty of the world, it was Karen Carpenter.

And when I began to deprive myself of food, part contest, part punishment, it was Karen's dulcet tones that harmonized with the singing from my shrinking belly. I believe it was Karen Carpenter who, without much fanfare, died for my, for all of our sins.

Annie Adjchavanich

Portfolio   3 Photographs from the series <u>Biological Men</u>

Ann as Marilyn

Boy Marilyn

Hope

Patience Agbabi

Pain Doesn't Hurt

PAIN
DOESN'T
HURT

he said
as he stubbed out
his cigarette
on his hand

as you
smack Smack SMACK
till I'm smacked out
on endorphines
you on adrenaline

pain doesn't hurt

it's a hit
a high
a hunger
it centres me
it's ecstasy

where you find passion
you'll always
find pain

I wanted to be touched
but no-one touched me
hands stroked tickled
the surface of my psyche

I wanted to be touched
so he fucked me
filled me
empty

My mother's nipple
forced solids
down my throat
to make me
BLACK Black black

and I clenched my soul
and retched up
my ancestors

Africans
who were whipped like dogs
and wept
for Africa

as those marks of civilization
were forged
skin deep

and ancestors
from pre- free ancient times
censored to a whisper

I wanted to be touched
by their sun
protected by their python

so injected black on black
hieroglyphic pain
and pain doesn't hurt

Emancipate yourselves
from mental slavery
Marley sang

my mind aches
to understand
itself

Pain doesn't hurt
in context
it's a medieval
blood-letting
in a modern day
complex setting

Pain doesn't hurt
where there's respect
for the deep dark
soul of
my sex

it's ritual
tribal
mutual
consensual
sensual

and I'm in limbo
so sate my libido
till my lips pour libation

where you find paSSiOn
you'll always find pain

don't leave my
mind on the rack
I want your smack
I want you to carve
a love heart
into my black
bark back

but
remember my roots
never forget
as you stub out
your silk cut
cigarette

as you light
your white candle
flame

where you find passion
you'll always
find pain

September 1994

Elizabeth Alexander

Washington Etude

After rain, mushrooms
appear in the park
but you can not eat them.

1967,
the year of the locust.
They come to Northwest

Washington by millions
and for days I crunch
shed husks beneath my feet

as they rattle and hiss
their rage from the trees.
Baby teeth bite baby

onion grass and honey-
suckle nipples, tiny
tongue balancing

the clear, sweet drops.
I am a humming-
bird, a cat who laps

cream from a bowl.
Dandelions
are yellow one day,

white the next. A mud-
puddle surrounded
by brambles and black-

berries is where God lives.
Buttercups under
my chin tell me all

I need to know. Nothing
blue occurs naturally
in Washington, someone

says, and I believe it.
I'm put to bed
when it's still light

and hear other children
playing out my window,
watch daylight bow,

regard the flare
of blooming stars,
the cicada's maraca.

Bob Arnold

Treasure

it's snow
falling

into her
hair

pail of
grain

pinning
onto a

heavy
wool

shirt
walking

back from
the hen

house
eggs

inside her
mittens

Jeanne Marie Beaumont

She Speaks from Experience

Felt like I
was a word being
erased. Itched every which
way, brushed
aside, blown off.

Later, I turned
calm & blank or
never blank again.
A disinterested third party
who witnessed second thoughts.

The word love
can be erased
just as the words
suitcase or serene or
is there a difference.

In this book
were many such words,
a whole spectral language
to be reformulated.
Old rubbings.

But the rubber-tongued
could never utter them
without further diminishment
although they twisted with pleasure
& their intentions were pure.

Photographing the Dolls

I wanted to invent a record,
one worth filing in a historical museum
of the future age.
If there was light from the window,
I used that,
or if lamps were lit
lending golden tints of posterity, good, good.

I pursued true illusion—
a recreation where the fake
takes on the psychic heft of the past.
Through each nuance of position: head
tilt, glance sideways,
balance on a half-inch foot
      —Look, I realize
they might all seem the same to you,
but I was schooled in subtle-
ties, out of fashion at the time as Latin
or home ec, which I skipped.
If you fail

to be charmed, it
matters little.
For myself I shod them, posed them,
shot them, exposed them.
From me they received books to read,
bouquets, a made bed, dessert.
I hung their walls with paper and pictures
and built them a room. Gave them friends
in abundance, conversations freeze-
framed for their tiny eternity.

Soon, a house. That is, many rooms.
The house made these words.

Paul Bennett
In the dark between dreams

A cat
aloof by daylight
deftly steps, one-two
across the woman's mounded hip
butts the man's fretful hand, and
kneads the hollow behind his knee
right paw, left paw, right paw
the both of them
probing for
comfort

The woman
nudged by the cat's passing paws
into a shallow backwater of sleep
slides until she touches bottom
to the belly of the man
and, grounded, drifts
deeper into dreams
of a younger
him

Who
aching to follow
fits his legs to her figure
deepening the hollow
where the cat, after one, two
paw probes more
curls.

Warm sleep wrapped in a dark tale.

James Berry
Bearded Old Sam

At first as if with bared teeth
a jackass had twisted his eyes and jaws

and later with hairy face shrunken
and side of the barefoot chopped
and mended stiff and grotesquely

he staggered about accumulating time
till unexpectedly he died
hugging himself on a village footpath

And that body with the life he inhabited
making that spidery scrawl about the landscape
was the big boss we saw who retired him

James Bertolino

Like Ripe Pear

Come, lie down
where your hair may yearn
into the earth, where fear
is but the last garment you fling.

Columbine & rain, azalea
& sunrise,
the world reaches
with two hands, two wings
over the hills.

Rest for a feathered moment
above the depths, then ease
your long-limbed spirit beyond limitation.
Stand naked
in the river of what is.

Now wave to someone you love.

Like ripe pear, like taut
persimmon,
you fill
with mystical sugars.

Kevin Bezner

To Think of Akira Kurosawa's <u>Dreams</u> One Morning Driving to Work

On the already busy
street

full moon
at dawn

pickup trucks and cars
pass me

by stirring white
Styrofoam

chips that swirl
in the draw

From long cut
peach trees

no petals
will fall

The Boy

When I arrive home, I check all the doors. I look out windows for foot-steps in snow. The door from the outside, not from the garage, in the room behind the kitchen, is unlocked, so I search the house. In the living room, hiding behind the television, is a boy about twelve and a man with a beard about forty. The boy stands up. I ask him whether he understands that he has broken into my house. He says he understands but that he has taken nothing. The man says he saw the boy break-in and kept him from stealing. I tell them I won't call the police but the man must make sure the boy learns discipline. He says I am too tough on the boy. Before I can answer, we are standing in snow to our thighs talking as if it were summer.

Valerie Bloom

Lizards

In youth she lived in fear of
reptiles.

She shunned the nimble poly-lizards,
each a red-gold inch of sensual sway
and suggestive slither,
sashaying boldly over the bedroom walls.

She mapped rights of passage,
bypassing the haunts
of shimmering ground lizards,
rainbow-painted hyphens
playing chicken round her feet.

When she was young,
she burrowed through boscage,
a bright monkey leaping over
bowing branches of starapple trees,
eyes watchful for saurian shapes
among the leaves.

Large brown croakers spoke with the
eerie voice of the obeah-man's cauldron,
the tongue of haunted dreams.

Green lizards,
with skins unnaturally translucent
and eyes that saw too much,
brought the gift of unwanted
pregnancies in their touch.

Once, thirty feet up,
she clasped one in her palm.
Reaching hand over hand
along the flaking roughness
of the branch, she stopped,
unwilling to believe the yielding softness,
the gentle prick of outraged razor on her skin,
the threshing of the captive tail under her fingers,
the purpling of the green.

Uncertain now who landed first.
Winded, they measured each other for a second,
then whirled and fled apart.
Echoes of the scream still rides now on the breeze.

They are different dragons, these
which drive her through the branches
of this mountain ash.

Seeing in the pale-green serrated foliage
the rounded bronze of
starapple leaves,

she contemplates the drop.

Katherine Burger

Paying For Your Girlhood Sins

All night long you visit once again
the narrow halls of The Museum of Menstrual Cramps.
Your feet tap an anxiety rag
on the slick, ungiving fundamental fact
of the unseeable pain crinkling in your abdomen
—fireworks misfiring like God's judgment
into the crowd of spectators, pudgy as bread,
a hotdog suspended between each hand
and each astonished mouth, opened in a pantomime of "oh"
so wide the saints could all go marching in.

You turn a corner like a fugitive;
a stairwell lurches down another level.
You find a room whose lock and key
have rusted through from damp salt air
that seeped in from the sea confined below.
This room has not been opened since you put away
those childish things
        a pile of Little Lulu comics tied with Xmas twine;
        your confirmation dress, its petals brown with age,
        a bruised white rose;
        a peevish girl on a disheveled bed,
        one thin wrist pressed against her fevered cheek
        while elephants on tightropes thud through her head.
A childhood playmate you had snubbed is there;
her blue eyes still brim up and spill.
Tears splat like stars on the dark concrete
        like rosettes of blood between your legs.
There is a the boy who rimmed the inner furls
of your left ear with his deft tongue
one Saturday during the matinee
and a secret chamber in your loins torqued open
like an avid flower straining for the rain.

48

A rainstorm broke one afternoon when you were ten.
The kids ran scattershot like bouncing peas
but little Jonnie Rivas spun round and round
in the amazing rain,
called "Olly olly oxen freeee"
in a voice so pure, so smash with happiness
that you knew this must be what love is like
and stood redlight redlight 1 2 3
while rain ran down your head, your neck, and to your toes
and washed away whatever sins you might have had.

Michael Collier

Moon Valley Country Club

After he walked through the arcadia door, unscathed,
like a saint, like someone materializing out of the fifth
dimension, the wall of glass parting in thousands

of deadly splinters, falling in front and behind him,
he turned to all of us watching from Tim Sawdey's
living room, and straightening himself, extended

his arms in a full benediction, hands upturned
balancing beer cans, like a chalice and ciborium,
and then he bowed and curtsied. And when

he straightened again, we could see the blood
drain from his face, cheeks and lips a gravid blue,
and his legs wobbly at the knees, so that when he stepped

back through the jagged maw of the door, as if to make
the glass reassemble, the breakage heal, he collapsed
on the patio and lay in sight of us, as if he'd come

a great distance out of the fairways and traps, skirting
the water hazards, and crossing the greens to perform this trick,
and now it was time for him to lie down and sleep.

In Achilles' Tent

His penis garish in the blue light
of the Sterno flame, a final jerk,
a rasping shudder, and then his hand
milking the rest. And with his dick
still hanging out of his pants, gobs
of sperm, like fat, on the orange ground cloth,
he collected his tributes: cigarettes,
a can of beer, a *Playboy*, then zipped
his pants back up, rolled out his sleeping bag
and said to all of us, "Go on,
leave me alone. Go fuck yourselves."

Lynn Crosbie

Superfly

Make your mind what you want it to be.
                    —Curtis Mayfield

Tired of waiting for him, I think of a plan to stick it to the
Man—he waylaid me with promises: protection, his valuable keys.
Nights of seduction, I would glide to the curb in my customized Eldorado,
black finish and cool bubble top

and turn it over to a superyoung girl with rags and a bucket of soapy
water, with a smile and a dead president, *make it shine my sister.*
He is inside listening to Curtis, his sapphire ring

he brings the moon with him, this cat, and his eyes glow like
mellow stones at my superfly threads. The cashmere white-stitched suit,
the maxi-coat trimmed in fox fur: *vixen,*

my pretty little hat with three blue feather plumes. I let him dig me
        for a while,
and lay a kiss, a spoon of cocaine on him, our secret meetings
a potent rush and I am hip to the hit to his fly hand on my thigh,

my ladies scatter in a cloud of Opium and he tells me,
you know me, I'm your friend.

I thought he was my man—I flash on him in the bathtub, its ledge of
        oils in flasks,
pulling a loofah sponge over my tired shoulders, passing a reefer
        in lemon paper,

on all the tired bitches working his keys, hustling his diamond rocks—
two sets of false eyelashes, micro-minis, freezing their asses off.

My .25 Beretta can't stop him, it's not real, I'm not real to him. He'll
use me up and kill me; I need brains guts and cool;
I put *fur* on your back, my baby, he says.

I am between him and death, *the greatest high of all,* and I ask him
     to step outside.
The pink flakes blow my mind and I turn to him with a flurry
     of karate kicks,
kicking out my left leg I bring him to the ground

and with my foot on the collar of his mohair suit I tell him, I took your
money and signed a contract on you: *I hired the best killers there are—*

men like you—*yeah, if one hair on my gorgeous head is harmed, it's
     all over for you.*
It's all over for you, I think, as I imagine I am Superfly; my mind is
     what I want it to be,
the Man is tired and suddenly he looks

old very, very old as he turns away from me, the things he cannot dream—
my brazen plans, my *body full of love.*

Paul Teale, Mon Amour

My story is a love story, but only those tortured
by love can understand what I mean.
                    —Martha Beck

Before you were apprehended you learned to calculate
statistical averages,
          that two and two would recur at random, I too
matriculate. Blonde on blonde, the malevolent look of love.

I called out to you as they folded you into the armoured car,
my letters secreted to your cell and examined
by censorious guards,

who are heartless and not divine.

You convey your affection with static hands, the demotic of the manacles
the metal links that mediate when I flush each night,
it is like a fever

when your innocent limbs collide with mine, your tender ministrations.
Combing the tangles from my hair, there are scissors placed safely
          behind you,
anaesthetizing me; your endearments enter the fragile tissue

the soft vistas of my wrists and elbows, drawing blood. And you
          draw tremors
on my spine with surgical intention, a theatre of lariats and silver
          duct-tape,
silver is the crown

that compels my silence. I am on my knees, subject to the
          choreography of zippers,
arcane briefs;

you have entered me, the song of angels in my sleep, such pretty girls.
I say that we are meant for each other, because you are blameless,
          your sweet
face an act of contrition, and I

petition for your release, and ask you to see. A room of velvet
        pillows, rich red wine,
opera, solitude. Cruel images hidden under your ties and laces; I will
        be stern, and
forgiving,

men have such obscure desires. Just look at his eyes, as untroubled, as
        clear as the sea that rages
in me; I will confess then, in the shadows of our secret evenings, you are
        not a stranger.
If you are kind to me, there is nothing else.

Their pristine bodies, helpless beneath saws and bindings that are not
        apocryphal,
the shock of flowers on their graves, my delight. Since you have
        spared me, I am singular—
remotely delicate,

your own duplicate, a killer without conscience, with an appetite that
        even you and your vicious
longings cannot requite.

Jim Daniels
Eating Drunk

Six of us crowded in a booth
at The Clock, a 24-hour dive. Drunk
so it doesn't matter if our legs touch.

What do we talk about?
Whoever was in the bar. Whoever wasn't.
Whoever didn't come out for breakfast
after closing time.
                          After awhile it gets
cold-toast sad. Egg-burp sad.

Nobody's gonna get laid tonight.
Nobody's gonna fight anybody
tonight. And the songs we picked
on the jukebox aren't showing up
anywhere. Not enough syrup. Too much.

✳

After dropping off my friends,
I smoke a roach from the ashtray
to try to take the edge off.

The car chills with absence. I crank up
the radio, run a stop sign or two.

✳

Back home, I slam the car door. Above me,
the hazy streetlight's fading out. Almost
light, sky greying.
                          I can feel the food inside me,
the fool inside me, everything mixed up.

✳

The cupboard bare once again,
night crumbs sprinkled in the dust.

Time leans its weariness on my shoulder.
I rub my belly under my shirt for luck,
for loneliness. God bless my shameless meals.
I can't help shoveling it in.

Accept the bacon and the eggs,
accept my loudness and my sadness—
my loudness for my sadness.
I open the fridge to stand
in its light in the dark kitchen.

Maybe that's all I wanted,
to stand in the light. But
while I stand there, I grab
a piece of cheese, shove it in my mouth

because it too is yellow
because nothing ever saves us.

Donna Denizé

Running the Big River

Put in: above a tributary from Mexico, above cross canyons;
take out: where the Rio Grande has been called
wild—scenic. Where help is several hours
or days away. You become a new
being so many miles from others, and
soon realize the river another way.
Today river is quiet and all life
moves slowly between great rocks, canyon
and river, mood and power. As the
 last hill above floodplain fades from view,
something breaks! Loose-drifted sand
disappears, and it's you and river, then
it's just river, taking all past yuccas, hidden except for great stalks
whose white flowers are borne in clusters, past
tree tobacco brilliance, yellow bloom
favoring hummingbirds. Here, in the mystery of river,
where mortal eyes fail, fail to comprehend such largesse,
 soul flows and the mind, caught in momentary
eddys of thought and silence, floats toward
something like prayer: a longing to see life
 that is different—turtle, spotted frog, river dove
or beaver become blessings breaking upon
 heart's yearning to know it is not alone
in the Big Bend; like water, imagination
 fills hidden spaces—track of coyote,
javelina, mountain lion, even
one brave who first bore this heat, and escaped its floods
 to praise Hooded Orioles' golden
crown and white wingbars—one splash
of color in a green floodplain.

Wish you could close your eyes and see
 ducks and falcons looking upstream in mid-air flight,
more certain of direction than people have been.
Close your eyes and
 a door opens on this side of the river, and
sometime before or after passion's
    flood-crest deposited silt
marking boundaries called "private" land, separate lives,
 In the heart that is not visible
 from shore, a door opens, and one can
see humanity's own sharp bends and big grassy

vegas where souls rest and move on
to a good, warm spring, accessible only
when waters are medium or low!

Above the river, sandstone and limestone
weather red; mottled rock and patches of cane
hide the black necked garter, and rattler.
From the river, cliffs tower running into
uplands known by various names, similar
names, confusing features, here even maps
fail! and living river, carved by gravity
 water, heat and cold, mirrors river
living in The Big Bend; the Cave invites, and suddenly,
only you   are foreigner to country of
Spirits whose dance, once upon towering
bluffs, made rocks slide, falls and channels, arroyos,
and warm springs rising from the bank
by a grove of cottonwood trees.

So it is, here. Strange, that above the river
miles from people, you come to know
 humanity as flow, traveling midst hidden dangers,
 each choosing his own Rio Grande, where walls
known by various names and confusing features rise quickly;
 there too, a canyon scarred
and fractured in places, rises from the
river of Arms until all beauty, or mystery
disappears, only pouroffs, rapids
and violent eddys command our eyes,
and so, having floated the soul's rugged lower canyon
                made the entire run without seeing
another human being in canyons
where "*choice is rare*," in the human river that is
crashing beneath us on rocky, stony hearts—
    do we portage, make camp
or simply go, in one, raging flow—content
with taking out, far down river in
a wilderness of dangerous crossings?

Or do we move to warm springs:
 human hearts', longing for life that is different,
life full of blessing and rapture breaking on souls
 praying they're not alone; and wonder this,
do we see city life like desert—
    missing hidden mysteries of hummingbird flight?
Out here, in The Big Bend, choice is rare
and canyons say mostly
"it's the river's flow, in the end,
flow, only flow will decide."

Denise Duhamel

My First Book Was Like My First Baby

since I don't plan to have children. I wanted people to love it
and make a fuss, and, in turn, tell me what a great job I'd done.
My book wasn't reviewed in that many places, and when it was,
one reviewer even called it sloppy. The grandparents weren't as doting
as I'd expected. They went on with their own lives
and didn't buy the book any presents. No one took a picture of me
holding the book in my lap. My husband wasn't jealous
that I was spending too much time with the book. My dog
sniffed the book and walked away, unthreatened. Other books
were getting cooed and fussed over, books cuter and more enchanting than mine.
There is no greater pain for a mother—seeing her child left out. Soon I knew
I had a book that would never accomplish much with its life,
that it wouldn't win prizes or be displayed in prestigious bookstores.
That my book would probably be a drop-out, that I'd have nothing
to brag about when my cousins showed me graduation pictures of their kids.
That my book wouldn't buy me dinner or take care of me
when I grew old. I tried not to let the book sense my disappointment
and love it for the book it was, but it began to have the telltale signs
of depression, hanging out with the wrong crowd,
dressing like a rebel. The book reminded me of myself as a teenager,
but when I told it that it shivered in disgust, blaming me
for bringing it into this world in the first place.

Lines

On our first date, instead of holding my hand, my future-husband looked
at my palm: *Here's your fame line   your heart line   the lucky M*
he said *you were in danger but you are coming out of it now.*
He said it like he meant it, the way the old women in the Philippines
had taught him.   *Now make a fist   these two little lines under your pinky*
these are the two kids you'll have.

My sister keeps waiting
for her third baby.   She has three lines.   Three kids, that's what the palm reader
at Rocky Point told her. *You'll get married next year*
and you'll have three beautiful daughters. My sister laughed and said
I'll get a second opinion because she was just a junior in high school
and sure she was going to college.

She went on the Flume
with her friends. She sat right in the front of the log, the dreaded seat,
the seat for the bravest, the seat where you got the wettest.
She put her hands in the air and screamed. Her sneakers squished
for the rest of the day, her clothes and hair stinking
like the polluted water.

On our first date my future-husband traced
the lines on my palm with his finger and I closed my hand around his
because it tickled.   *If the pad near your thumb is fleshy,* he said,
it means you're very passionate. His own palms were chubby and pink,
his brown fingers tapered and elegant. He wore a silver and turquoise ring.
He said, *You'll get married only once*

but later there'll be an affair.
Now that we're married, he can't find that wrinkle of infidelity.
Our palms change, he tells me, especially our right palms
that mutate through our behavior. He examines the bunch of tiny X's
that look like windshield frost, the wishbones, the spider webs,
the triangle dragon teeth.

My sister will most likely have that third baby.
My husband sees those three lines though my sister groans,
Two are enough. Her oldest is already fourteen, and my sister
is finally able to start taking classes at the community college.
My husband says to make everyone feel better: *I was only kidding*
1 don't really know that much about predictions.

                                        My sister
brings her daughters to Rocky Point which isn't as fun as it used to be,
which is going bankrupt, she says, like everything else in Rhode Island.
The rollercoaster is broken down, the cars off the tracks, lying on their sides
like cows. The fortune teller is gone and there's just a machine
in which you stick a quarter
                              and a mannequin holding a crystal ball
nods her wooden head that's chipped near the nose and a piece of paper
shoots out with your lucky numbers. The boys who run the rides,
the ones who used to be cute and my sister's age, all have tattoos now
and nose rings and moody tempers and smoke near the rides' fuse boxes.
She doesn't like the way they look
                              at her daughters who run careless
in their flip-flops, their ponytails gleaming. The booths are still there
with water guns you can shoot into clowns' mouths, fat balloons rising from
the tops of their heads. Skee Ball and the Ring Toss and Whack-A-Mole. And
hanging from the booth's roofs, giant Tweety Birds and Pink Panthers
the cuddly neon elusive ones that hardly anyone ever wins.

Russell Edson

Getting the Doctor into the Kitchen

They decided to have the doctor cooked ...

There he was, smoking his pipe and reading a medical journal that described a radical new treatment that would take the dead and resurrect them as house plants.

They may have to handcuff him and march him into the kitchen like a prisoner of war.

Meanwhile, the doctor is reading about a breakthrough treatment for those who have never been born to conceive themselves, and to be born of female clouds.

They may have to stab him in the back and drag the body into the kitchen. Still, they'll have to convince the cook that this is a perfectly natural thing to do, that is, to make the doctor into a stew smelling faintly of disinfectant...

The Sitting Organ

There was a father who spent many pleasant hours sitting on his daughter's lap.

They would be sitting in separate places, but pretty soon he'd be on her lap...

Get off my lap.

I'm not on your lap.

Then where do you think you are?

None of your business; where I sit and where I don't is strictly a personal decision decided by an elderly gentleman with the acquiescence of his sitting organ; and far too personal a thing to be discussed with young ladies. Have some manners!...

Elaine Equi

Beauty Secret

The beautiful
and the hideous

often conspire
in an empire
of appearance.

So which side
of the equation
would you rather be on—

or NEITHER

like the one
hurrying by,
eyes averted,

arms full of packages:

"These are necessities
not beauty aids.

Excuse me and
thank you very much."

✳

It must be
like losing your
fear of death

to just stop
worrying about
what you look like—

no longer tied
to that lamppost

like a dog
in the rain.

✳

From my mother
I learned to fear beauty

the lack
of it

and from my father
to distrust it.

Like eyes,

the heart too
turns away

sets its sights
elsewhere.

❋

If only people aspired
to the charm
of odd things:

miniature golf courses
or buildings
in a certain light

but, of course,
they don't.

❋

The sun sets.

The vase rests
in the center

of the poem.

It is all
a matter of arrangement.

Relationships
of power

made to seem
natural
and right.

Sunil Freeman

The Performance Artist Recalls

We were kids goofing off at the mall when Dave got this
flash. Here's the scene: There's a water fountain
by the elevator; the set-up's the same on the only two floors,
and the clincher: a stairway.

Bingo! Picture Einstein riding his beam of light, or
maybe just The Far Side on a good day. We gathered
around the fountain, five junior high kids in, let's see,
1971? It actually was [she laughs] the year of "Stairway
to Heaven." Our cue was adults at the elevator:
The door opens, they enter. The door closes,
we dash up the stairs and spin into the same scene
around the second fountain. [She lights a cigarette.]
Years later seeing Buñuel's rascally characters
re-enact *The Last Supper* I had a pang of such longing.

We were loud to seize their attention, but it was more:
with practice, we could recreate the exact texture
of chaos—body language, rhythm, jive, same unruly tableau
[she takes off her sunglasses] with no incriminating excess
of laughter on our new stage.
                              This, after a breathless sprint
up the stairs. That fast cool whiff of industrial concrete
was time travel for me, like racing through King Tut's tomb
to complete a work of art, which was that we played
with time and space; in a friendly way we fucked
their minds. Once we got the choreography right,
and the speed, they would see us and blink. They'd even
go back for a second try while we died not to bust
out laughing.
             Just before they understood, their eyes grew
soft, unfocused, as if some central gravity had hiccuped,
and like babies that instant they were in a new world.
Sometimes I cheated and caught peripheral glances.
I pictured their brains grown big and airy as beachballs,
warm and bright, lovely and goofy, in the sun.

Outside Looking In: Psychedelic Syllabics

for Timothy Leary

Forehead pressed against the window so breathing
makes clouds that half smudge out the stars.
"Would you look at this tree?" We wait for John
in a house full of clocks that'll still be
here in the morning, clocks like a tick tock
convention, a syncopation seminar

hiccuping triplets so color swatches dance—
red, blue, gold, red, and then Mary
takes the incense, patchouli; its red tip
arcs time-released waves that gyre and gimble
against the haze. "Guys, this is a great tree."
"Dark Star"—Garcia's solo turns bright silver

as Mary questions a clock which tocks right back.
John arrives—five miles on a bike,
twenty-five degrees—he changes our world:
chunks of air shear off him; the room grows cold
then absorbs him. Someone lights up a bong.
The kitchen floor goes 3-D, stars beneath us.

Garcia's now jet black, then gold, black and gold
as I watch the walls and wait. Soon
a film will lift from them, funnel and twirl
with words inscribed, like on a coke bottle,
my private hallucination—these words
I'll never be able to read—still, *language*.

Two walls shudder and release that translucence.
The friendly cartoon tornado
forms, words spinning barely too fast for me.
Three ferns are dancing with the funnel cloud
and far across the room I hear a voice,
my old friend Dee: "This *is* an amazing tree!"

John Hegley

The Reward

They lost their cat
and put up a notice that
said there was a reward
for the finder.
When it was found
this hopeful chap on welfare
brought it round
and was told that his prize
was the happiness in their child's eyes.
You can give her Fluffy yourself
said her father
and see the flowers
of her tears flow.
That will be your reward,
she'll be back from
ballet in a couple of hours
or so.

Michael Horovitz

West London Breakfist Morning, November 1996

As we sweat dripping crushedness
from sardine-tin tubeholes
the dregs of dawnstrained orange ooze
barely sustains us across rush-hour's cutthroat corners
to blunder aboard the supercharging buses.
    You'd think the broiled tomato chips
still sloshing around our gulletshafts
athwart His or Hers elbow-stabbing breast-gunnels
bulging baggage trolleys & clattering armour
of anguished co-computerized commuters
might leaven with their fleeting eructations
of pungent softness the arduous trek
for a few of the squillion frayed and flaying
through the edge-worn Edgware-to-Oxford Street traffic jams
to a stoical moment of hard-won bliss
    —but more likely only God knows (& only
dogs sense) anything nice about the usual
diesel fume-fartwinded half-hour standstill
at merciless stridently parp-harangued
marmoreally impervious, undelectable, unspreadable
Marmalade Arch.

Barbara Hurd

Imagine Hope

The winter I was ten, my father took me
to the middle of a dusky pond,
made me sit side-saddle on ice,
the way my mother had in the old photo he loved,
her head tilted, finger scratching frozen surface,
as if, for her, hope was what
she had cupped in her hands as a child,
set down in a bowl,
glazed over with a sheet of ice.

His was the hope of heaven,
hers of the coming to rest,
the whole family, except for him,
a school of Pisces, at home in mahogany deep
where learning to feed
means opening the mouth,
letting the universe enter.

Years later he mails me a photo
taken by the Hubble Space Telescope:
monstrous columns of cold gas
six trillion miles high
like raised forearms and fists
against the backdrop of infinity,
the end of each finger larger
than our solar system and embedded with fire.

Imagine hope as these hands on a piano, he writes,
Mahler's "Resurrection Symphony"
rising from each billowing pillar of interstellar storm,
the birthplace of millions of stars.

And imagine, I write back to him,
each newborn star like the flash of a fin
above water for only a moment,
and hope like the coolness
of what takes us back,
hand on feverish brow,
water dissolving the body
in tideless pools where moose
lean over the edge at dusk,
nuzzle the water with their lips.

Reuben Jackson

Love #49

this is how i felt
hearing gato play
"don't cry rochelle"
in '77.

a saxophone playing
lines lovely as your
hair;

the winter nights
dark as vinyl.

i was probably
lonely and high;

years from believing
there was something

to view at dawn besides
the glorious disk

above this room
where you turn

like the score of a song.

5/96

One More Once:

(after Frank O'Hara/for Jeanne)

It is 6:25 in Washington,
an autumn-like Monday in May,
and I am washing a head of lettuce and wondering
how the editors at *People* could have omitted you
from their *50 Most Beautiful Individuals In The World
1995* issue.

For who in their right mind would not choose you over
Courtney Cox, or Steve Young or Halle Berry (this year's lone
African Americans can be kind of attractive entry).

It's clear none of their editors have seen
your face in the day's first chorus of sunlight,
witnessed a night of your sighs and laughter—
or eaten pastrami with you in Midtown Manhattan.

What passes for stardom these days
is not the charisma in your touch,
but competent thespians
with amazingly savvy agents.

The disappointment is enough
to make me start my own magazine.

5/2/95

Mahmood Jamal
No Comment

There was a time when words
like love and hate, came easily to me
Like so many faces they jostled
smudged and edged out spaces
from the page, pried out furtive sounds
from their silent hiding places
and made a song and dance
about the way the world was made.

Now that so much has been granted
voices, signs and icons all abound
I feel a desperate silence all around.
Ambiguities increase with every doubt
The silence grows however much we shout.

So I must learn to contemplate
Poetry on a stubborn blank screen.
To pixilate it with phantom loves
Or smudge it once again with hate
Is, to say the least, obscene.

Ron Kolm
Open File

Distant sound of thunder
From way beyond the bypass
Draws me out of the house.

Lying on the lawn, spread-
Eagle, I remember I forgot
To turn the terminal off.

Inge Elsa Laird

"....They give birth astride of a grave...."

(For Frances Horovitz, 1938–1983)

balance
lost
in a cancer ward

balance
our first meal

balance
a liquid formula

balance
a voice   locked
unlocked

balance —
balance

balance
lost
in a jewellery box

Michael Lally

More Than Enough

there's more than more than more than
more than enough so why isnt enough enough and where is it
written that enough will never be enough xcept
in the amazing arrogance of societies and
institutions and governing bodies of immune deficiency
allowances of tabloid mentalities that breeed breeeed
breeeeed breeeeeeed breeeeeeeeeeeeeeeeeeeeeed infinity when
all we are asking for is food.

all we are asking for is enough space to live a life of
enough space to enough space to live a life of gratitude

when all we are asking for is no more hope no more dope no
more ways of being anything less than the stewards of all
that god has created including each other which means
caretakers which means taking care of which means caring for
each other and every other living thing and everything *is*
living from that star that is supposed to have died so many
thousands of years ago and yet still shines in your eyes to
that grain of sand in the shoe of the man sleeping on the rock
of all our past discouragement—

I'm talking about the reason we are here today
to look at each other and say what can I do for you
to help you get through whatever lack is causing you pain or
sadness or fear or anger or feelings of victimization—

there is only one nation, and it is the nation of
love, we weren't wrong in the 60s we were just too
self-righteous about it thinking whatever made us shout
also gave us the clout to have it all our way so I ask
today for the humility of the saints and the bodhisatvas,
the courage of the martyrs and the *kama sutra* the love of
every god who ever gave solace to any lonely soul like
mine and yours, I am reassured by that love no matter how
many tanks and guns and chemical weapons our collective
greed has ignited in the hearts of even lonelier souls who
have no recourse but belligerence and death to satisfy the
myth of their invulnerability—

we are all vulnerable, today's success stories, tomorrow's
homeless, let us all be warriors for love as if we were
sent from above to heal these wounds of neglect, because,
hey, guess what—we were.

Fran Landesman

Epiphany On the A Train

The train shoots out of the dark
And on to the bridge.
In a dazzle of daylight the billboard sings:
"Believe on Christ the Lord & thou shalt be saved."
Why do the words thrill
My unbelieving teenage soul?
The message I receive
Has little to do with a crucified Jew
And everything to do with the sound of the words
Marvelous in my mouth
"We are poetry" they sing to me
"And poetry is the way & the life."

Priscilla Lee

After the Bird

His momma was sixteen when she had him, named him Jay
after the bird so he could be free. Saturday haze, hot summer
breaking, Jay packs shirts for Maine. He's why Grampy lives,
will live longer if he visits. Jay says he wants his family to die
so he can get on with his life. Once, he mixed sleeping pills
with rum, climbed up a treehouse. The drugs were time-released.
Grandpa, up at dawn in dungarees, slops the hogs, grafts three
different apples on one tree, doesn't come home till supper.
Jay imagines his grandpa so tired, he could sink in dirt and die.
Last night, he dreamt the family shopped for washing machines,
climbed into a dryer, were trapped spinning. On the farm,
Momma shoots a woodchuck tearing at her turnips, bites
her cuticles as the other woodchucks drag its body away.

Gwyneth Lewis
The Field

1. Anything might happen here.

2. The brave, protected by rituals of rules,
    play ball in the middle, while above
    the busts of Roman emperors in clouds
    parade past sunsets. Anything
    could happen.

3. Gypsies might come to live on it,
    camping in stanzas that spill out words
    in running children.

4. The secret: let everything come to you.
    Love, and the weather.

5. The guilty skulk with spliffs around the edge,
    near bushes that nobody planted, which just came
    to hide forgotten corners, where all dogs find balls.

6. Water, when it falls, just lies in pools,
    enjoying the flatness and the open view.

7. Lovers are subject to weaker gravity
    so are forced to pin each other down
    on grass, or else they'd surely float away....

8. The goal posts sigh with a capital H
    (Huh, the playing field, then Huh).

9. Be still and wild things might approach
    to snuffle around your trouser legs.
    Be still. Here comes lightning.

10. Or you might see the dusk-bellied frigate birds
    land, like ideas of greatness one night
    and a loose dog chasing them all away
    before running around the field, just for joy.

The Device

This poem is a lie-detector test. Begin.
Who are you? I am different. I've softer skin
than all the others, finer feelings. I deserve
more cushiness, as fits a special case.
The centre of the world is always me,
the rest all outback. *Ego always lies. The sin*
is following. Begin again.

This poem is a lie-detector test.
I was wronged. She did it.
The baby in the blender wasn't my doing,
nor the shaking hands. My friend the knife
loved me; my unlived life
was my loyal gift to her. Poor me.
Go back. Too many rhymes with 'she'.
Blades best used for cutting free.
Begin again.

She gave me grief like necklaces,
blackened the pap so I sucked on air—
bitter, but bracing. The greatest gifts
are given like curses. "Trust no one,"
a Jewish father said
as he dropped the child who jumped into his arms
for the last time foolish. *This*
you didn't want to know. You pass.
Fill in the questionnaire below.

Paul Lyalls

Writers on the Storm

Into the engine room of Saturday night
A spin cycle of light, noise inhalation
Overcrowded expectant fashion
Body-wrecking dream-spilling
Life-bending seconds
A slaughter of library books—
All knowledge is just agreeing
It's better to be lucky than smart
It's all just a postcard from nowhere
God exists and he lives in a sugarcube
Watch it mate you're spilling my life
On this night a cup of coffee
Gets more sleep than your average Josephine
My drop dead gorgeous launderette
And she beckoned with Come To The
Supermarket eyes and she said
'I wanna be loved in a way that
I don't understand'
Saturday night is a dog with two tails
Whilst hangoverland is a scary
Faraway place and the taste of fame
Just got tastier
Saturday night is between thought
And expression
Saturday night is being caught in possession
Of a good feeling Saturday night is a weapon
Saturday night is being so drunk
You don't know where the ground is
Rave new world in a silver dress
Mugging people's sub-con-scious-ness
I'm not tired I'm hysterical
I know what the words mean
But I haven't got a fucking clue
What you're saying
Saturday night has them dancing in the gallows
Buzzing like an electricity sub-station
If you can't be kind at least be vague
Saturday night is a long night's journey
Into night

And we are as much influenced by the
People we've met as by the people
We've never met
Saturday night is Saturday night
And the ocean's in motion all the time
While tomorrow is a derelict day
The road ahead was clear
But it was the wrong fucking road.

Joanna McClure

Respite

After all that bootstrapping
I lie, content,
     full
        fed by my fire
          and Colette
The taste of
        fresh soft sweet
        green apple
           mixes with
Long neglected
        black clear coffee
        roofs, tree tops, sky
And haze behind which
        lie low mountains
        whose profile
Keeps me company
        thirty-five years later.

               ✳

A new tree in the foreground
        Reminds me—It is a
        New life.
I make my own fire,
        Heat my own coffee—
        Tired from the struggle
          To separate
          To let go
        Tired from
          The grief.

The sound of the dishwasher.

Outside—pine needles
        Point to the sky.

2 a.m.

       Me
Alone at last again forever.
The unexpected spider crawls
Quickly to the ceiling—
     Hangs
        and
            Drops.   Swings
              So gracefully
I catch my breath
As the leaf catches the late night
                         acrobat.

Jeffrey McDaniel
Billy Idol

In 1983 I went by myself to see a Billy Idol concert at the Spectrum. I was sixteen and wearing a skull and crossbones t-shirt, tight black jeans, ankle-high combat boots, eyeliner, and lipstick. I was sitting a couple hundred feet from the stage, when I experienced this moment of total synthesis with Billy. He was singing "Eyes Without A Face," and even though there were fifteen thousand people watching him, I knew in my heart it was me he was look-ing at, because he could feel my presence and was telekinetically acknowl-edging me as his protégé. I was the young Billy, except I was taller and had more depth. When the show ended, I wasn't ready to go, so I headed for the real party: the parking lot. There I found the true rock and roll fanatics, who undoubtedly would recognize the Billy in me. Before long I made friends with Joe, a plain-looking, seventeen-year-old boy from New Jersey, who liked to ride dirt bikes. I could tell by the way his eyes sparkled—he could see the Billy in me. We talked to strangers in the parking lot for hours, and when they praised Billy, I knew in my heart they were secretly praising me. It started to rain. The subway was closed, and I didn't have enough money for a taxi. I began to wonder what Billy would do in this situation, when Joe said, "Come with me. I have a car." Joe, my savior, my one true believer, the only one who really saw the Billy in me. While driving me home through South Philadelphia, Joe asked, "Have you ever thought of having sex with a man?" "No," I said, "Have you?" "No," he said. There was a long pause. I realized how dark and empty the street was, how we were miles from my house in Center City, how it wasn't plausible to jump out of a moving vehicle, how I was sitting next to a seventeen-year-old boy from New Jersey who was madly in love with the Billy in me. "Are you sure?" I said. The next thing I knew Joe was saying how attractive I was, how I reeked of sex and he just wanted a kiss. If I'd seen a hint of Billy in him, I would've done it, I would've grabbed him by the ears and kissed him and been his Philly slut, but he was Joe from New Jersey, and his hobby was rid-ing dirt bikes. "I'm really flattered by your interest, but no way." Joe got very quiet. I asked him if he got excited looking at other boys in the locker room, if he'd ever touched a woman, if he felt alone and depressed. Yes, yes, yes. Joe was very depressed and often thought about suicide. This was becoming too much. All I wanted was for him to see the Billy in me. I told him to drop me off at the 7-Eleven on the corner of my street, so he would-n't know where I lived, so he would go away and never come back. As I got out of the car, I leaned forward and gave Joe the kiss of his life. I sucked his face like it was the last hit on the last joint in the whole world, then I left him there, all worked up, amazed at the Billy in me.

Heather McHugh
Busy Dot Com

Not decorative falls
but quick declines by cliff,

not slow o'rwhelmings but a fast and-ese,
not swoon but groan, not throb but throe,

we took last looks and (to the woeful wood)
a willing ax. From there

we toll-wayed fifty Taco Bells
to our new cul-de-sacs.

Not So Fast

First a dimming overcame me
then a wind, and then the whole
sound waveletted, aroused.
I was extremely gradual in my
misgiving, looking (things did *not* look)
up—and there

in the buffeted high race of K's a man could see
the fabled column in the clouds (which theretofore I'd only
known from books): and it had one
long eyehole through it
to a blue too light

to trust. (The lightest blue is heaven's founding
oxymoron.) It's not there for us
to understand; it's there for us to be
looked down on
through—
I made my dash to cover—

made away. But now I know it's up there,
and my whole life long, while I'll
be bearing up, it will be
bearing down: a mind
for legalism, slow. My airs

mean nothing: it has grounds.

E. *Ethelbert Miller*

Co-Star

my sister
a philosopher
in 1959
made this remark
in midtown Manhattan:

Why do all the beautiful
women have such ugly men?

Whispers, Secrets and Promises

afternoon
and your eyes walk
across the table into
my hands

this is the beginning
of confessions and faith
or how you braid your
hair

a metaphor
for things left
unsaid

George Myers Jr.

Mrs. Shapiro's One-and-One-Half Prayers

If love be not in the house there is nothing.
　　　　　　　　—Pound, *Cantos*

My God, My God
why has thou

—and then she is pierced.
(The ghost of love climbs out of any old coffin.)

My God
Take me

or let me
and this

be nameless

Mrs. Shapiro Remembers the War, Mum

It is already late when you wake up inside a question.
— Anne Carson, *Plainwater*

If you can't find perfect pitch, strive for rhythm.
   They killed you, Mum, they killed you.

If you can't hear well, go where you can't hear anything. Your hearing will
   /improve.
   They took your shoes and stole your country.

Tune the instrument, tune the spirit.
   Dry, dry, the grasshopper's bones.

The athlete has his audience; the mother, inquisitors.
   I see, hear and feel nothing.

A few words about style: Some don't have it.
   And what does one wear to 6 million funerals?

Nature abhors a vacuum. Think: STONE.
   We buried you; you're under one.

Which reminds me, if you can't tie good knots tie a lot of them.
   So be it. Amen. God help us.

Expect nothing else to come to you but what is here before you now.
   Three geese sail overhead; I almost see them.

Victories, losses: Splurge, prepare.
   The horse has left you. The horse and all that rode it.

Everybody likes a little sauce, but no one wants a meal of only gravy.
   The black dust swirls in my hair.

Stay with someone whose mind has not stayed put.
   I have eggs, bacon, milk, but not time.

Be a foreigner in your own country; be a native everywhere else.
You are buried in no one's home.

To slake the moment, brace the past.
I hear gossip from across the Styx.

Judge a person's generosity only by what she offers.
Something makes me grateful for nothing.

Literature is written by individuals; remembrances, by the dead.
You are not one. You are now the many.

Life comes to you in spears
and goes carried off on shields.

Peggy Pfeiffer
Harbinger

Look to the signs.

Go when the call says go
back to bedside
through halls that narrow like
your first night terror.

She looks older than
you ever thought possible.
She believes that what's
put her here
will return to
take her next time.

Here let it all go:
      the million times she said: I did my best
      the warnings not to trade virginity for love
      and the sentence if you did: life without orgasm
      even your burned diaries—all.

Bury it and tell her
she's not going anywhere,
don't even think it.

But know she's right.
Hasn't she always been.

Look to the signs.
There's a house of guilt
that comes
in after-wishing.

Margaret Randall

Hunger's Table

pain is not a flower pain is a root
—Paul Monette

Now they sleep with the plague
beneath their pillows:
dancers and teachers, doctors and florists,
truckers and lawyers and priests.
Now they duel with her night sweats,
remembering they will soon forget,
and die with our love in tow.

> The woman I was
> keeps setting this table,
> announces she is putting
> forks to the left,
> knives and spoons to the right,
> petals of night bloom
> curling.

Your skin tells time, a map
inviting me to contemplate
the loss of gardens.
There is no choice when choice
commands you turn your back on passion.
Lover and teacher, writer and friend:
come sit at my table
while you can still dine
and a Canyon Wren floats her song.

> Water glasses are Mexican green,
> wine goblets rimmed in fire,
> dishes perfectly empty.
> The woman I am
> kicks off her shoes,
> sits down to eat.
> She thinks about
> what taunts her on the plate,
> devours its body,
> repeats its name.

These are the years of love letters
written in granite
protruding over gentle hills.
One beside another,
and another, stones
that remind us you were here.

This is our defiant rainbow,
its broken stump still hidden
within the darkness of the storm.
Brother let me keep you company,
rub your tired feet. Let me
see you home.

        The woman I will be
        invites good friends to table.
        Serves memory's food.
        Tells stories
        between the soup course
        and her dream time.
        Holds a granddaughter on her lap
        and flies.

Hunger's table is unreachable in waiting,
its settings embrace discordant music,
noises that fill the head,
dishes bone-clean and scraped,
a sound that courts the pain
of these brave times.

Welcome to our dear ghosts,
men whose historic flesh
plumps once-emaciated features,
who discreetly lift a saucer,
remarking upon its place and date
of fabrication.

Our brothers have forged
a terrible river.
Their return
has made them more than hungry now.

Simon Scardanelli

Uncommon Times

These are uncommon times
When worlds collide and nations fight for vanity
These are contagious times
When love divides and hate inspires insanity

Infected all around
A million loved ones underground still rising
We search for clues in vain
And look for someone else to blame

Hold on
Hold on to something
Hold on to someone
Hold on to anything at all

We climb these dizzy heights
Only to fall as sure as night
But wisdom seems so hard to gain
Must everything be so explained

We light the fires at night
To keep the wild beasts out of sight
But nothing burns like hell on earth
Is nothing really what it's worth

Hold on
Hold on to something
Hold on to someone
Hold on to anything at all

Maggie Smith
In His Hand

He hears tapping at the lower corner of his door.
he beats his hands bloody on an expanse of wood.

He puts down a box of dead sparrows and answers the tap.
he is blinded when the wood gives way to light.

He thinks: here we go again.
he wants to run, needs to pee, almost does.

He bends, picks up the little fellow.
he goes slack-jawed, blanches, swoons.

He pins the feet in the crook of two fingers.
he falls into a leather acre of palm.

He brings the man close to one eye, breathes him awake.
he sees himself huge in the curved mirror of God's cornea.

He knows pandas were a better idea.
he begs: set me free and I'll tell everyone.

And the man runs off to start a religion
and God causes thick bamboo to grow in China.

Rose Solari

Abortion Elegy: What I Know About Her

There are times I can see her face as if
she were here, as if she had lived—hair darker
than yours or mine, your cheeks, my mouth.
She stands over my bed as she did almost
a full year before we knew of her, or runs
through the living room, both hands spread,
chasing a shadow.
              I don't talk about this
to anyone, although I want to, want to be able
to say aloud when she would have been born,
how old she'd be right now, and how much
I would have loved her. If blood were fire,
she and I might have burned through circumstance,
might have been waiting, pure and calm,
whenever you came to us.
              I imagine
too much, I know. It gives me rough dreams.
But sometimes, when it is very quiet, I know
I hear her. I ask her forgiveness one more time.
I explain, as if from the beginning, how we decided
she could not be, that there was no room for her,
and believe she understands. And returns
out of love, not vengeance, to where she started.

Sparrow
Beautiful Cowards

I have seen many cowards, many beautiful
    cowards:
Women with long black hair,
Men with large, well-shaped chests.

They are beautiful when they stand, beautiful when
    they speak, but most beautiful when they run
    from danger: their strong legs lifting,
    their hair flowing.

A New Poem

This poem replaces
all my
previous poems.

Darrell Stover

Ethnopharmacology of Snake Bite Cures

Hedychium stem paste with garlic
Tacca tuber scrapings
Simaba fruit infusion
Ziziphus leaf juice
Rubus flowers unknown

You paved over some good bush
and oh so many snakebite cures have been lost
like colonial rosehips stolen from native arboreta.
The sting of fang stops the brain
unless a spirit world tripper
applies the proper plant salve.
A swollen ankle, purple and pulsating,
awaits the spit of jungle-brew.
An early earth garden,
an ethnobotanist's dream,
sits in some places unseen,
untouched except by the blessed hands of the shaman.
Extraction soaked leaf applied to thigh
says you will not die; but do not try
to steal the elixir.
Caterpillar tractors bite the land
and swallow tons of unearthed minerals.
Monstrous chains coil around trees as fire burns bark.
The cures we need are for a venomous breed of man.
Picture the deity of life
holding the surgeon's knife
and a long brown stem in the other hand.
The plants are silent, dead and disappeared
and the deity throws her hands up in surrender.
The operation is over.
The wealthy man dies.
His money can't buy good health,
only more and more of greed's greatest construction,
the destruction of Gaia's balance and sustenance.
The wellspring of knowledge
deep in the genes of the jungle college
repose in the souls of rain forest people.
Indonesia. The Congo. Amazonia.
Where did they all go?

You do not deserve their magic.
You do not know their pain.
The forests are now broken down towns,
uncivilized cities.
The earth screams an echoing curse
of dead soil, plants and cures.
Plagues of migratory mosquitoes,
resistant malarias,
and vengeful viruses
spew forth.

The blue and green ball fries.
The planet dies.

Datura root bark paste with cow urine.
Philodendron leaves with beer.
Piper nigrum seed paste with ghee.
Calathea root decoction.
Goodyera leaf paste.
Cissampelos root juice.
Ocimum twigs unknown.

Silvana Straw

Our Lady of the Unauthorized Biography

1.

At the Department of Infectious Diseases, I learn DNR means Do Not Resuscitate.
I type up the instructions and tape them to the wall,
hold a little piece of ice to his lips when he's thirsty.

2.

I've used up my sick leave. The office timekeeper wants to know
how many days till my friend dies, he wants me to give him a deadline.

3.

In the blood transfusion ward Mark pretends he's a vampire to make me laugh
and sucks at the dangling tubes of blood. I carry his spit cup to and fro,
I'm scared and happy and can't sit down.

4.

The credit collector calls for the forty-seven dollars and seventy-four cents.
Three days later, he calls back. "Ms. Straw, this is Mr. Green,
I've given you enough time to get over your personal tragedy,
now I am forced to resort to other measures."

5.

He is so tall they divide his ashes into two urns.
In the second urn they put his father's ashes,
so his mother can sneak her husband and son
out of the country without the required paperwork.
The stewardess insists the woman place her handluggage
beneath the seat in front of her, she refuses, and carries
both her loved ones on her lap in her suitcase across the sky.
She wonders where she'll spread his ashes, 'perhaps a little sprinkle
on her breakfast cereal every morning,' she cries.

6.

The psychiatrist's best friend died this week,
a double-suicide with his wife in a hotel in Georgia.
He tries to convince me religion is a learned behavior,
do you believe everything your mother taught you?
isn't this life enough?
I wonder what the bandage on his forehead covers, a horn perhaps,
maybe he's having bits of his left brain removed.
In between sessions, he takes a peek inside,
those little angels dancing around in there drive him mad,
he shoves a pencil through the hole.

7.

The volunteer from the AIDS clinic is a journalist who writes a biography
about my friend which he tries to publish after the funeral.
When I try to stop him, he accuses me of thinking I'm my friend's protector.
I am, I tell him. I am his protector.
Our Lady of the Unauthorized Biography, that's me.
Some nights the journalist can't sleep, he dreams he is digging up corpses
and interviewing them, and just when they're about to lay it all on the line,
he can't find his notepad.

8.

I love the way your skin looks pink, how untamable and sweet you are.
When I'm thirsty I hold a little piece of ice to my lips, blow kisses at the sky.

9.

He tried to take me with him the morning he died,
for a moment the white light almost went through me but I resisted.
We meet each other halfway through dreams, I feel his smirk in the night,
I am repeating myself in sleep, cleansing my blood.
I have to admit I was scared of his blood
and the night he cried in the kitchen after dinner,
I was even scared of his tears.
If only you knew how I wanted to get down on my knees
and lick them from the floor.

Andrea Tetrick

Olympia Deluxe

I bought a typewriter off a man I know
Lugged it from Brooklyn to Washington
Olympia Deluxe reads the frame & its case
Olympia Olympia Deluxe.

Once it belonged to another friend
Who blew out his brains in the wilderness
Left a suicide note dated ten-thirty-one
A note he had scribbled by hand.

It's old but it's clean I paid fifty bucks
The keys all strike & the ribbon is sound
Olympia Deluxe reads the frame & its case
Olympia Olympia Deluxe.

David Trinidad

Fortunes

You are just beginning to live.
You are original and creative.

You have a yearning for perfection.
Your winsome smile will be your protection.

You are contemplative and analytical by nature.
You will take a chance in the near future.

You have an active mind and a keen imagination.
Listening is half of a conversation.

You love sports, horses and gambling but not to excess.
From now on your kindness will lead to success.

Your luck has been completely changed today.
Be direct, one can accomplish more that way.

You will get what you want through your charm and personality.
You will enjoy good health, you will be surrounded by luxury.

Someone is speaking well of you.
Now is the time to try something new.

Laura Ulewicz

The Prologue of Demon is Spoken

(for Piro and all my fathers)

Fifty.   The dreams blur.
You are not sure anymore
how good they were. But the rebels
still come daily, so young,
daily, to your house on the Via
Babuino in search
of a father. Only you,
they tell you, have not changed.
Again you are caught in your role.
Every day you mean to tell them,
Listen, it was not ALL
selling out. A man
has a right to grow old, has a right
to move out of rebellion
into philosophy.
You young, stop hugging ghosts.
Every day you MEAN to tell them.

Fifty.   The dreams blur.
Your flirtation with the Party—
you've been mocking that
for 20 years now. Your fellow
anarchists haven't met
in your house—for how long now?
All those greetings in the warm
dusk over, those long
disciplined debates.
Schimsky's wife. Her fingers
fluttering her purse
like timpani. You'd watch
her grow away of her womb
while the flies on the ceiling ate
your brain. Often you think
now of your dead friend.

Fifty.   The dreams blur.
You broke free. Hoping they'd be
as you were you urged them to follow.
Why did you need them, you wonder.
You were strong. They could not
bring you down, so around
you they built a cyst, a cyst
of acceptance. You were the verb
they modified. Now
that the young and the old-time
anarchists agree
(time of fertility
you argued for), you are not
sure the old distinctions
exist. In the order of spirit
you move toward, there is no
such thing as the middle class.

Fifty.   You have learned
how to live in order,
how to create, and you
create in order to make
order you have come upon
your order. You have strings
into the universe.
Your veins connect Monkey
Flowers to politics.
Inside your being wild
grasses, old cars,
the paintings of Hundertwasser
become emotions. You are
and you are, and you are.
With so much worthy
of understanding, how
can you ever find time to die.

Fifty.   The dreams blur.
The woman comes who did not come
before. She is all nipples
and nervousness. Like
an Iris in bloom behind
swords. How she is rooted
in waters; her loins empty
of you. Yes, you still want
what you waited for. Night
after night she burns a hole
in your sleep. Move her, you say,
into that space. It is
she who helps you build
inside emptiness
she has reminded you of.
Bewildered she waits. You speak
to her of Hundertwasser.

Lee Upton

Hand-Made Pin, Madonna: Book of Kells

She was painted handsomely:
down-sloping eyes,
red mouth like a tiny bat wing.

A people's image repeats
fear in their virgins.
Flesh for all to see

with sea scuds of crosses.
As she is my witness,
her image is pinned to me,

a shield against sickness.
I was taken aback, so earnest
was the woman under the tent

with her boxes of velvet,
pronouncing a blessing
but not a bone of the sibyl

in her, nothing of curious fortune
but for the strains
of assumed virginity.

Janine Pommy Vega
The Politics of Insomnia

I waited til dawn for the postcards
of Frida Kahlo sleeping, of
Diego Rivera with his mouth open
under the covers, of Pablo Neruda
snoring loudly next to the waves
They never arrived

I thought then of lesser pictures
portraits with steel lines
of artists caught and mummified:
Lorca, Max Ernst, Isabel Eberhardt
in her sailor suit
but I could not keep them

You admitted you could not sleep
either
we were mutually guilty
of pouring no pure milk of love
over bodies
tangled like piano wires

More than wanting to sleep
I wanted
not to wake you up
my lungs rattling like cellophane
with every breath, persistent
coughing ripped the silence

There is no going back to former times
when I could lose myself, and come up
like a swimmer
blessed by the deeps, spreading
drops of sea water hugely
over the blanket and your mouth

There is no getting around
death leaning on my chest
with bony elbows
If I could accept her
embrace her thigh and cover her
with kisses

If I could harbour no hidden
instincts of denial
and open the tomb of my heart
so the same music played inside
and out, and bathed us, you and me,
then possibly I could fall asleep.

Cholula, Mexico, August 1995.

Dana Weimer

Women with Big Shoulders

Anonymous as lost girls,
They walk down streets
Past mannequins
In store windows...
   Don't worry,
      These shoulders aren't real.
That's their secret,
Like the impossible weight
Of faux jewels, a necklace
To cast a spell.
   Make me over!
      Make me over! they cry,
Looking for truth
In the silhouette—
The size of shoulders
A definite asset.
A flick of hair,
The head cocked
To one side...you can see
The long eels of their bodies
Wiggling in and out of clothes
Inside dressing rooms
Of Macy's and Filene's.
There's got to be a way out
Of this, a way out of these clothes.
The opening's got to be
Large enough to get free—
Free from a blouse
That's caught at the shoulders,
Too small to get loose, past
These big shoulders struggling.

Valerie Wohlfeld

Vespers

I lived inside my hair
as a sea animal
inhabits an abandoned shell:
a silkworm's petit point unsewn,
a solitary lair not my own.

Against his backbone
my array: jewel
by jewel the vespers bell
and I, in tortoise-shell-
variegated-light, loosened our apparel.

On my wedding day
I cut my hair away.
I arranged my bed of hair
as sickled grass,
tips of flowers, sassafras.

With my scissored hair
beneath our bodies, the vespers bell's
vibrations fell until the threadbare
room seemed a diamond's cell
of light, set solitaire.

Karen Zealand

If Watermelons Were Confetti,

you'd get the picture when a tractor-trailer
overturned in a couple's front yard.

An amazing number were still intact
and seemed to have sprung from the lawn.

One knocked a bird bath from its pedestal
and fell into the basin.

Rescue workers in hazard gear
cradled the melons like newborns

and it seemed indecent to expect
them to proceed to supermarkets.

They'd lost the demeanor of fruit
and assumed a stature that humans

assume reluctantly.
As, for example, a motorist hung 30 feet

on the top deck of the Nimitz Freeway
in the San Francisco earthquake.

When asphalt rolled like the sea
and a concrete wave broke 15 feet

above his hood, he said, I'm hallucinating.
He decided to leave his golf clubs

and was rescued exiting his vehicle
with a bag of groceries.

Silvana Straw

How I Was Terrorized by a Poodle in the Elevator of The Empire State Building While Visiting New York with My Boyfriend

The poodle stands on her hind legs in front of us.
She's wearing a red cape and high heeled black boots.
She barks quietly to an older gentleman in German.
Arching her back, front legs pulled in, teetering slightly,
she turns her head back to look at my boyfriend, just so...
She's got that dreamy look, that sleepy look,
that just been groomed and want to fuck look,
she feels so "poodle" today.

As the elevator ascends she starts to turn for you,
and turn and turn and turn for you,
68, 69, 70, suddenly
the elevator becomes the Luther Jackson Junior High
girls locker room going up.
I'm 13, it's the day of the 600 yard dash
and I can't put on my sleeveless gymsuit because my mom is from Italy
and won't let me shave my underarms, and I'm really hairy
and the poodle knows this
as she parades about freshly shaved, her legs,
between her legs, her many tiny purple bows,
purple toenails, and invisible perfumed anus.

There I am in my knee socks and big underwear
and I want you to make her stop
but instead you close your eyes—
Just what she's been waiting for!
She takes this as her cue
and like all good poodles do when they think you're not looking—
she starts to hump your leg!

Humping and humping—your girlfriend watching—
This is the best fun she's had in weeks!
I want to scream, Pig Dog! Pig Dog!
I want you to shake her off your leg
but instead I just stand there and watch her hump.

When we reach the top, she walks out of the elevator like nothing happened.
I feel a sudden need to call my mom, Hi Mom,
I'm on top of the Empire State Building...

Every time the poodle passes us on the walkway,
she looks down at your leg and whimpers slightly.
I want to say, I saw you humping his leg!
I want to say, I saw her humping your leg!
I want to impale her on the spike of the building,
the instrument she uses to measure your desire,
the antenna by which she catches you flinch,
the antenna glistens, the better to feel you my dear,
and in the end the poodle wins because every man wants a poodle.

In the car, on the way home, I ask,
Did you see that poodle humping your leg in the elevator?
Yeah that was pretty weird, you say.
I can't believe how rude she was! I cry,
Why didn't you kick her?!

I see the poodle everywhere now, at People's,
on the cover of *Glamour*, her name is Daniela.
I call my friend in New York who photographs poodles
and tell him to bring me her heart so that I may eat it.
He tells me poodles don't have hearts.

I lock myself indoors, turn my room into a dressing room,
shave all the hair off my body till I look like
one of those hairless Mexican dogs,
put on a red cape, paint my toenails,
practice saying things like, Mirror, Mirror on the wall,
and, Get down on your knees and lick me.
I wonder what it's like to hump someone's leg.
It's not good enough.
I decide to take out his eyes.

It's been years since I've let him walk me.
Some nights he begs me to take him down to the Monument.
There's no elevator, he pleads.

I wear a leash now,
I've got one for every occasion,
I'll never be a poodle, honey,
but I make a great seeing-eye dog.

Claudine Schafer-Legrand
Portfolio   3 Photographs

Jodi Bloom
Teenage Vixens from the Netherworld

Before she became the youngest Avon Lady in America, Nell Madigan was a Nobody. Worse than that, she was somebody who could turn you into a Nobody just by talking to you. Dad always said, *There's something wrong with those Madigans, reproducing like jack rabbits when they haven't got two nickels to rub together,* but there wasn't really anything wrong with them; they were just Catholic. *It obviously waters down the gene pool,* Dad would say, *so it can't be what Mother Nature has in mind for the human race.* He was right because the Madigan kids were ugly and borderline retarded, all thirteen of them. *Well,* the Madigans would say, *it's what the Pope has in mind for the human race and he can kick Mother Nature's butt any day.*

From a distance—and you always wanted to keep a distance between yourself and a Madigan—you couldn't even really tell the Madigan boys from the Madigan girls, with their matching long greasy hair, black K-Mart sneakers and their scabby knees and grimy elbows. The Madigans couldn't kick anyone's butt, even if they did have the Pope himself on their side.

Nell was the 9th grade Madigan, and the sixth or the eighth kid in that long line, depending on whether you were counting from oldest to youngest or vice versa. I had never heard Nell Madigan say much of anything except for reciting that endless list of her brothers and sisters, middle and confirmation names included. Which was a fairly impressive memorization achievement, along the lines of reciting the 50 states in the United States of America. But not impressive enough. Not by a long shot.

The boys in our class called her Smell Bad Again. I forgot to mention that; the Madigans stunk. Like a combination of fried chicken and sweaty feet. Maybe that's why it was such a big deal the day Nell Madigan came to school wearing Hawaiian White Ginger.

✳

Most of the teachers at our school still believed that alphabetical was the "perfect system for imposing order upon the chaos that is Junior High." So I, being Sue Marshall, got stuck behind Nell Madigan in almost every class. This was one of those curses that turned into a blessing. See, I had to smell Nell Madigan every day of my life, but then, I was the very first to smell Hawaiian White Ginger. I actually discovered it. And I think I deserve some credit for this, the way Christopher Columbus got credit for discovering

America. Like, it was there the whole time, you know? Someone intelligent just had to come along and go: *Look, it's America.*

At first, I could still smell the fried chicken and dirty feet, which was gaggifying, really it was. Especially on Monday mornings in Homeroom, when I had not been tortured with the smell of Nell Madigan for an entire weekend. I was just sitting there daydreaming about Danny Bellacardio, a boy I had a crush on who didn't know I existed and who wouldn't give me the time of day if he did because he was in High school.

So there I sat, dozing in the land of dreamy boys when along came this smell—riding on the wave of the fried chicken and sweaty feet—the most amazing smell I ever smelled in my entire fourteen-year-old life—and I thought I had smelled my share of amazing smells. Like the perfume my mother wears, Wind Song, which stays on your mind, just like the ad says. And those miniature donuts at the Ohio State Fair at the end of summer, which smell greasy and sugary, but in a totally irresistible way. And like Danny Bellacardio who smells like Ivory soap, has the most beautiful long hair, and who played guitar with his hard-rock band, Blind Deer, in the school talent show last year—when he was still at Eastland Junior. Hawaiian White Ginger was better than all of those things, better than all of those things *combined*.

✳

By Wednesday I thought I was going crazy. Was my mind playing tricks on me? Maybe the men in white jackets would come and take me away because I could swear that the smell of Nell Madigan had mutated from the worst thing that ever travelled up your nostrils to something so sweet and delicious that it gave you like an instant vision of Heaven. Of course at the time I didn't know it was Hawaiian White Ginger, so it didn't give me the vision of a beautiful tropical island with exotic flowers and sexy dancing girls wearing grass hoola skirts and lei's around their necks. That came later.

I started following Nell Madigan secretly through the halls of our school in order to find out what it was, even though this was a major risk to my reputation. By Friday I was hoping someone else would notice. But no one did. And that was why I asked myself: *Am I going crazy?*

✳

The answer was yes.

Evidence. On Friday afternoon I did the unspeakable, completely insane thing of talking to Nell Madigan. Thereby risking my entire reputation, which I had worked extremely hard on and which, as you know, could be damaged for life by one simple bad move such as talking to a Nobody. But the smell had infected my brain. That was my "rationalization," to use my mother's favorite word for a lame excuse.

I thought about it in Algebra II. I thought about it in English instead of concentrating on The Subjunctive. I thought about it in Study Hall, where I took a seat dangerously close to Nell Madigan. It finally happened at lunch, which was actually the perfect place, right there in the middle of the banging trays, and the screaming immature boys throwing food, and all the "noisy ruckus," as our principal Mr. Clutch called the school cafeteria.

No, I didn't sit with Nell Madigan. *Are you kidding?* I sat on my side of the cafeteria, at my table, with my friends, Annabelle Bradley, Mary Kate O'Neil (who was Catholic but whose parents had some common sense because she only had two sisters), and Julie Nelson. I sat there with my friends, but I kept my eye on Nell Madigan. When Annabelle asked me: *What's wrong with you today Sue Marshall?* I said: *Oh, nothing. I'm just thinking about Danny.* Because everyone knows that a crush on a boy is the perfect excuse for all kinds of unusual behavior.

Then Nell got up and walked across the cafeteria with her tray. She was in her Madigan trance of Nobodyness. I said to my friends: *This pizza is really grossing me out and it's going to cause World War III on my face.* Which was pretty dumb since the truth is that pizza was like the one edible school lunch. But I stood up with my tray and walked over to the trashcan where Nell was dumping out the remains of her moldy homemade PB&J, her perfume floating around her like a cloud of peaches and roses covered with melted white chocolate. My heart was pounding so hard I thought it would burst. I cleared my throat and Nell turned around and looked at me.

"What..." I started to say, but the cat had my tongue. Nell was staring at me and I had the thought that underneath the Madigan-itis she was sort of pretty. But I also had the thought that I was becoming the victim of a major evil curse. "Nell, what is that perfume you're wearing?" I finally said.

"Hawaiian White Ginger," Nell said and she smiled like she knew something I didn't.

"Oh," I said. I couldn't let on that I was having like a total schizo-phrenic obsession over something belonging to Nell Madigan. "It's...well, it's so...*different.*"

✳

The plain white envelope, with my name—Sue Marshall—printed on the front, was jammed into our mailbox with Saturday's mail. Inside was a small square packet. The front of which showed exotic white flowers with big green leaves on a black background. On top it said, in bright red letters: *Hawaiian White Ginger the Exciting New Fragrance by Avon.* And there was a scrap of looseleaf paper, on which was written: For Sue Marshall, compliments of your Avon Representative, Nell Madigan. And her phone number.

I am pretty sure that I went into shock right there at the breakfast table. My Dad was like, *Secret admirer, Sue?* I didn't answer because all I could think was, *Did anyone see her walk up to my mailbox?* My mind went crazy trying to figure out what I would say if anyone did.

Luckily, I spent the day at the mall with Annabelle and Mary Kate and Julie and I didn't have to think about it too much. Danny Bellacardio was at the mall too. He didn't look at me or any of us, but his divine presence took my mind off my problems. Of course, when I got home, the sample of Hawaiian White Ginger was there on my dresser where I'd left it. Like Mom says, *You can't run away from your problems, they'll follow you like a shadow.*

My fear of total ruination kept me from opening that packet all the way through the weekend. Then on Monday morning, while I was getting dressed for school, something got the better of me. I'll admit I was thinking how jealous my friends would be of my new perfume. Well, no one's perfect ok? So I opened it and pulled out the white folded-up square, which looked exactly like the moist towelettes you get with your fortune cookies and orange slices at Mr. Wong's Family Taste Chinese Restaurant.

I rubbed the moist towelette on my wrists and neck and behind my ears. I pulled up my t-shirt and rubbed some on my stomach and between my titties the way Mom does. And suddenly it was like a breeze from the most beautiful place in the universe—in the entire *galaxy*—had surrounded me and was whispering in my ear: *Sue Marshall, whatever your heart desires is yours...yours.*

Julie was the first to notice my exciting new fragrance and finally, after she asked me a million times where I got it, I told her. I told her everything. Then I held my breath waiting for my reputation to self-destruct before my very eyes like the tape on *Mission Impossible.*

Which did not happen. What happened was Julie made me get out the moist towelette—which I had carefully preserved in a plastic sandwich baggie in my purse—so she could rub it all over herself too. By the end of school that day, orders were placed with Nell Madigan, our Avon Representative, who had left the land of Nobodyness forever.

✳

In just two weeks the entire 9th grade smelled like Hawaiian White Ginger, which came in every possible perfume formation known to man. It came in spray atomizers (regular and purse size), Eau de Toilette (cheap and unsuitable), Cologne (medium-priced) and Eau de Parfum (too expensive for us but I heard that Miss Mayfield, the only young and pretty teacher at our school, bought some and got engaged to be married the very next week). It came in a hand cream, body moisturizer, bath beads and even talc, complete with a pink powder puff for application.

In another two weeks the 7th and 8th grades were in on it, although the boys in 7th were grossed out, but what could you expect of those immature babies? The 8th grade boys were split down the middle which made it very easy to figure out which 8th grade boys we should bother talking to. In the 9th, the boys were goners—following us around, getting worse grades than boys usually got—acting weirder and more like showoffs than ever. Which was too bad for them because even a 9th grade boy was hardly worthy of any attention at all.

Of course we let Nell Madigan sit at our lunch table. She was rich and had lots of new clothes, and it was like she had a brand new identity—as if she had never even been a Madigan in the first place. I felt sorry for her for still being one. It was me that came up with the idea of Nell legally changing her name to Ginger White which would have been a totally unique and sexy name, like a movie star. But we found out you had to be eighteen. Still, she loved the idea and said she looked forward to the day.

✳

Avon kept those free samples coming. Our new best friend Nell gave all the samples away, thereby turning us girls into a sick and deranged mob of starving make-up addicts. Always hungry for more—more colors, more flavors, more, more, more. Lipsticks and blushes with names like First Kiss and Berry Extreme, Pink Fantasie and Dare to be Bare; Timeless Blue eye shadow the color of the sky; Green Velvet and Midnight mascara. And the most dangerous thing of all, Black Smoke liquid eyeliner. Eyeliner was strictly prohibited. According to our mothers, eyeliner was for Sluts. And the only thing worse than a Nobody was a Slut.

You can call it rationalization or whatever, but me, Annabelle, Julie, and Mary Kate didn't agree with this old-fashioned theory of eyeliner. Neither did the other girls in the 9th grade. I mean, if you wore eyeliner AND went past second base, ok, you were a Slut. But just the eyeliner? No way. Next to Hawaiian White Ginger, Black Smoke liquid eyeliner was the most popular item in Nell Madigan's catalogues. In the privacy of the girl's bathroom at school, we circled our eyes with perfect curvy lines. A spritz of perfume and off to class we went.

Finally, one day at the mall, Danny Bellacardio said hi to me, and that was how I knew that Hawaiian White Ginger had powers beyond our imaginations.

That was about the same time that Mr. Clutch waddled into the main hallway at school and, in that ridiculously short three minutes between classes—when you're trying to talk to your friends, ignore some boys and spy on others—scrunched up his fat bulbous principal's nose, and hollered at the top of his lungs: *"THIS SCHOOL SMELLS LIKE A FRENCH WHORE-HOUSE."* It was like the funniest thing that ever happened at Eastland Junior. Then he stomped back to his office, had a total fit over the PA system, and declared Hawaiian White Ginger, and all Avon products, contraband.

✳

Of course you guessed what happened right? The black market for Avon formed overnight and the craze was worse than before. We spent at least 47 minutes of every 57-minute class secretly trading and testing each other's lipglosses and eye shadows, poring over the catalogues and counting out our dimes, nickels, and pennies for more Hawaiian White Ginger.

Nell Madigan received a special plaque with a note on the official Avon stationery that said, and I quote: *To the Youngest Avon Lady in*

America, Congrats on your Entrepreneurial American Spirit and Thanks for Keeping our Customers Happy. Signed, Christina Gold, President of Avon Products, Inc., NY, NY.

We were very proud of our Nell.

*

I was thinking about NY, NY—about what sort of totally amazing place it probably was—the day I walked into the girl's bathroom at school and found my friend Julie Nelson ready to spill an entire 3.4 ounce bottle of Hawaiian White Ginger Eau de Cologne down the toilet. "Do you think it means I'm a Slut?"she was saying in between hiccups and sobs. I finally got it out of her: Julie Nelson had been *raped* by none other than Danny Bellacardio himself.

I was furious. I mean just exactly what was she doing with my Danny to begin with? Still, I didn't see any point to wasting all that perfume so I grabbed it out of her hand and tried to think of what to do next.

"I don't know Julie, I really don't know," I said. "But I guess we should go see the nurse or something."

An ambulance came and took Julie Nelson away right before lunch because the school nurse was not equipped to deal with "an emergency of this stature." Then double assemblies were held in the auditorium, boys and girls separately.

Someone had given Mr. Clutch a bottle of Hawaiian White Ginger, which he used as a prop in our assembly. He held it up above his head, gave it a little shake and said: "Boys at this age need *no further provocation*. It's bad enough that hormones are speeding through their bloodstreams like race cars at the Indy 500...they simply do not need the continued torment of a bunch of teenage vixens from the Netherworld." He reminded us that all Avon products had been relegated to the school's list of illegal sub-stances along with alcohol, cigarettes, and marijuana, and that anyone caught selling, purchasing, or using them would be dismissed from school. Permanently.

*

Danny Bellacardio said: *No one raped anyone.*

The whole world was suddenly divided perfectly in half—people who believed Danny and people who believed Julie. Of course I had to stop lik-ing Danny Bellacardio the Rapist even though that was when I started hav-ing dreams of being raped by him.

*

I kept my dreams to myself. Me, Annabelle, Mary Kate, and Julie held a special ceremony swearing not to become teenage vixens. At the end of which we dumped all of our beautiful Avon products, including over a dozen different types of Hawaiian White Ginger, into Mary Kate's trash compactor. When Mary Kate turned it on and the grinding noise started, I had this awful sinking feeling. Like my very heart's desire was being destroyed along with the O'Neil's leftovers from breakfast, lunch and dinner.

Everyone but Nell Madigan stopped wearing Hawaiian White Ginger and Berry Extreme lipstick and Black Smoke liquid eyeliner. Nell started going out with Danny the Rapist and earned a new reputation overnight: Slut. She colored her hair Penny Red and changed her name to Ginger Vinaigrette, even if it wasn't official. I was dying to tell her that having a salad dressing for a name was barely any better than being a Madigan, but we were no longer friends.

Danny Bellacardio changed his name to Danny Bell because it sounded more like a rock star. He cut his beautiful long hair into these short crazy spikes and started a new band called Teenage Vixens from the Netherworld, with Ginger Vinaigrette as the lead singer. They bought black leather jackets at Wilson's Leather at the mall. In class I had to sit and stare at Nell Ginger Vinaigrette Madigan's leather jacket—on the back of which was spraypainted the word: Slut.

She would have been expelled except that school ended a week later.

✳

That summer we found out the big secret that Danny Bellacardio had never really raped Julie Nelson. How we found out the truth was that Mrs. Nelson—who said she wanted to clear her daughter's good name once and for all—decided to press charges against Danny, taking him to a court of law where he would *stand before a jury of his peers and get the punishment he deserved.* That was when Julie admitted that what really happened was that Danny only forced her to go to third base.

Danny said: *No one forced anyone.*

That was the start of the biggest problem of my life—I believed Danny Bellacardio and not my friend Julie Nelson. And the worst thing was that even though it was wrong, I still thought of Danny all day long and dreamed of him at night. I dreamed that I was the one being raped, I was the one going to third base...and beyond. And the problem was it was like the most delicious thing ever, having Danny Bellacardio's hands all over me—and the smell of Ivory soap mixing with Hawaiian White Ginger, which in my dreams I was still brave enough to wear.

For the second time I started waiting for the men in white jackets to come and take me away. I asked myself again: *Am I going crazy?*

✳

You guessed it. The answer was yes.

Evidence. I went over to Nell Madigan's house one hot summer day. Instead of hanging out with Annabelle and Mary Kate and dumb old Julie the liar, I went to that forbidden zone of our neighborhood, the true land of Nobodyness and Slutness and total ruination—Madigan Land, 375 South Chesterfield Road, Columbus, Ohio, 43209. There should have been a KEEPOUT sign on the front lawn, which wasn't a real lawn; it was a pile of dirt with broken toys and scraggly weeds all over the place.

Mrs. Madigan answered the door. "Hello," I said. "Is Ginger...I mean Nell, at home?"

Mrs. Madigan stared at me while a half a dozen kids came out of nowhere and stood around behind her, squinting and eyeballing me and probably cursing me for life, but I didn't care. Then Nell was standing there too. "Hi Sue," she said, and she smiled that same smile as last year when I first asked her about Hawaiian White Ginger.

The Madigan's house smelled like fried chicken and dirty feet, exactly what you'd expect. It was dark and cluttered and messy and horrible, and it was impossible to picture Nell Ginger Vinaigrette Madigan living there instead of in some fancy apartment—maybe in NY, NY—with her red hair and black leather jacket and Danny Bell on her arm like the perfect fashion accessory. I had a case of The Sorry's sneak up on me...sorry I had been so mean to Nell, sorry about trash compacting twenty-five dollars worth of perfectly good make-up and perfume, sorry about *everything*. Luckily I am good at hiding The Sorry's and no one noticed.

Upstairs in Nell's room we sat on her bed. "I know why you've come," she said, opening a dresser drawer, which was crammed so full of Avon products it was like totally mind boggling. Then she pulled out that familiar bottle, a miniature 1.7 ounce purse atomizer of you-know-what, while I held my breath and tried to act at least sort of calm.

Nell giggled and yanked off the top and started spritzing us both with Hawaiian White Ginger. She just kept spritzing and spritzing like a maniac, using up practically the whole thing and laughing hysterically. I had never been drunk or stoned in my life but I knew that's exactly what was happening. Me and Nell Ginger Vinaigrette Madigan were high as kites on the smell of that perfume—both of us laughing so hard we fell over backwards on the bed—laying there helpless while our heart's desires floated right up out of our bodies and filled that room from end to end.

Alison Bundy

Western: I Am Produced

Gently now. Memory is a thin-legged thing.

How did I come here? A remarkable tale.

You have seen prints, photographs perhaps, where the front darkness conflates with a background of deeper dark. That is the quality. And here, a father is stretched on the ground in the forefront, while behind him, toward the back, is evident a simple structure partaking of the geometry of house, and this house levitates, rises like a cloud above the dirt.

It is dark but the figure, the structure, these shine faintly. They are like pearls washed in thin ink.

This was in West Texas. Who was that father? My father. The photograph, the print, is black and white, but the close observer discerns an aura of red, a glow. That is murder.

Where is the mother? We shall see.

✳

Now there is but one sun in our sky and that same sun shone then. It shone on the small rocks as well as the large and it offered no shelter. And if there was a bird in the sky it was a falling bird and if there was a bird on land there was only one, and if either let out a song it let out a falling note. The father had a broken car. It had stopped on the empty road. Money fell in the cloth against his leg. He carried his watch in his coat pocket.

The mother was special. She walked beside him. They had not yet had sex but he had chosen her for her neatness, her tiny waist. He would like to bow down before her. He was an American with a car albeit broken, some learning, panoramic ambition. She had gotten out of the car in the heated day. She took off her white gloves and waved them close by her face. She would soon break a heel. No one had hit her, she had seen shelter. She had been in a broken car before and nothing bad had come of it.

First they walked on the tarred road. The father had some knowledge of the gasoline engine. He predicted, It's the pump. He put a hand to his throat. Or the lines, maybe the lines. This was in the heat and light of day. The light revealed a red dusty land. The car was a black Bantam coupe and he had been driving it on the road to the Chisos mountains. He was a seller of hams on a vacation tour. He had met the mother in Northern Mexico.

Look, the mother said and she bent down and picked up the heel from the road. It was white and like a delicate funnel stopped at one end. I'll break the other one for you, said the father. No, she said. She walked unevenly due to the heel. Like a person with a limp. Like a person ascending a stair who finds the stair withdrawn. Like a woman, a woman. It was bright in the day, and hot. She had read more than the father and her head was filled with abstract knowledge but she had no knowledge of the gasoline engine.

They came to a wide dirt track leading off to the right. The track stretched out, rising to a ridge that described a horizon. Tires had pressed patterns into the dirt. Riders had passed in metal through the air.

This was before they had come to the house. It was a tall, thin house. They did go onto the track. Not a car had passed them on the tarred road. But it was a long track and the sky was purple and gray with dusk when they finally stood on the ridge and looked down at the other side. They were tired with walking and they saw down there: the drop. They saw the house and the low building behind it. It was in a near low curve of land.

The father, my father, pointed out. Propellers, he said. There was a pile next to the low building. He started down the slope. The dirt was soft and deeper, and he went pointing his feet to one side. He went faster. He held his arms away from his body and the arms made little circles in the air. He hit the bottom of the slope. He had gone that distance without looking back at the mother my mother. She also went down the slope. Her shoes sank into the dirt and the dirt seeped into them as she went. The shoes had been white but now were changed.

They looked for a human being. They knocked on the door of the house and waited. They knocked. They went to the other low building and stood in the frame of the large doorway and called out. It was darkening out. It was darker inside the building.

There were two men in the building. They slammed something and came from a room. The shadows fell like cloth in the building. The father my father said, Hello. He thought the men looked dark. He said, Mexicanos? They looked at him and did not reply. *Habla Espanol*, the father my father asked. One man put his hands in his pockets. The men looked down at my father's torso and then his shoes. They looked up again. One man, the smaller, said I'm a Texan. And his voice held no regret. The other man said, I'm a Texan. They came toward the father my father and the mother my mother. My father's hand crept to his pocket. It felt the ticking watch. My mother bent her knee and lifted it up. She bent down and took off the shoe without a heel. She poured dirt from it. The men were now quite near. The smaller one said, I'll fix you a new heel.

The father my father told about the broken car. The men said, It's late. They said they could stay but they wanted to play poker. Alright my father said with the politeness of a guest. This was before they had shown my father the knife. One man hit a switch and a light went on. The room was a square cavern. My father said more about the car. The men did not respond. Alright let's play poker said my father. One man the smaller man touched my mother. He put his hand on her arm. It stayed there for some seconds. The room smelled of smoke and gasoline.

There was a room in the back with some wooden chairs and a square metal table. They all went into this room. One man closed the door. The men sat down at the table. There had been games in the room before, one man said. A man had been cut there. He had his own rules, the taller man said. The men said they would show my father a new kind of poker. They said my mother could watch. My mother sat on a stool with her legs crossed. She sat away from the table. The men evinced interest in her legs. The legs were dirty, the white stockings soiled and with runs. There was a map on the wall depicting the state of Texas and the territory shown on the map was set against a background of deep blue and a bird which was perhaps the state bird was pictured hovering over the shape of the land. The taller man started to deal the cards. They were cards which had seen better days. What game do you play asked my father.

It was a game called Stumpeye Poker. It's easy said the tall dealer. I never heard of it said my father the willing guest. Must be a local variety. Must be said the dealer. We'll give you one or two hands before we put in.

It was a game of shifting rules. It was a game like a maze. I'm tired said my father and he tried to laugh when he did not understand the rules. Do you have any water he asked. The men said they didn't have any water. The tone of their voices was surprised and they emphasized the word water as if they had hardly heard of it. The dealer said in a nasty way, This is Texas. Can you live on dust said my mother. The men paid her no attention. My father's eyebrows went up. He smiled. I guess it doesn't rain much here, he said.

My father did not think himself a poor player. He picked up his cards and assessed them and made conversation. Now what I do, he said. He said this to the men. He told them of selling hams. It was a conversation like a story and he told the story in a loud voice as if he were addressing a person standing outside the closed door.

Now the Negroes, said my father. He put money on the table. Generally speaking they can't afford my product, toward the south they smoke their own. But up around Chicago I can happen on some that's not farming but that's made it more. Or maybe it's Christmas and the man buys a leg or shoulder for his woman. Excuse my being blunt. Now I got a little gimmick to sell more than that roast. It's a little thing I thought up myself.

The men pulled his money toward them. The deal did not move and my father took up some fresh cards. It's just a gimmick but it works he said. I don't have alot of coin, he said. Put it in bills then, said the dealer.

Now what is that gimmick my father inquired. How do you get rid of the hocks, tongue, snout, all smoked, understand, and wrapped. He frowned now as the play continued and it seemed he had a stronger hand and the men took some more of his money away. I show 'em the parts, he said. After they buy the roast see. And I say, Give her the whole thing, the whole pig. They get quizzical. Why what do you mean sir? Why with this!

I tell them. With this here make-your-own-pig package!

He smiled at the men and they were looking down at their cards. He looked at my mother who did not smile or laugh. Why they love it, said my father. I sell more parts that way.

Now what are the rules asked my father again. How much money do you have said the smaller man. This was at night. The light in the room faltered but did not go out. My mother drew a glove from her belt and passed it over her face. Where you from the small man who had touched her asked. They were playing a hand and the coins were on the table now. He made a friendly face at her. Wisconsin, she replied. The land of snow and cows! he said. The men laughed but it was not in a friendly way. Can you live on snow he asked and he raised one eyebrow in an upside-down V over his dark eye. He showed his cards and my father showed his cards and the small one took the money away. My mother folded the glove back over the belt. A fly came down from the light onto the table. Hit that fly the taller man said to my father. What said my father. Hit it, he said again and the fly buzzed away.

My father played the men's game and some time passed. He felt the cloth and money against his leg. The money fell fainter against the leg. It was warm and close in the room and he had walked all day in the sun. He laughed. It was a laugh like a cough. Some funny rules you have. He was not from Texas, he was a tourist. The smaller man put his hand to his side and brought up the hand and it had a knife in it. The hand set the knife on the table. I'm showing you this knife, the man said. My father stared at his cards and put a hand on his stomach. His stomach was soft and he had pressed it in with a leather belt. His hand moved down to his leg.

Are you threatening us, said my mother as she watched the knife. She had read widely and had much abstract knowledge but nothing she had read went in the direction of the knife. No man regarded her.

Here's a story, said the dealer. He had taken money on several occasions even though he had had weak cards. He did not have a knife in front of him but maybe he didn't need one. He dealt a card to his friend and one to my father.

There's a white man. He needs some water. He's in a dry country. He meets some nigras walking.

Some what asked my father. The man dealt him another card and my father looked at the two cards as if they made a map to tell him something.

Some nigras. They got water. In a bucket. He says he wants it, see, but they don't give it to him. What you want white man they say to him. The man dealt more cards. No one else for miles around. They make him get down on his knees and talk to the water. Say Water, I want you. The man puts down his head and says it. Beg for it, they say. Please water, please. I want you, says the white man.

The other man giggled. He rocked back and forth on his chair.

No one else around, said the dealer. The white man crawls for the water. And when he gets there one of the nigras unzips his pants and pisses into the water and then they dump it over his head. The water goes into the ground. There's your water, white man, they say. Who's the nigra now?

The other man went back and forth. He put a hand on the hilt of the knife and knocked it on the table to make a sound like clapping.

The dealer looked at my father who had all his hand now. Who's the nigra now? said the dealer. You hear that one before?

No said my father.

I didn't think you did. You hear that story, asked the dealer to my mother. No, she said.

That's right said the dealer. You wouldn't hear that one in Wisconsin. He found his words funny and laughed. Who's the nigra now.

Oh, said my father. He took his cards and turned them over, spread them face up. It was a paltry hand. Look, my car, he said.

You saying you won't play this game? The light still faltering from time to time but not going out. The man swept a hand over the cards and took them up. He added them to the other cards and threw the lot on the floor. The smaller man picked up the knife he had been showing.

My father lifted his hands and showed them. I'm saying, my car.

You saying you won't get down and pick those cards up?

My mother started to move from her stool and the small man exhibited the knife closely to her and she moved back. She took the gloves from her belt and threw them on the floor.

Mexicano, said the dealer and scorn rode heavy in his voice. He said, Get down, Mexicano.

The fly came back to the table. My father tipped from his chair. He put himself on his hands and knees on the floor. A mistake he said. He looked at each man and he watched the knife. A mistake, it was dark. We walked all day.

The small man made an X in the air with the point of the knife. He said, Who's the nigra now.

My father gathered the cards. He had been sweating all day but now he was not. His hand shook and his knees pressed the hard floor. He reached a hand under the table to get the cards there and when he did this the man showed the knife at his back and then the man's hand ran the knife down my father's back next to his spine. The knife went fast as if my father's back were easy as liquid and it ripped the cloth and cut into my father's skin. My father called out. My mother stood up from the stool.

The man with the knife sat back. My father up on his knees with a hand at his back.

A mistake, said the man with the knife in his hand. A mistake Mexicano.

My father started up with a hand on the metal table and pushed and the table went over. Jesus said my father. He turned to my mother and spread out his arms and went toward her as if he were about to embrace her. Get out, he said to her, get out. The dealer had a knife in his hand also then. The small man, the one who had offered to fix her shoe and who had put his hand on her arm and who had first cut my father, that one took my mother out of the room. He took her to the square cavern of a room and tied her with rough rope by the hands and ankles to a pole there. She heard my father call out again. Look, the small one said to her. I'm not so fond of women, really. You stay here and be a good girl. Delicately the man ran the knife up the back of each of my mother's legs, cutting the seam of her stocking, leaving a pinpoint line of red. You be good.

The worst happened then to my father. He was not quite dead but maybe he would have liked to die and that was when they dragged him outside past my mother and dumped him by the pile of propellers. The dealer went into the house and the small one came back to my mother. That's what happens when you stray he said to my mother. But you're lucky. I got some shame. He cut the ropes binding her and took her to the mouth of the building. Now get out of here he said. Your Spanish boy's out there.

My mother ran and stumbled and knelt down. My father's face was red and purple and blood came from places on it. All her book knowledge had receded and her breath hurt her throat. He put a hand on her and it was a weak hand. My god, said my mother trying to hold him but what was the proper way. My god.

It's a tunnel, said my father. The one moon had come out and it made a strong light and the propellers gleamed in a muted tone. Men come out of that space, he said. My mother pressed him against her and felt her shirt absorb the warm blood. She felt it sticky on her skin.

They go through the trees, said my father. My mother moved gently back and forth with him like that. She had read many books but never in her life had an enemy had a face and set it against her.

Ah Jesus, said my father, come down. He put his hand up and pressed her and she conceded and they lay down together in the dust and moonlight. Jesus, said my father. I smell roses. He moved his body against hers, rubbing, pressing as if he wanted a certain thing. My mother moved a hand to his pants. The pants had been ripped at the waist and the belt was gone. She pushed the pants down and away and her hand slipped on the blood of his skin and awkwardness. She felt for his cock and rubbed it. Come down he said again and he pulled at her shoulder. She kept the hand on him and moved in the dirt. The dirt moved with her and the father was heavy. She pulled her clothes up and down and felt him bleeding more with the abrupt movement. Shh, she told him. It was bright from the moon but his face was dark and surrounded by darkness and his eyes were like an animal's peering out of its lair. Did he recognize her? He was pressing his cock against her and she took her hand away and moved onto it. He grabbed at the ground and she tried to reach his hand. He pushed against her but without force and the blood seemed to pour from the places on his chest where the men had cut him. No she said and his hand went to her face and then to her hair and clutched at the hair. Her back was on the dirt and rocks and he moved in some rhythm now and the stones cut her back. She looked at his face and it moved and he was raised up slightly looking into the night at the tall thin house. He shuddered deeply and he looked in that direction. The house, he said. My mother tried to look, were the men coming back? The house is going up he said. She saw the corner of the house and it was not like a curtain lifted on hooks it was the corner of a sturdy but slim building. That house up there, my father said, and then, The pain. He pushed himself off my mother and fell toward the pile of propellers. He said, My mouth. He pulled himself along, one foot, two feet, three, away from my mother toward the house. It had been an effort, a long walk, the car still unfixed. And now it was pain and he could not tell it. It was sensation so strong it made language useless. How can it go up, he asked. He lay down then. He breathed the air in a skimming way and turned his face against the small stones. He breathed one more time and then something took his breath away and did not give it back.

Did my mother weep? In that night when she saw he no longer moved? Did she go to the body that was my father's, that was my father, and kneel and weep and rend her clothes? I was in my very beginnings and the body of that man stretched out on the plain like a plain itself. My mother was crawling into the night. The light on the propellers still was the light from the one sun reflected by the mirror of the one moon. I was just beginning within the bruised body of my mother and I was leaving my father who had died seeing the house rise up, whose body was revealed and then shown, exhibited by strangers who had misunderstood him. I was in the body, the body of my mother, then, at that time.

Chihuahua Primer

Every person has an idea or two about chihuahuas. Some feel it is proper to dress the creatures in festive, seasonal outfits and invite them up on laps for a visit. Others are concerned about the shape of the chihuahua's skull: its divergence from the common dog skull form causes them worry and even gives a few sensitive souls nightmares. But the chihuahua cannot help it if he has a skull which looks like a simple cap, the type of cap knit by an unpromising beginning knitter.

The chihuahua, like many other dogs, is not allowed to exercise his will very often. This was different, of course, in ancient times, when chihuahuas ran wild in the forests of northern Mexico and burrowed into the ground there in the deep secret folds of nature. Now and then ladies or men, happening by, lost perhaps, or hunting the colorful hypomyces lactifluorum, would catch sight of a chihuahua and they would clap their hands and emit small cries of pleasure, for the little smooth-haired creatures were considered good luck indeed.

And then at some point—it is difficult to say exactly when, history of this sort being always shrouded in darkness—, at some point unknown to most of us but not, one suspects, to the chihuahua, they were lured out of their forests, promised treats, no doubt, caught in cages, ambushed in the dark of night. Their captors may well have had good intentions, may merely have been down on their luck, in need of a charm to start their way back. Such is the attraction of the chihuahua.

We do not, of course, know the names of their captors, but it is a few mere steps from that violent night to this day, when chihuahuas are carried through cities in boxes and bags; dressed in tutus and clown suits and petted unceremoniously by every Tom, Dick, and Harry, as the saying goes; kept on leashes in parks and required to stand on two legs at odd hours of the day and night, waving their front paws helplessly before themselves.

So it is that for some of us, familiar with chihuahua history, a faint coldness clutches the heart when a Lincoln Towncar pulls beside us, carrying a lady who herself carries upon her lap a chihuahua dressed in a miniature and perfect Santa Claus suit. It is winter, snow begins to fall, the chihuahua's tender dark eyes look out and meet ours, and we try to signal to the delicate creature, to put into one glance between species knowledge of a distant and honorable past. But already the car has pulled ahead, is turning, the tiny Santa hat rides out of sight, and we must continue on our way in the snow that is falling everywhere, over houses, cars, and people, over the strange heads of chihuahuas, those beautiful creatures the sight of whom provokes a sense of loss, as they suggest to us another time....

Erotic Adventure

On the street a round-faced woman wearing a black hat speaks to a man. Although she does not know it, he is a man like a watch wound up, set in motion by the tight spring of sexual desire.

"I hate movies," she says to him.

"All movies?" asks the man. He is a man like the sun, his face emits light.

"Yes."

Thus they part. The woman, happy to find herself alone, walks quickly to her house. There she removes her hat and sits down at her dining-room table, folding her hands in front of herself. Immediately she falls into a reverie, recollecting her favorite moments and scenes from movies, how this one lifted that one's shirt, unzipped pants, skirt....

The man also repairs to his abode, passing on his way several delightful-seeming females to whom he nods and smiles. Well, he thinks as he opens the door to his house, the ladies are like beautiful silver fishes and my only desire is to swim along with them in a pleasant state of nudity. He sits down at his dining-room table and thinks of the round-faced woman and his heart is like a calendar, filled with the days that stretch out until he sees her next, when he will perhaps remove her hat, unbutton blouse, lift her skirt....

Primary Rule for Writing Popular Romance

If the woman is beautiful she must be undressed; if she is not beautiful she must be transformed.

Frank Costello
The Bet

I owe my life to Julie Krone, the nation's winningest female jockey.

"Going to Saratoga," I told the Congressman, when he asked what I would be doing during the '92 August recess. He knew me well enough to know the answer. He didn't mind me going to the track on or off recess, as long as I churned out the speeches and reports. He didn't mind my other, less lawful, gambling activities, tolerating the annoying phone calls and the unusual people—even by his low standards—passing through my office.

He could tolerate my vices because he knew that I would let his slide in return. He was my shark. I was his remora. If only my ex-wife had some vices I could have ignored, maybe the marriage would have lasted.

I had left introspection behind with my English degree. I had no ambition beyond the next bet, no career goals, no family. I had a place to live but I was homeless. But I did have Saratoga in August.

For all I knew, Saratoga didn't exist from September through July. It was my Brigadoon, arising out of the Upstate New York smog at the end of each summer with a happy crowd of locals singing and dancing in the white mist. I could imagine Willie Shoemaker and Angel Cordero riding through the Adirondack foothills on a busman's holiday, like Gene Kelly and Van Johnson hunting in the Highlands. Suddenly, a race track appears before them, surrounded by the relics of a society relegated to a part-time eternity by the graduated income tax. "How are things in Aqueduct," sing the locals. My magical holiday begins.

The romance of Saratoga, like most romances, was shallow. The boarding house I had stayed at for the last nine meets hadn't improved, although it did double its rates last year when Minnie, my August landlady, learned about the B&B markup.

Minnie was an ex-hooker turned bookie from Buffalo. She had backed into the landlady business years ago by collecting a marker on the house— she needed a place to stay in Saratoga, and if she could make a few bucks on the side, even taxable bucks, so much the better. Minnie didn't take any betting action during August, at least on the horses, and the house was as close as she had ever come to making an honest living. Then she learned about B&B's, from a source I have never been able to pin down, and got the house listed in a soft cover directory: a "quaint Victorian B&B with five guest rooms, numerous antiques, a proximity to the oldest thoroughbred race track in the nation (the races are only run in the late summer–check ahead) and Miss Minnie, your charming hostess."

Any thoughts about taking my business elsewhere ended that August morning when the unsuspecting Yuppie couple, still stooped over from sleeping in a "quaint Victorian antique" that Minnie had picked up at Goodwill, came into the kitchen and asked about breakfast. "Fuck if I know," said Miss Minnie, charming as always. "Try the McDonald's down the street." Miss Minnie was my kind of person.

My own situation in August '92 was more hopeless than Minnie's promise of breakfast. It wasn't the horses that killed me. It was the ball games. Basketball, baseball, even Jai Alai. If you could roll it, I bet on it. I was on the losing streak to end all losing streaks. Like most, it had started strong. I dead cold nailed the college basketball regular season but gave it all back and then some in the NCAA's. Sweet sixteen, my ass. It was the suicide sixteen, eight big losses on my account. I began to do stupid things in an effort to win it back, but the nut kept getting larger and larger. By July, I was almost fifty thousand down. My bookie, George, told me that it was time to see Rock.

Rock represented the big books, the books that took the money laid off by guys like George the Barber. I had dealt directly with Rock a few years back, a Super Bowl bet that we syndicated. He paid off and thanked me for the action. No one knew why they called him Rock. He was short, overweight, wore a rug and favored white linen suits, summer and winter. His mannerisms were more effeminate than tough guy, Capote not Stallone.

No one ever pointed that out in his presence. It wasn't that Rock was scary. It was the people behind him. They wouldn't hurt you. You should be that lucky. No, they would just find a way to make you their partner, to work off the debt with your services. They wanted your soul, not your body.

"You're in pretty deep, kid," Rock whimpered. "Got a plan to get out?"

"Going to Saratoga," That was pretty much my standard response to all the big questions.

"Robbing a bank in Tharatoga or thomething?" Rock's lisp was unnerving, but it was not wise to laugh.

"You know Saratoga, Rock. It's my mortal lock, a sure thing. All I can do is make money there. I won't lose, guaranteed. The worst that can happen is that I break even, and we are where we are. But I got a good chance of taking down the nut. You've stayed with me this far. Just give me August in Saratoga."

I could sense Rock doing the arithmetic in his head, figuring the odds on my finishing in the money. "We like you. kid, we alwayth have," said Rock. "You're a pro, juth having tough luck. We can give you Tharatoga, but at the end we thettle, one way or another."

"Thanks a million, Rock," and I meant it.

"By the way, kid, how'th the Congrethman doing?"

*

148

The first three weeks at Saratoga went by quickly. I was about ten grand ahead as the fourth week began, Travers week, the week when the big money could be made, the temporal and geographic point at which the laws of random chance became clear. My target day was Thursday: lots of tourists driving down the odds on the wrong horses, and up on the right ones; lots of shippers being brought in from other tracks by trainers trying to make a quick killing; and Julie Krone fighting for the rider's championship.

I loved the smurf. I made a lot of money on her when she was fighting the odds in Maryland, and she was as tough down the backstretch as any boy I had ever seen. But that was before *Sports Illustrated,* and *People,* and the Letterman show. Now she was famous with people who didn't know a trifecta from a tricycle, who didn't know that the best jockey at a track would still lose four out of five races. She also was politically correct, the enlightened way to lose money gambling. She was made a favorite in twice as many races as her mounts deserved. The result was that you couldn't make a cent betting on her, but you could make a fortune betting against her, and Thursday's program looked perfect for the Krone factor.

The lead up to Thursday was great. I hit some big exacta's and went fifteen grand ahead for the meet. Only thirty-five to go. My box mates could see that I was hot. No last names. No real first names for that matter.

Willie the Conqueror, Peter Paul and Bullfrog had been sharing the same box with me since '87. They called me Shorty, I guess because I am several inches taller than the others, or maybe because I sometimes favor short odds. Willie made the purchase each year, and we just showed up. No details. No explanations. Just the impersonal intimacy which single men share. The little glimpses of past or other lives that came out were all track-related.

Willie had been a hot walker at a track when he was young—I wasn't clear whether it was during a college break or on work release—and he was one of the few people I knew who could honestly read the physical condition of a horse. Not the phony "he's on the muscle" jargon of the TV commentators. The Conqueror could look in a horse's eye and know if he was ready to run.

Peter Paul may have been in the seminary. Maybe he even was a priest. All we knew was that he was a virgin and that he sure blushed liked a bishop whenever Minnie told stories about the old days. He plainly had a priest's eye for sinners and could spot a trainer or jockey trying to pull a fast one with one quick read of the program.

Bullfrog had a four-pack-a-day voice, an easy call. He was the one we least expected to see back each August. But he always was there, croaking and puffing. He was the scientist in the group, a student of the arcania in the *Racing Form.* Bullfrog said that he once shared a box with Andy Beyer before he got his Pulitzer, and that Beyer got his "speed ratings" from an idea that was originally Bullfrog's. Everyone at the track had a "what if" story like that, but Bullfrog did know his numbers. Who can tell?

Anyway, I was doing better than all of them, and they knew it. No room for jealousy in the box. We all enjoyed each other's successes. But they didn't know I was fighting for my life.

Thursday couldn't come soon enough. Ten races, with at least three where I had locks with long odds. But I wasn't in it for the win money. Today was the day I was going to take home the Pick Six.

The Pick Six was the toughest of the so-called exotic bets that racing commissions invented to compete with lotteries and casinos. The public loved big payoffs, no matter how impossible the odds. The Pick Six pandered to that weakness. A two dollar bet picking the winners of the fourth through ninth races, with the winners taking 75% of the money in the pool—and at Saratoga that could mean a payoff well into six figures on a single ticket. If there was no winner, part of the pool was carried over to the next day. That's a big payoff, particularly if there is only one winner, but with an average of nine horses in each race there are over half a million possible combinations.

I had pieces of the Pick Six in past meets, going in on syndication bets with my box mates. I even made close to eleven grand once when we split a Pick Six winner during a rainstorm several years back. But I had never hit the big one on my own. Now was the time. Even the weather report over the track PA system was favorable: "Sunny, light wind, high about 75 and a carry over in the Pick Six of $131,000."

I had three horses covered in each race, a $1,458 bet on 729 combinations, all put down in a few seconds with the help of a computer. In the fourth race, Kent Desormeaux took a filly named Soul of The Matter wire-to-wire over nine furlongs to start me off. Thank God for the kid, another old friend from Maryland. In the fifth race, a sprint, Gary Stevens beat out my second choice with the favorite, but I had the favorite covered. Two down, six to go. Time to make some money.

The Krone factor was at work in the sixth race, three-year-old maidens at nine furlongs. A maiden is a horse that has never won, and three-year-old maidens are the toughest call in handicapping. Julie was riding a horse that was otherwise undistinguished, but the Krone factor had picked up most of the win money. I had the second and third favorites as well as a shipper from Finger Lakes that was out of Secretariat and had been brought along slowly. Krone's horse broke in bad position and my shipper, a big colt named Jade Factor, took the rail, saved ground all the way around and pulled away down the backstretch. He didn't just win. He paid twenty-one dollars. This was getting rich.

"Only ten tickets hold the Pick Three," Bullfrog groaned, as he looked at the odds displayed in the television set in our box. "There's going to be a big payoff today if someone goes all the way."

"You're looking at that someone," I said. No point in keeping it a secret.

"Way to go Shorty." "Lord have mercy." "Get me some Camels when you collect." The excitement in the box was real. It was my money, but it was our team. High-fives and a round of beers. As I called the waitress over, I saw Rock, white linen and all, smiling at me from a seat up above.

The seventh and eighth races were no contest. My horses had win and show in the seventh and all three finished in the money in the eighth. No extra money for me, but the box was betting my horses race by race and hit an exacta and a trifecta, each at long odds. We were cooking, and it was contagious. The boxes around us, more familiar strangers, picked up on the excitement. There was nothing like it. Only the ninth race left.

"One minute to Post Time."

"Don't keep it a thecret kid. Are you alive after five?" Again, the lisp from hell.

"Yeah, Rock, I'm having a good day. I told you I would."

"Tell you what, kid. You give me that ticket, and we cancel the marker. You don't owe nothin, and we start over. But you don't give me that ticket and you don't hit the ninth, and we got to have a long talk about the Congrethman."

"Give me some credit, Rock. I've got three horses in the ninth, and the Julie Krone fanatics have driven up the odds on all my horses. I'm looking at a payoff of two, maybe three hundred grand."

"Your choice kid. Maybe Krone winth and you lose. I'm just trying to help you out. I won't be able to do that once the race is over. No replayth at Tharatoga."

I broke into a sweat. The biggest payoff in my life, the answer to my problems, was a few minutes away. Either that, or it was the end of my life. I couldn't move. I couldn't answer Rock.

"It is now post time."

"I guess that's the answer, Rock. Let the horses decide, as always."

Rock moved next to me. "This window'th sthill open kid. My offer holdth until the bell ringth."

The horses loaded quickly into the gates. The sixth horse was another of my shippers, a four-year-old claimer named Turbulent Kris. "Must have been named by a startcr," Peter Paul said, as we watched number six break loose from the gate crew and buck sideways against the green metal doors. He broke down the track in the opposite direction. An out rider caught up and brought him to a stop. We could see the crew and a vet going out to check him over. The other horses were growing impatient in the gate. The crowd was getting impatient at the rail. I had stopped breathing.

"Turbulent Kris is being scratched by order of the track veterinarian," the PA system announced. "All bets on Turbulent Kris will be shifted to the favorite, Bucking Bird."

Bucking Bird and Julie Krone, I thought. The Krone factor, sucker bets, my odds at winning going up, my odds at a big payoff going down. Damn Julie Krone. Does she have to make it this difficult.

"Sthill no bell, kid," Rock said in my ear, "sthill no bell."

I watched my body make the decision. My hand, the one clutching the ticket, went out to Rock on its own.

"Thankth kid," Rock said. "We're thquare now."

"They're off."

151

"At the quarter pole" I was even with the betting windows. "As they pass the half-mile pole" I passed the paddock. "As they enter the far turn" I was past the elms, even with the Big Red Spring and gaining on the Union Ave gate. By the time they started the stretch run, I was beyond hearing distance, sprinting all the way to Minnie's. I never looked back. I never said good-bye, even to Minnie. I just kept going.

✳

To this day I have no idea who won the ninth race that Thursday at Saratoga. I stay away from the track. I don't bet on anything, unwilling to take the chance that I might meet see someone who was there, and who remembered. I have a new wife, a new job. Some might say I have a future.

Minnie, Willie the Conqueror, Peter Paul and the Bullfrog may miss me every August, or maybe they don't give a damn. I try not to give a damn about them.

All I remember about the track is Julie Krone, the nation's winningest female jockey. I owe her my life.

Donya Currie

Land Mines

Jacob hasn't been the same since he stepped on a land mine on his way home from Sunday market. Refusing to try the prosthetic legs offered at the Red Cross clinic, he's stuck with crutches and an eerily flapping pants leg that scares his younger brothers and sisters.

"Leave me alone," he tells the social worker who visits once a week. He will not look at her, only turns his face to the wall and waits for her to leave. Sometimes she will sit for hours, hoping to break his will. She never wins.

"You know, antipersonnel mines kill 25,000 people each year," she tells him one spring afternoon, the sound of giggling children seeping in through the walls of his family's hut. "You are lucky to be alive. You are lucky you didn't lose your eyes like some of them. You could still make something of your life, be useful to your village."

She might as well talk to him in another language. He refuses to listen. He thinks about the way his legs used to carry him swiftly, how he could run faster than anyone his age or younger. How the smallest children looked up to him. Now they laugh.

And the dreams continue to haunt him. First it is Winnie the Pooh.

"Cottleson, cottleson, cottleson pie," the yellow, furry Pooh says, perched on the edge of Jacob's cot. "Come outside and see the honey. Come outside. It's so very nice outside."

Jacob follows Pooh and they romp in the fields, Pooh runs and Jacob hops, hops, hops quickly behind him, reminding Pooh of Kanga and Roo.

"Now you're getting it," Pooh squeals. "Ah, so very nice."

Jacob always wakes from this dream sweaty and disappointed, wishing he could hop that fast. He's afraid to try, picturing himself pitching over into the dirt, face-down, looking like a fool. A crippled fool.

Sometimes, Nowhere Man visits, bringing his nonsense that often makes sense.

"For what you sit there with blue banana trying your clock so sad?" Nowhere Man has a hard time, the way his brain and body are dislocated like a Salvador Dali painting, pieces of him floating about the room, his words mixed with the surreal images of other people's dreams.

"Come on, Jacob," Nowhere man says, extending a rippling, caramel-colored finger toward the cot. "Get a move to your shave run outside."

Nowhere Man leads Jacob outside, where Pooh waits. They all go hopping toward the horizon. Jacob hops fastest because he's had the most practice.

When Jacob turns around, pieces of Nowhere Man are floating toward the sky, becoming smaller and smaller. Then Pooh hops onto a mine and fur and stuffing fly into the air. Both his friends disappear.

Jacob never tells anyone about these dreams. He knows he is going crazy.

"It's not like you mushroom soup to be good and find oranges planted to give up," Nowhere Man says one night, the three of them stretched out under a small tree, taking a breather from the night's hop.

"Leave me alone," Jacob says aloud, waking himself with his own voice. He lies in the darkness and listens, thinking he can hear Pooh giggling in the distance.

Jacob eases himself up on one elbow and peers out into the night, searching for Pooh. His brothers and sisters are sleeping on pallets on the floor, wrapped around each other like puppies. The oldest brother, Kaleb, snores gently. Little Oshwa is smacking her lips in her sleep. All the tiny chests rise and fall with easy breathing, the kind Jacob can only imagine now that the craziness and fear from losing his leg make his breath anxious, sometimes painfully so.

"Perhaps if you could pray," the social worker says during one visit. "You might find a way to reach peace. You might find that losing a leg is not the worst thing that could happen to a person."

"I was wondering through the woods one day," Pooh says. "No, I think I mean I was wandering. Um, oh, well now I'm confused. I can't remember why I was telling you that story, anyway. Come outside with me."

When Jacob first stepped on the mine, he had a kind of strange vision, knowing exactly what was happening as the hot pain shot up his leg. His parents had died this way. They walked through a field of multiple mines and somehow managed to trip five of them at once, the Red Cross volunteer told him. Their bones and chunks of flesh were scattered for two miles.

"So many junk heartache and the lost bad time because of the mines," Nowhere Man says, spreading himself across Jacob's bedroom ceiling like a constellation. "You are feeling alone like candles flowers no one is here for you?"

"Yes," Jacob says, once again waking himself by talking in his sleep. His eyes are wet with tears.

A United Nations team came the day after Jacob's accident and swept the village, taking 234 active mines away. Some of them blew up during the team's search. They lost a beautiful German shepherd early in the morning, before anyone realized how many mines had been buried in the village fields.

"I want to ask you," chubby Pooh says one night during a particularly long hop, "Where did the mines come from in the first place? I've never heard of such a thing."

"Civil war," Jacob answers as he hops. "The entire country was at war for seven years. Towards the end, the government forces tried mines as a way to end the rebellion. After 1,000 soldiers and twice as many civilians died from mine encounters, the war ended."

Pooh's yellow fur looks like gold in the moonlight. He searches for honey in the hollow of a stubby tree. Jacob hops home alone.

The morning of the six-month anniversary of Jacob's leg loss, he wakes up to the sound of crying. The hut is empty. He wonders if he is hallucinating.

"Hello?" His voice echoes in the empty hut. His crutches scrape the dirt floor as he searches for signs of life. He limps outside and finds the village deserted. Even the animals are gone.

"Where are your brothers and sisters?" Pooh asks.

"Get anthem out of brisket here," Nowhere Man says fearfully, gripping Jacob's arm.

As Jacob heads toward the edge of the village, he comes across a dead goat, bloodied and dismembered. Then there is a small dead child, curled into a fetal position in the dirt. Then a mother, her face blown away, a basket of laundry spilled by her feet. A few feet later, he sees Kaleb with an arm missing. The rest of his brothers and sisters are scattered nearby. All dead. All bloody.

"You go," Pooh says, breathing heavily in Jacob's ear. "We have to tell someone about this."

"Out, out, bubbles now!" Nowhere Man screams.

"No!" Jacob cannot stand the sight of so much death. Then he wakes.

He is alone. He doesn't know where he is, if his brothers and sisters are still alive. He can't seem to get thoughts to straighten out, to form like they used to and connect one fact to another.

"I am not crazy," he says to the empty room where a hot breeze is lifting the curtains from the open windows. Jacob's leg begins itching, not at the stump but in the place his leg would be if it had not been blown off. The itch grows hotter, into a burn. He thinks of Pooh and the first time his mother brought him a stuffed yellow bear to comfort him as a small boy. He remembers his Animal Man comic books, the vegetarian super-hero, and how Nowhere Man showed up in a late edition as one of the creepier villains because of his jangled speech patterns and his dismembered body.

Somehow Jacob's mind has strung together these gruesome dreams from his childhood comforts and the horror of the mines in his village. He slaps at the blanket where his non-leg itches, lies back against his thin, mashed-down pillow and vows to try hopping without his crutches. Tomorrow night. When no one is looking.

"And you will be gentle not looking down but thinking hats scarves gloves up, at the sky," Nowhere Man whispers.

"If your hands are free from those crutches," Pooh adds, "you will be able to grab an awful lot of honey."

Lucinda Ebersole
Auden's Toothbrush

It was called The Colony. It had some official title on legal documents but everybody who was, is, or wanted to be in the literary establishment called it The Colony. The Colony sat grandly on sixty lush New England acres with a large house that served as the dining hall and meeting room. Scattered around it were a series of duplex living quarters that housed the visiting writers.

Over the years, each side of each duplex had become known by a specific article left behind by a writer. Every year subsequent writers tried to leave behind something to top the item their room was known by. It was a foolish contest that meant each bedroom in The Colony was filled with inane bric-a-brac without the slightest rhyme nor reason.

When she arrived at The Colony, her packet of information said she would be in Duplex 8, Room 2, the room with Auden's toothbrush. She was told by the director of The Colony, known as The Director, that this was the room with Auden's toothbrush as she set her bags down in the living room. Each duplex had a living room and kitchen on the ground floor with steps on either side of the living room that led to the second floor, where there was a bedroom and bathroom on each side but no hall. According to The Director, this was the ideal writer's environment because you had your own private space but also a communal space so you could spend time with your fellow writer. It was clear that The Director was not a writer.

As they stood in the living room, the door opened and The Director greeted the other inhabitant of Duplex 8. "Ah," he said, "It's the Yale Poet." She was the Yale Poet, not to be confused with the Yale Younger Poet, who was not at The Colony. One of the things that separated The Colony from MacDowell or Yaddo or Ragdale was the pecular, almost tribal use of nicknames for the visiting writer's. These unfortunate labels, came from The Director, but were readily accepted by everyone who crossed onto the colony's lush green pastures and were bestowed for three things: your last prize, your last teaching gig or your last *New York Times* review.

"And this," said The Director, "is The Feminist de Sade." She cringed momentarily but knew this was to be expected, after all, she had won no prizes and hadn't taught in a year. All she had was that damn *New York Times* review. Never in a million years should the *New York Times* have reviewed her arty little novel on the front page. It was a fluke really. She met the agent through a friend and she knew no agent would represent a writer with not a single piece of work published, much less a writer with a literary novel that she would not allow to be edited in any way.

"So, The Agent said, "what do you write."

"I've written a novel," she said before she was known as The Feminist de Sade.

"What kind of novel is it?"

"A good novel."

"It's about good and evil?"

"No, it's good. A good literary novel."

"Well," The Agent tried a different tact, "Who do you write like?"

"I write like I write."

"But, you have to write 'like' someone. Is dark and gothic like Flannery O'Connor? A voice for our age like F. Scott Fitzgerald? A new-age *Gone With the Wind*. Who is it like? I can't sell it if it's not 'like' someone."

"Then you can't sell it. It's my voice. It's unique to me."

"A unique voice," The Agent said. "I'll need more. Genre? Romantic? Detective? New-Age? Experimental?"

"Yea," said the future Feminist de Sade. "It's an experimental chick novel. No plot. No narrative. No characters. Just language. Page after page of words. The End." Surely now the Agent would politely leave her alone. She watched as The Agent shifted in her chair and then smile broadly.

"An experimental chick novel. That's perfect," she said, and it must have been, because two months later she called with news that the novel had sold. Bypassing the normal small, literary imprints, The Agent had sold the book and the option for the second to the biggest, most conservative mainstream press in America. By the time the book was published, there were several good reviews and The Agent called with news of a review in the *New York Times*.

"They're definitely going to do a review and that's really all that matters. Who does the review is really unimportant," the Agent told the impending Feminist de Sade.

"Who's doing the review?" she asked.

"It's no big deal," The Agent said.

"Who?"

"It's really a good thing," The Agent said prefacing her remarks, "I mean she is really famous and besides most people think she's a nut so what she says really, really doesn't matter. What's important is that she writes about you. But if you really want to know…"

This was the kind of information that makes writers prone to alcohol and suicide. The reviewer was to be America's Most Controversial Lesbian Social Critic.

"Don't worry," said The Agent. "Her last *Times* review was flattering."

"Her last review was for a book entitled *The Hidden Erotic Foreplay in Byzantine Art*."

"She liked it."

"She hates fiction. I've heard her speak. The last fiction she read was *The Odyssey*. She said it was too character driven. She'll trash the book."

"Look," said The Agent, "Press is press. There is no bad press and if she hates it, everyone else will love it. Trust me."

The advance copy of the *New York Times Review of Books* arrived several weeks later and below the grand masthead sat these words: "A Feminist de Sade is Born." The byline read, America's Most Controversial Lesbian Social Critic. This couldn't be the review for her book. She looked closer and saw the title and her name and she read on.

It was true that the main character did have a penchant for seducing women and tying them to the bed, but that was just a metaphor. She only did it four or five times. She never so much as kissed them, never touched a one of them, except to tie their hands. The women were never hurt, in fact, they rather enjoyed it.

The National Organization for Women did not enjoy it. They organized a boycott. The boycott sold more books. The press called. Talk shows called. Obscene callers called. Every time her name was printed, it was followed by "The Feminist de Sade." Two years later, her name didn't matter, especially at the Colony. She was The Feminist de Sade and she smiled at The Yale Poet as The Director closed the screen leaving them alone in the living room.

"Look," said The Yale Poet, "I know about you. I've read the articles. I want you to know right from the start, I'm not into that stuff. I'm as liberal as the next person, but I don't want to be recruited."

"It was a novel," The Feminist de Sade said. "It was a novel. "

She was shocked that The Yale Poet would think that she might be the slightest bit interested in her. The Yale Poet was in her early forties but looked ninety. Ninety years old and ninety pounds. The skin on her body was wrinkled and her eyes sunk deeply into her head. She had long hair hanging nearly to her knees. She turned abruptly and headed up the stairs to her room—the room with Marjorie Kinnan Rawlings' map of Florida. From the back, she looked like Cousin It on a bad hair day. The Feminist de Sade stood alone in the living room. "It was only a novel."

At The Colony, dinner was served at 6:00 p.m. Dinner resembled the food in a condemned high school lunchroom. The Feminist de Sade looked for an empty seat. The Director motioned her to his table. She took the only seat, next to The Yale Poet. The Director introduced her to a Lannan, whose husband was also a Lannan but he was teaching and couldn't be with her, Miss Nominated for a National Book Award, Pen/Faulkner, and Mrs. Giles Whiting.

"The Feminist de Sade is in the room with Auden's toothbrush," The Director said.

"How is it?," asked Pen/Faulkner.

"O.K., but I wouldn't have thought that Auden would have had a pink Reach."

There was a pause as everyone at the table looked at The Director who choked on a fish stick. The Lannan smiled, "You live up to your reputation." There was nervous laughter followed by curious whispers as the star of The Colony's season entered the lunchroom and no one gave a second thought to Auden's toothbrush. Last year he had been the star when he was The Pulitzer, but this year he was back and known as The MacArthur. "The Mac Arthur," people said it with the same reverence as they said "The Pope."

The Feminist de Sade had no interest in fish sticks. She played with her food as she watched The Yale Poet do the same. The Yale Poet had known better than to take the fish sticks, she only had some salad. As the writers talked, she arrange and rearranged the salad on her plate, occasionally eating a small piece of iceberg lettuce. After careful arranging, the lettuce, carrots, radishes and onions resembled a woman's face lying on the plate. The Feminist de Sade pushed her own plate back and excused herself from the table as the salad face watched her leave the room.

She sat at the desk in the room with Auden's toothbrush and thought about all the other writers who had been there before. They all probably sat at this desk and wrote wonderful novels and poetry, but she stared at the blank space. She wrote several letters and rationalized that it was writing of some kind. Sitting on the bed and fumbling through the magazines in the bedside table, she read a story by John Cheever in *The New Yorker*. Realizing that Cheever had been dead for quite some time, she looked at the cover and found that the issue was dated 1968. Perhaps it was time to clean out the night stand she thought when she noticed that this particular *New Yorker* was addressed to Truman Capote. As she stuffed the magazine back in its place, she caught the cord of the lamp, pulling it off the night stand. The lamp fell to the floor, shattering the bulb in an explosive crash. Sitting in the dark, the only light visible was the blinking time on the alarm clock that read 3:16 a.m.

The Yale Poet wandered into the kitchen, her hair hanging in an enormous braid that resembled an anaconda resting on her spine. She was groggy as she sat down at the tiny kitchen table.

"Sorry about the noise," The Feminist de Sade said, "Want some coffee."

"O.K. What noise?"

"I crashed the lamp about three. Didn't it wake you?"

"I'm a heavy sleeper. Nothing wakes me."

"It could have waked the dead."

"Didn't bother me. I'll see you at lunch," she said as she left the kitchen.

"Probably not until dinner."

At dinner, The Feminist de Sade was again unable to eat as she watched The Yale Poet arrange her salad. Tonight the vegetables were arranged in alphabetical order, the next night in a palette of descending color, the next by country of origin. Each night the salad arrangement was a puzzle, the more she played with the food, the less The Feminist de Sade ate. She was growing increasing cranky and unable to think of anything but food, she even dreamed of food.

In her favorite dream, she found herself in a kitchen with a gigantic refrigerator. The refrigerator was filled with poultry of every kind. There were squabs and quails, capons and turkeys, Cornish game hens and ducks, and chicken in every conceivable fashion: legs and thighs, breasts and wings, whole and quarters. She began cooking. Duck a l'orange, quail in Pernod, roast turkey, duck flambé, pate de carnard, squab a la creme, and chicken: Cordon Bleu, Henri IV, Marie-Louise, Napoleon, Provençal and simply fried. Her last dish was a poulet bonne femme. In a giant kettle, the chicken cooked in a thick broth. She cubed and sauted potatoes, crushed garlic, added onions and mushrooms. As she added the last sprigs of rosemary, she saw the Yale Poet floating in the stew, her head resting on chunks of mushrooms, potatoes surrounding her body, the gravy gently covered her as she sank under the chicken.

The Feminist de Sade woke famished. She went down the stairs to the living room and then up the stairs to the other bedroom. The Yale Poet slept on her side, her braid following the line of her body. The moonlight came through the window, illuminating the faded and tattered map of Florida, tacked to the wall where Marjorie Kinnan Rawlings left it. She walked carefully, making as little noise as possible. The desk was ordered with poems stacked in a pile on the left, a notebook and sharpened pencils on the right. Venturing into the bathroom, she examined the medicine cabinet and now understood how the poet slept through the noise. The cabinet contained Valium, Xanax, and a large bottle of syrup of ipecac. The visits to the poet's room became nightly excursions. Each visit, growing more bold.

One night she dreamed of crushing garlic and herbs with a white mortar and pestle. To the fine paste she added a virgin olive oil, stirring until it was velvety. As the poet lay naked on the bed, she rubbed the mixture over her body. The emaciated frame soaked up the oils and herbs, growing plump and strong beneath her hands. That night as she sat by the poet's bed, she stroked the braid, holding it away from her body. The hair was heavier than she expected and it smelled of strawberry conditioner. She touched the end to her cheek and felt the rough split ends as she breathed the rich fruity fragrance. At that moment, she knew she would have the braid for her very own.

At dinner, The Feminist de Sade sat at the table with the Boys of Bennington. They were the youngest members of The Colony. Each had published novels before their graduation from Bennington. They had been roommates and had written graphically violent novels. The Colony put them together and they spent most of their time playing tennis and being picked up in limousines to do interviews in New York.

"We're the low score tonight," Boy One said or maybe it was Boy Two, they seemed interchangeable.

"Not a single prize winner," says the other, "but we do have The Feminist de Sade."

"Do I count for something?"

"Oh, yea. You're one of those extra point kind of people."

"There's a point system?"

"Sure, this table is the *Times*/teaching table. You get a point for being in the *Times*. A point for teaching. Another point for teaching at a good writing program."

"An extra point for odd things, like being "The Feminist de Sade.""

"You boys have given this way too much thought."

"Look babe, this is a business and you have to know where you stand. You've got about another year with that de Sade thing and then you're going to need something else."

"You guys are tough. Tell me more."

"O.K., prizes are scored by prestige and cash. A Whiting is three, a Lannan is four."

"More money for the Lannan."

"Right. Nominated for an award is two, winning is three."

"Unless it's a Pulitzer, then it's four and five. A Nobel is ten. You just keep adding points."

"The MacArthur is a 29. Nine for the MacArthur, five for the Pulitzer, two points for Iowa, two points for Columbia, one point for Syracuse, one point for Florida, three for reviews in the *New York Times Book Review*, and six for the two National Book Award nominations."

"Now you try one, de Sade. Try the Lannan."

"Let me see. The Lannan is four, the *Times* is one, Columbia is two, so I'd say a seven."

"No, she's an eight. You forgot the bonus point."

"Bonus?"

"Her husband's a Lannan. That's a rare thing and worth a bonus."

As the table continued to evaluate the writers present, a bat flew through the window into the lunchroom. As people shrieked, the Boys of Bennington jumped from their seats, brandishing tennis rackets and taking wild swings in the direction of the bat. At Yaddo, the bats are considered sacred, but no such rule exists at The Colony. One racket made contact and the dazed bat hit the floor. The Feminist de Sade stepped in to protect the bat.

"Leave it alone. God, it won't hurt you, it will eat its weight in bugs."

She scooped up the bat, feeling its heart pounding against her hand. As she was headed toward the door, she passed the MacArthur who said, "That bat should make you a fine roommate."

"Yea," she said, "I think I'll call her Justine. You know, Auden's toothbrush would make a fine bat comb."

With that she disappeared out the door. She held the bat all the way back to her room and then opened her hand, releasing the bat out the window, but Justine flew back in and hung on the rafters. This is great she thought, from now on Duplex 8 will no longer be the house with Auden's toothbrush and Marjorie Kinnan Rawlings map. Duplex 8 will now be known for bats and syrup of ipecac. The Feminist de Sade sat at her desk and contemplated the fact that she would never write another word.

That night, she dreamed of sleeping naked in her bed. Mosquitoes flew through a tear in the screen and swarmed around her body. Sitting on her shoulder, a mosquito injected the anti coagulant and sucked the sweet blood until Justine dove from the rafters, the beating of her wings startling the mosquito who was consumed. All through the night, Justine soared and sliced through the air eating mosquitoes like popcorn. The beating wings fanned the sleeping body that twitched as a fly buzzed overhead. Justine hearing the fly caught it in her teeth, crunched the thorax like a hard caramel glaze and licked the soft custard entrails. The Feminist de Sade woke up fighting the covers as the sun came through the window. Justine was nowhere to be found. She sat up in the bed and knew that there would be no peace until she had the braid.

The Feminist de Sade was walking across the grounds when she saw The MacArthur crossing her path.

"How's your bat, what's her name, Justine?"

"She's fine. I'll tell her you asked."

"You know, I read your book. I usually don't read something with such hype, but it was really good. I don't think most people understood the women tied to the bed."

"It was a metaphor."

"Yes. It was a kind of poetry."

"So, what famous room are you in."

"My favorite. The Carson McCullers room."

"Did she leave a toothbrush?"

"No. Brandy. But it's gone now."

"Too bad. I guess we can't have a nightcap."

"Don't be so sure. Stop by after dinner. And, bring a toothbrush."

The Feminist de Sade watched The MacArthur walk away and she renamed him The Alibi. He had two things going for him. One he was notorious for his conquests of other writers. Two he could no longer hold his liquor. After five bourbons and some light petting, The MacArthur was out cold and she was on her way to The Yale Poet's.

Standing under the map of Florida with a sharp pair of scissors, The Feminist de Sade lifted the thick braid, pulling it away from the nape of the sleeping poet's neck. The braid was secured by a coated elastic band that held the hair tightly. She slipped the scissors through the hair and clipped a section, another section and another until the braid lay separate and alone on the bed. She lifted the prize and hurried down the stairs, stashing the braid in a bag under the porch and made her way back to The MacArthur's bed where she slept without dreaming.

The MacArthur reached over and pulled her close.

"Oh, please. Give a girl a break. You've kept me up all night. I'm much to sore."

"Oh baby," he said stroking her hair and he held her close.

"Let's just lay here a while," she said as she watched him smile. She fell asleep and woke up to the sound of the shower running.

"Why don't you grab a shower and we'll get some lunch."

In the lunchroom, the air was buzzing with gossip and whispers. As they walked in, The Director met them and asked to talk to The Feminist de Sade.

"I have to ask you this. Something has happened and I need to know...I have to ask you..."

"What? What is it?"

"Where were you last night?"

"Why?"

"The Yale Poet's hair was cut. Cut off in the night."

"What?"

"It was a sick thing. She's gone home. But you're her roommate and I need to ask you where you were."

The MacArthur stepped up and said, "That is really none of your business."

"It's O.K. We'll have to tell him."

"She was with me," he spoke up.

"With you?" The Director looked at The Feminist de Sade and then at the MacArthur. "All night?"

"Yes, all night," he said as he put his arm around her shoulder.

They walked her back to Duplex 8 and The Director suggested that she move to a new room.

"You can always stay with me," The MacArthur said.

"I'll be O.K. I'll keep the door locked."

"We never had to lock anything before." The Director told them, "but I guess times change."

The Feminist de Sade locked herself in the duplex and sat down at the desk in her room. She hadn't been sitting there long when she heard the murmur of voices. Looking around, she found her room filled with characters, all trying to tell her their story. She began to write. She wrote for hours, stopping only a short time to retrieve the braid from under the porch. She laid it out across the desk and she continued to write.

By the time she left The Colony, she had a first draft. The next few months she rewrote her novel and finally presented it to The Agent.

"This is great," she said, "Tell me about what happened at The Colony."

"The food sucked, The Yale Poet got sheared, I slept with The MacArthur, and wrote a novel."

"I hope the novel is more descriptive."

The novel was a hit. It got great reviews, though most of them referred to the writer as The Feminist de Sade. There had already been four printings when it was nominated for a Pen/Faulkner. Then it was nominated for a National Book Award. It was not nominated for the Pulitzer. Finally, it won a new prize whose name she could never remember. The prize was presented at an awards dinner. The Agent was telling her, "And guess who's going to introduce you?"

"Who?"

"Guess."

"Just tell me."

"The Yale Poet. Can you believe it. No one has seen her since it happened. It will get you tremendous publicity."

The Feminist de Sade dressed for the dinner. The first person she saw was The MacArthur who grabbed her and kissed her.

"I'm really proud of you," he said.

The Boys from Bennington were there.

"You're up fourteen points," they said.

The Director came up and hugged her.

"Would you consider being on our board?" he asked.

A shy young woman caught up to her as she left the ladies room.

"I can't tell you how much I enjoyed the book," she said as she looked down and soft curls caressed her full pink cheeks.

"Oh my God," The Feminist de Sade said, "I didn't recognize you. You look great."

The Yale Poet lifted her head and laughed.

"It's funny how many people don't recognize me. Sometimes I don't even recognize myself. I thought it was the end of the world, but without the hair, I saw myself in the mirror. I was a mess. So, I checked into a hospital. I've gained twenty-five pounds. I feel a lot better."

"You just look great."

"Thanks."

At the dinner table, The Feminist de Sade and The Yale Poet ate salad with blue cheese dressing. They drank Cabernet and ate crisp white rolls with sweet butter. They ate lamb chops with cranberries in wild rice and sautéed carrots and creamed spinach. For dessert, they ate a chocolate cake, with thin fluffy layers of cake separated by a mocha mousse and covered in a thick, crisp dark chocolate icing.

The MacArthur stepped away from the table and The Yale Poet leaned over and asked in a whisper, "About that night..."

The Feminist de Sade felt the cake tumble in her stomach.

"Did you really sleep with him?"

She laughed, "What did you hear?"

"That you had an affair."

"We did."

"Was he good?"

"What do you mean, 'good'?"

"Well, he's got a reputation as a ladies man, but..."

"Did you sleep with him?"

"Yes. But it wasn't great. In fact, it wasn't at all."

"It happens."

They laughed. They were laughing when The MacArthur returned.

"I'm glad to see you both having such a good time, he said. "I can't think of two women I'd rather have dinner with."

"I'm glad you feel that way," The Feminist de Sade said as she winked at The Yale Poet, "But if you reallly cared about us, you'd give us your dessert."

He slid the cake across the table as the women raised their forks in the air. As the forks headed toward the cake, the tines caught forming a solid wedge of silver dividing the chocolate cake cleanly on the plate.

Janice Eidus
Travelin' with Jack K.
(for Ron Kolm)

So Jack K. asks me to go *on the road* with him, and he says it just that way, like he's speaking in italics. Meanwhile, he's also giving me some long song and dance—while he's packing away scotch after scotch after I don't know what-all-else, since I'm not much of a drinker myself, and I only came into this bar in the West Fifties in the first place to use the Ladies Room to freshen my Ultima II Sexxxy Red Lipstick. Anyway, his shpiel is something about how he came back to life just the other day—he's really hyped up, talking a mile a minute, his words running together, like there's no punctuation, no time to stop and take a breath, nouns, verbs, adverbs, adjectives, all piling up so fast they're just one big blur to me—but he's saying something about how all the alcohol in his system had kept certain vital body parts alive inside him all these years, and then some voodoo-guy dug him up, and between these still-vital body parts and this voodoo-guy's secret potion, well, old Jack K. is now back on the scene, ready to head back *on the road*, one more time, baby.

So I'm thinking, why shouldn't I go with him? What's keeping me here? I'm completely broke, I've just been laid off from my job as a salesgirl at Macy's, and it's the third job I've lost in as many months. I've been out of college two years already, and I'm going nowhere fast, that's for sure—because my bosses don't like my attitude, or maybe they're turned on, or turned off, by my Ultima II Sexxxy Red lipstick, or something, but anyway, I keep getting fired. And I'm totally out of love at the moment with both of my boyfriends, the pothead guitarist, who, as far as I'm concerned should rot in Hell, and the depressed, Prozac-taking poet, who, as far as I'm concerned, is *already* rotting in Hell.

I ask Jack why he's chosen me to go *on the road* with him. I say it in italics, too, just like he does. I mean, I read it back in high school, like all the kids in my rebel-crowd did, and I can't believe that he's chosen me to be his next road buddy. It blows me away. I figure maybe he chose me because he's drawn to my lush red lipstick. But he says no, it's not the lipstick, and I listen real hard, trying to make sense of the way he strings those words together, and all I can figure out is that he chose me because I'm wearing earrings that look like the ruby slippers Judy Garland puts on her feet as Dorothy in the movie version of *The Wizard of Oz*. This makes me feel a little guilty, because these are very expensive Columbus Avenue earrings, bought and paid for as a gift to me by my depressed poet boyfriend one day when his father sent him a check to pay his psychopharmacologist, and then his dad practically killed him when the shrink called to say he'd never been paid, and my poet boyfriend had to confess he'd bought earrings for me, instead.

Still, they *are* beautiful: big, shiny, red earrings in the shape of Dorothy's magical slippers, decorated with all sorts of *faux* shiny, glittering jewels. Jack reaches over and strokes the earrings, first the left one, then the right. His strokes are totally asexual, and I know he's not coming on to me. He tells me that when he saw me sitting in the corner of the bar, he knew that my earrings were like karmic cosmic things, like pieces of zen attached to my earlobes, like "brilliant words that poured out of some misunderstood genius's mouth," he says, "and that reassembled themselves into a pair of earrings, man, do you know what I mean?"

I nod yes, even though I don't, and then he begins to ramble about how boring society is, and how it would have been much more fun to have come back to a cooler, jazzier, bebop, hipper place than this same old uncool, repressed, unspiritual one. "*Oz* now," he tells me, stroking my *Wizard of Oz*, ruby-slipper earrings again, "where Dorothy went with Toto, and the Tin Man, and that wild lion, and the straw guy, now *that* was a deeply spiritual place, Dorothy and Toto were on a quest, a spiritual journey, you know, fearlessly, like they were wild, never scared, never complacent."

I nod again, to show him I'm with him, I'm keeping up, even though that's not the way I remember *The Wizard of Oz*, but I'm not about to disagree with him.

"In Oz," he says, "those Munchkins, they were the true Beats—living their lives in states of exhalted exhaustion—skipping up and down that yellow brick road, and even if that old guy, the Wizard, wasn't really the real thing, he was such a character, he had vision, he was an adventurer, a really cool old guy, and that good witch, the nice one, what was her name, she wasn't a slut or a whore like most women, not her, she was a real sweet babe. Dorothy *never* should have left Oz," he insists, downing another scotch. "She never, never should have gone home, man. Like, what did her home have that Oz didn't, answer me that?"

I just keep nodding, pleased that I can follow his sentences, at least for the moment, and the ruby-slipper earrings bounce along with each nod of my head.

"I *read* you, chick," he says to me. "And I like you. You're cool. You can handle this, so let's do it—let's go *on the road!*"

I pay for my ginger ale, and I ask his permission to go to the Ladies Room before we split. I realize I'm sort of "the girl," and he's going to be "the man," the one giving orders, that that's part of the deal. But I figure, better Jack K., who wrote that really cool book, giving me orders, than that nasty, tight-lipped fart at Macy's who barked orders at me all day long, and then fired me for staying out an extra five minutes on my coffee break.

In the bar's bathroom, I reapply my Sexxxy Red lipstick one more time, I stroke each ruby-slipper earring for good luck, and then I pee for a really long time, pushing myself to keep peeing and peeing, because I don't know when we'll be near a decent bathroom again, if we're really going *on the road,* and then I zip up my black jeans, wash my hands with a ton-and-a-half of soap, again because who knows when I'll next have a chance to. And then I smooth my black tee-shirt, take a deep breath, and I head back out to the bar to meet up with my new road buddy, Jack K.

We walk out the door of the bar together. He really doesn't look bad for someone who's just come back to life. A little bloated, but that's all. We start walking along together. I can't tell if he has a specific direction in mind, or if he's just walking aimlessly. Then all of a sudden, he starts to cry, although he doesn't stop walking, but he's crying about how much he misses his mother, who worked in a factory and never complained when he lived at home with her and wrote books that didn't make any money, and this upsets me, because my own relationship with my own mother, who wants me to get married, have umpteen babies, and live in the same suburb she does, is pretty awful—and I feel as though he's guilt-tripping me, even though he doesn't mean to be—but then I realize that his mother is dead, and so what he's saying is really, really sad, and I begin to shiver all over.

Then, suddenly, he stops crying. "Big Sur," he shouts. At first I think he's addressing someone he knows in the street—"Big Sir!" But I look around, and the street is deserted, so I realize he's talking about the place in California. "That's where it's at, man, that's where it's cool, where it's spiritual and jazzy and rebellious, not bourgeois, a West Coast Oz." So I nod, again, what do I know, after all, I'm only "the girl," and I've never been to Big Sur. I've seen some photographs, though, of some extremely expensive looking houses out there that only some awfully bourgeois people could afford to live in, but it's Jack's show, and if he says Big Sur is where we're heading, then I'm ready.

"Okay, but first I've got to stop at Macy's," I tell him.

His mouth hangs open, like he's never heard of it.

"You know," I say, "it's like the biggest department store in the world? On Thirty-Fourth Street?"

"I know what the hell it *is*! Don't condescend to me, you little twit," he shouts out. And then he starts to call me names, bourgeois, hyper-feminine, cockteaser, bitch, slut, he's ranting on and on about how I'm like all the rest of them, all I care about are clothes and perfume and making myself desirable for every Tom, Dick, and Harry, like every other slut he's known. I can't imagine where all this stuff is coming from—it's got nothing to do with me or Macy's—it's like he just can't stop certain words from pouring out of his mouth once he gets going on a particular subject. So I don't take it personally. Then, when he seems wound down and exhausted, near collapse, I say, "Look, I used to work there, and I've got a last paycheck due me, okay? So come on, we need the money, it's some bucks for us to head to Big Sur with."

This cheers him considerably, and he doesn't call me another name after that. But when we get there, after I pick up my paycheck from a snotty little clerk in Accounting who's wearing earrings that look like cheap chandeliers, I confess I do make a quick stop at the Ultima II cosmetics counter on the main floor to buy two more tubes of Sexxxy Red lipstick, because I feel absolutely naked when I don't have any on, it's just one of those things about me, the way Jack can't control his words, I can't control my lipstick habit. But Jack goes crazy again while I'm doing this. He sulks, and curses the poor saleswoman who's ringing up the lipsticks for me.

After I pay for the lipsticks, I get this idea of how to make Jack happy, so I take him upstairs to the Lingerie section. I have this strong hunch that he's the kind of guy that'll get very turned on by all the racks of bras, panties, teddies, garter belts, and corsets. And I'm right. He immediately begins running through the Lingerie section like a little boy, from rack to rack, aisle to aisle, fingering black lace thong-style panties, burying his face in pink satin teddies, mumbling something into a large-cupped Maidenform bra about his saintly, dead mother. Unfortunately, he's starting to attract a lot of attention, and I know how brutal the Security Guards at Macy's can be. So I drag him, protesting all the way, down the escalator. "Come on, Jack," I say, in as pouty and cute a voice as I can manage, trying to be "the girl" again, "we gotta go. The road, Jack, let's go *on the road, buddy*."

Now he's happy again, he hasn't had a drink for a few hours, which is good. "West," he tells me, "Big Sur is West." So we cross Broadway and start walking west. When we get to Ninth Avenue, we pass a large group of homeless people sitting over a grate on the street, and he immediately stands over them and begins preaching at them, in that stream-of-consciousness way he has, about how if they travel west with us, they too shall find the independent way, the zen way, the Oz way, and then he starts telling them all about what a saint his dear, departed mother was.

"Hey, man, fuck you," one of them says, looking up at him, "give us some spare change, or blow your crazy, drunken, mother-lovin' speech out your asshole and begone!" I start to look around for a cop, because I'm getting scared in a major way. But Jack just keeps keeps preaching and preaching, telling them that this spare change they're so desperately interested in is not zen, not good for their creativity, their independence, their deepest spirituality, at all. So one of them, a big burly guy who looks like a former boxer, stands up and is just about ready to punch Jack in the face, and I'm still playing "the girl," pleading, "Oh, please, pretty please, don't hurt him, we're *on the road*," but nobody is paying any attention to me. But another one of the homeless guys stands up and stops the first one. He says, "Nah, man, he ain't worth it, he's just another one of them zombie writer types, I can pin them a mile away, they never got any money on them." The first one says, "Yeah, you're right, he's a writer, for sure, he ain't got nothin' worth taking," and he sits down.

So now everyone seems calm. "Let's go downtown, Jack," I say. "West," he insists. "Big Sur."

"Well, yeah, but downtown, first, you'll see. That's where it's really cool now. Trust me." I figure we'll take the subway, but Jack steps out onto Ninth Avenue and expertly hails a cab, and pushes me inside. Naturally, he expects me to pay for it. But I'm so grateful that we're both still alive, that I don't really mind, and I even give the driver an extra-big tip.

The first place I take him to is St. Mark's Place. We walk around. Jack suddenly produces a ten dollar bill and buys twelve identical pairs of earrings from a street vendor. The earrings are hideous. They look exactly like those cheap chandeliers the snotty woman in the Accounting Department in Macy's was wearing. "They're for my mother," he announces, which gives me the heebie-jeebies again. I'm starting to think that maybe I've made a big mistake, and that being on the road with a recently-returned-to-life Jack K. who's still obsessed with his mommy, is not where I'm destined to be. "Thanks, man," the earring vendor says to Jack, "you're a good son to your blessed mother."

Then I get this brainstorm and I take him into St. Mark's Books, and I show him all his paperbacks on the shelf: *On The Road*; *Doctor Sax*; *The Subterraneans*, all of them, shelves and shelves of just his books. I figure this will thrill him. "You're still in print!" I whisper. "Do you know how incredible that is? Most writers go out of print in, like, three *weeks*, and you've been dead for so long, and *you're still in print*" I figure this will give him some peace of mind, when he sees how well regarded he is, and then he'll calm down, and we'll just head out west to Big Sur.

Well, I'm right that seeing his books in print makes Jack happy, but I'm wrong about how he responds. Now he insists that we remain in the bookstore, so that he can peronally sign all the copies. "That way," he whispers to me, suddenly sounding very savvy, "the bookstore can't return them to the publisher, if they're already signed, you know what I mean. It's good for sales."

Before I can try to convince him that sales aren't his problem, he begins to shout, really loud, "Hi, everyone, it's me, Jack K., back from the dead, and we've got a booksigning here, a party, man, a reading, bring out the booze, bring out the drugs, the espresso, the bongos, the singers, the poets, bring out Allen and Neal and Bill, we'll party, come on, everyone, let's bebop right here, right now!"

Everyone is staring at him, but apparently nobody believes he's who he says he is, and everyone just goes about their business. A lot of people look embarrassed, like, oh, how sad, another nut who wishes he'd been a beatnik and who now thinks he's Jack K. come back to life. This enrages Jack, who pulls a flask of whiskey from his pants' pocket, and begins to drink. Then he begins to cry, curse, and shout. He calls everyone in the store heathens and morons who aren't fit to read a word he's ever written, and aren't worthy to inhale the same air on the same planet that his mother had inhaled. So now all the customers are growing nervous—"this guy is really a *nut*," I hear one whisper to another—and everyone is backing out the door. The salespeople don't know what to do, and I'm miserable, becoming increasingly convinced that I made one big mistake here. I wish I had never, ever read his damned book back in high school, because then he never could have convinced me to head on the road with him in the first place.

"Jack, Jack," I shout, near tears, "this isn't working. I want to get away from here, far, far away from here!" Suddenly I know what I need to do—so I click my ruby-slipper earrings together right there in St. Mark's Books, three times, just like Dorothy does with her own ruby slippers in *The Wizard of Oz*. And to my own shock, it works, and I'm transported far, far away, not back home to the hovel on East Third Street that I share with my two other chronically unemployed roommates, but to the land of Oz, itself!

I'm in Oz! The *real* place, not a movie set, with a real yellow brick road, real Munchkins, Good Witches and Wicked Witches, and even the Wizard of Oz, himself. I don't have any idea where Jack is, though. I hope they let him out of St. Mark's Books, and that the police didn't lock him up. I hope he made it to Big Sur.

As for me, well, I've been here in Oz about six months now, and I'm pretty happy, even though Jack was totally wrong about it: it's not beat, or spiritually deep, or jazzy, or rebellious, at all. The Munchkins aren't in states of exhalted exhaustion. They're not even really cute, not up close, they're actually pretty ugly, and most of them are perverts who keep trying to get me into bed, so that they can perform various acts of bondage on me. Glenda, the Good Witch, may not be a slut, but she is so filled with syrupy, sacharine-sweet platitudes that she bores me to sleep. And I constantly have to avoid the Wizard, who's an alcoholic old pedant, with an obsessive grudge against Dorothy and Toto, who he never, never shuts up about, constantly wishing them various terrible fates back in Kansas.

The reason I stay, though, is because of the Wicked Witch of the West. She's just about the greatest friend I've ever had. She and I have great times together—we love to play old Motown records, for instance, and do those silly old dances—The Swim and the Hitchhiker—all up and down the yellow brick road, and we laugh and laugh so hard together until we have to pee, and then her trained flying monkeys come and swoop us up and fly us to the nearest bathroom.

She keeps me laughing constantly. I never laughed so hard back home. She tells me the best stories about what a little, snotty priss Dorothy was, and how Toto was really a vicious animal, not sweet at all, and how the scene in the movie version in which Dorothy throws a bucket of water on The Wicked Witch and kills her, and The Wicked Witch shouts out, "I'm melting! I'm melting!" was a complete fake, staged because the director was worried that little kids around the country wouldn't be able to sleep at night if they thought The Wicked Witch still lived. "And they paid me a pretty penny," she tells me, "in cash, up front, for me to let them get away with it, let me tell you!"

And I make her laugh in return when I tell her about the nasty fart I used to work for at Macy's, and my two ex-boyfriends and what jerks they both were, and about the rich landlord of the hovel on East Third Street who wouldn't even fix our heat and plumbing when they broke down in the middle of winter, and how we tenants banded together and took him to court, and how we lost in court—that part, about the judge telling us we had no rights at all, absolutely cracks her up, every single time.

And then one day, when we were just sitting around not doing too much—she was trying on some new witches' hats she'd ordered from a catalog—I told her all about Jack K. And she said, in her cackling, booming voice, tossing away one pointed black hat and trying on another with black and silver feathers sticking out from the top of the point, "Oh yes, my pretty, I read Jack K. in high school, too—Witches High, you know, located just to the left of the field of poppies—but his writing just didn't do much for me, because, you see, my pretty, he wasn't *really* wicked, not really, he was really so very innocent, all caught up with his mother and his need to prove himself so pure and spiritual, he was really just a big overgrown baby, you know."

I sighed. "Maybe you're right," I said. "But he did have a way with words. And, besides, I sort of liked him. Do you know where he is now?"

The Wicked Witch has amazing powers, and if she wants to find out where someone is, she can. But, for some reason, she just didn't want to give me that information. Instead, she made a big joke out of it. "He's *melting*," she shrieked. "Oh, my dear girl, your road buddy is *melting*!" I laughed, despite myself, and never asked again.

So like I said, I'm pretty happy here, even though it's not Nirvana, or even Naropa, or anything like that. I wear my ruby-slipper earrings every day, and I'm never tempted to click them together three more times and say, "There's no place like home," like Dorothy did. I really don't want to go home. I don't miss my hovel on East Third Street one bit, or my dead-end jobs, or my two ex-boyfriends, or my two ex-roommates, or anything. And the Wicked Witch has trained her flying monkeys to fly off to Macy's and pluck tubes of Ultima II Sexxxy Red lipstick off the cosmetic counter for me, so I never run out.

My only sadness, really, is about Jack K. I do feel guilty about leaving him that day in St. Mark's Books. But what I do, when I start to miss him a lot, is this: I reread an old, dogeared copy of *On The Road* that one of the ugliest, most perverted of the Munchkins gave to me in exchange for a three-minute-long French Kiss, which made me want to puke, but which seemed to make him very happy.

And once I open the book, and start to read, and all those words come tumbling out at me, I feel really, really close to Jack, and then I think that whereever he ended up, he's just fine, because all of his words—that endless, endless barrage of his words—will gather themselves up together and reassemble themselves into a great big, woven blanket to keep him safe and warm, wherever he ended up, somewhere over the rainbow, I figure, either above or below ground, who knows.

Eurydice
As I Was Walking
From <u>Scree</u>

When I was fifteen years old, I went abroad to discover the world. It was a clear blue day, a Tuesday without foreboding. I felt I had a right to anything and that nothing could touch me. So I cut class, put my finger on a map at random and touched New York. Three days later, on the plane to JFK, the young soulful TWA steward proposed marriage on his knees and gave me free cognac and a rubber Mickey Mouse ring with his hotel room key on it. During the landing I felt dangerous like a conqueress; I looked down at the unknown city spread out before me like an openlegged bright young whore and I was aroused.

I'd left home with nothing but my blue schoolbag so my parents wouldn't get in the way of my exile. In it I had my three favorite rocks (lava from Etna, petrified wood from Lesbos, a crystallized fossil from Santorini), motleystamped English translations of my school transcripts, Breton's *Nadja*, handrolled cigarettes, and bubblegum. I wore my blue school uniform—a cotton dress that zipped from cleavage to knee—sensible walking shoes and thick black eyeliner. It was September, but JFK looked like an impromptu Mardi Gras. The natives were dressed like billboards. The sun was tepid, lite. The American blue was murky. I felt myself floating just above the magnetically maneuvered crowds that opened before me like the renovated Coliseum from the old grassy stands. I began to suspect that this was not a nation. And at the same time, almost immediately, I began to lose sight of detail. The size and polyformity of the numerous multiple choices of America overloaded my inner circuit.

My first host turned out to be an angular adolescent with legs like stilts and German-anarchist wire-rimmed glasses who loitered around JFK after seeing his parents off to Europe for a month. He brought up Nietzsche and Nietzsche's Nazi sister. I spent the night in his parental Laura Ashley bed amidst a barrage of fake flowers (wallpaper, sheets, comforter, towels, tapestries, furniture were all covered by dead images of flora). My host argued, "Try me out, I really have no performance complex," but I said: "I don't screw Americans." I was ad-libbing, my brain being the only thing I had to protect my small body with. He said I was generalizing, and I said generalizing was the only way not to get lost. How could you have any opinion otherwise? But I admitted that it was hard to generalize in America which contained everything and everyone heaped together in a brimming motley pot where nothing was melting, and I was making up my theories on the spot, so I conceded to give him a try. I don't remember the sex act, except for his cum-splattered glasses looking up at me cockily. I also can't remember his name—some classic American name, Paul, Scott or Steve; local names coincided so often, they were insufficient to identify people. When Paul came, he cried out "Beam me up, Scottie." I had never seen a circumcised penis before.

He fed me Cracker Jacks while we watched *The Twilight Zone* and a mare's dilated cunt on PBS that looked like Munch's *Scream*. But TV made me feel irredeemably foreign. Then his friends came and we all did high speed blotter acid. I had my first sniff of the rank bittersweet odor of marijuana and my first headtrip. I treasured my initiation into the American drug experience which struck me as the indigenous equivalent of Orphic mysteries. I had to fight my tenacious reluctance to abandon self-control. Everyone was desperate to talk. Most of what they said passed me by, because my knowledge of English was too literal. I just wanted to stay absolutely motionless for a while and process things, but Americans couldn't be still. People were jumping out of windows at parties all over the city, they told me, and gave me meth. I was picturing myself as the Marco Polo of the 80s and New York as my epoch's primitive jungle. If I were Gretel, New York was my forest and the drugs were the crumbs I dropped behind to mark my way. Drugs were America's integral bonding stimulant, like its ouzo. My adventurer's duty was to never abstain from my hosts' communal rituals.

We ended up in a woody bar that wouldn't serve me cognac. Having had wine with every meal at home and grappa for my insomnia, I couldn't comprehend being forbidden from drinking, and put up a fight against madness, arguing that a non-U. S. citizen shouldn't have to abide by quaint regional laws. The bouncer said, "You shoulda stayed home, toots." So I learned to drink on the sly like in black-&-white detective flicks, and it actually felt romantic. Romanticizing obstacles and things was easy. My imagination had always been my survival mechanism.

Next, Scott and pals took me down to a smoky stripclub where cross-legged men ogled catatonic naked girls parading their slits on heels or roller-skates. The white men wore ties and suits and grim drunk faces; the other races just looked scared and lascivious. I got to touch my first silicone tit and wanted one for my rock collection. Women in g-strings strolled in our midst, leaning precariously toward gravity; it was like seeing Mom sauntering about in the nude, cheeks jiggling, rippling arms akimbo, displacing the stale air above the stove. In America so many things turned perverse that its nakedness was paralyzing. The strippers liked me and wanted me to do the last number, they took me backstage to outfit me and took out a collection plate for me in advance; it was my first and only paycheck. They said I learned fast.

America was dizzyingly fast. All night we cruised from club to club, running from the drinking-age police or the setting of ennui or time or that aforementioned urge to fly off the edge of the solid world, running into dozens of memorable characters in the process of our fall down the rabbit hole. People did this every night, driven by an unfathomable instinct to undo. All day long, in streets, trains, offices and shops, America was on the run, chasing its famous dream. [There was no such thing as the Greek Dream, so I had trauma understanding.] And all night America ran from its nightmares—or chased after them.

Bartenders liked me—they called me "lady," gave me free drinks, and thought my two-year-old hooters were valuable by virtue of being free of gravity. After they poured me an illicit drink, called a "stiff," I'd put one of my old rocks in their palm and say "May you always be as hard as this." They thought Greece was Eden. Smelly cooks and waiters who came out during last call for tequila shots also liked me. People drew strength from repetition. They taught me to sing "King Caractacus." Little else was stable.

On that first night Paul's friends took me to a dykeclub because I was born on Lesbos. I met a black top who called herself Outcast and rented a booth where she demonstrated whippings, spankings and riding crop tortures once a week, like in old freak shows. She wore a chain and ball in her vagina with a weight hanging from it that obstructed her movements, and she passed around ballots with questions evaluating her performance. She asked to put me in a wedding dress, my bodice pulled down and my feet locked apart with spreader bars as part of her show. She wanted me to speak nonsense while she did needlepoint on my skin. She called this "sexwork." This was how she seduced and got laid. America had forgotten that sex was just a comforting pleasure. It thought sex was just a symbol. I'd thought sex brought order and cleansing to the world, release, emptiness, center. But in America sex was chaos. And chaos ruled.

On that first night out, I met a barfly at a dim Soho bar who was a Hell's Angel. Hell's Angels, like starving Biafrans, had been mythic symbols in my childhood. I'd been forcefed for them. I propositioned him so I could reclaim my awe. He wore a rancid bronze-hued hat shiny like Johnny Appleseed's pot. He was 69. I said "Where do you plant your seeds, Johnny?" He was my first fullbody fuck in America. It was like screwing a baby. Soft and careful. He proposed to me, despite all his slipping out. His penis was lucid and vulnerable, quietly pure, typically American. He gave me a bracelet that read Padded Cell.

When I caught up with Paul and Friends that night, they were passed out on his floral carpets. My brain throbbed with overstimulation, ready to crack open. This is America, I thought exhilarated, now I've got to live as if history has ended. It shocked me how many moments and incidents were vanishing unaccounted, lost in the anonymous mass of America's plenty. It pained me to let them fade unconfirmed, unadorned, undigested, and therfore irretrievable. I was always left wanting. That was America's secret of success. Back home, people practiced endless, immobilizing introspection; there was time to reflect, index, mourn; we lived in an abundance of time and had more of it in our hands than we'd ever use. Now I couldn't stop running. I was in flight, as if on intergalactic mission. I had come *looking* for Action, and to find it I had to give up doubt. But doubt had been my compass so far. America taught me that in life everything is meaningful and everything is insignificant. That first dawn at Paul's synthetic garden, I dreamed of disco-slamming crowds ecstatically chopping off their genitals to eat, their bloody knives reflecting me distorted like the scoop of a clean spoon.

Idi Amin was eating his enemies at the time, and Bokassa, dressed as Napoleon, was serving journalists' brains to President Giscard d'Estaing. I kept thinking, "I was raised on that continent." A Latin couple in L.A. found a human finger in a can of Menudo soup. But no one claimed it and the company trashed it. I walked around the grimy cab-infested streets suddenly conscious of being edible. I had come to a world whose major bonds of trust had broken down or never existed, and so anyone could take a knife to my flesh and cut off a few choice steaks and grill them before my eyes. There was no governing logic, no single unified body, nothing granted. The gulf between my body and my mind was widening dangerously.

On my second day we ran into a guy my host called Chickenhawk who wore jumbo diapers and Sears plastic continence pants. He bought us a junk-food feast at Taco Bell and explained why wearing a diaper was 'wonderful.' He said lying on his tummy masturbating against his diaper as a baby was his first and best memory. Then he whimpered about 'making weewee' in his panties. Americans abhorred growing up. It made it easy for me to catch up.

Luckily my youth made me a member of America's elite. So did my philosophy of life. [I had gone to school later and had been too busy scaling social ladders, protecting myself and lying *ad nauseam* to learn anything valuable.] My fundamental education had been derived from children's books which I read from a personal point of view so distorted that I never recognized them when I reread them and so they remained new and defenseless to my imagination. My early bedtime adventures—abductions, decapitations, mass burials, cannibalisms and mutilations—prepared me for my migration. My books told the same story over and over: how a child's fearless resourcefulness, unburdened by knowledge, conquered a great unknown world. Curious George, Mole, Little Black Sambo, Alice, Charlotte, a myriad Grimm and Andersen peasant preteens, were innocents abroad like me who, when tested, turned out to be braver, wiser, firmer, wilder, wilier than anyone could have suspected. Even Mary Poppins had nothing but her immense conceit and sense of herself to get through all that happened. The lesson always was: my own devices would prevail. If I had a faith, it was that I could eat 164 pancakes and slay the Gorgon and trick the Giant into not seeing me. And that was what made me an American. [Americans would rather self-destruct than grow up.]

During my first week of transition, I went around nauseated, like a sane girl walking into an enthusiastic outbreak in the madhouse. I was too far from home to find comfort in the old logic. I'd been used to marble edifices and edifying epics that time couldn't affect—the jailbars of that life being aesthetically reassuring, venerable, timeless. New York was hardscrabble and free like a wind-blown agitated beast alone in the storm on a rickety skiff. I, picturing myself as the veteran Argonaut, reveled in the fearful frankness of its cacophony, and in the dim suspicion that there was meaning in it I would distill. This was humanity stripped down, I thought, real.

Up close, America was nothing like its gilded movies, its famed endlessly-pecking desert-drilling oil wells, or its foreign-aid parcels of pink frills and powdery foodstuffs we had known it from, back home. America struck me as an uncoagulated mix of lightweight fun, deep-seated uncertainty, and silent unexplained rage—a grating unBlakeian marriage of opposites that put everyone's nerves perennially on edge. I'd never seen so many people who did not resemble one another—and it struck me as sacrilegious. But if I judged what I saw, I couldn't join it. So I suspended thought till the morrow like Scarlet O, and devoted myself to my senses. In return, America surprisingly never treated me as an immigrant or a freak. A rumor was spread by kids at school that I was a Getty incognito; it persisted throughout my life in NYC, catching up with me on the oddest days—even though everyone who knew me, soon knew how to say "Fuck your Virgin Mary" and other filth in modern Greek. It was obvious America wanted me to make up my identity in a universal unencumbered way. No one ever inquired about my parents, my ethnic eccentricities, my religious needs; I was received as a naïf.

Being a geek, my host proved efficient: he took me to his high-school, sanctioned me as his family's exchange-student with forged letters, and by Thanksgiving, having taken some lengthy tests, I was a graduating senior in his class. We had a sunny French teacher who worried about me and said she hoped I would live but somehow knew I wouldn't. Our English honors teacher, a silver-haired cerulean-eyed spinster, pronounced me a genius. On my first day in her class I'd stood up waiting for her to sit down first as was done in Greece, until she finally said "Please sit," to which I'd responded: "You shit firsht" (hadn't lost my thick S's yet) making the class laugh—not a mark of genius, unless she meant Lycidas, Genius of the Shore; she sponsored me for AP credits. I slept with the leggy fascist D.A. who was our U.S. Government teacher and used the word "twat"—his stiff self-conscious white-bread machismo gave me the uncontrollable urge to watch him come. He looked like Abe Lincoln.

After my geek's parents came back, I became the school's unofficial itinerant guest, staying over at any kid's whose parents wanted an exotic oddity to parade or a wounded pet to care for or happened to be absent. American houses had a transient look of neatness, an absence of clutter and detail that unnerved me. The familial jealousies and power dynamics would choke me, and I liked to move on. One girl—Diane? Denise? Donna?—threw herself at me with that clingy social shamelessness that is endemically American; she supplied me with herbal tea, incense, joints, *Playgirl,* lip gloss, not-animal-tested cosmetics, and a spare bed in between richer hosts. She and her hippie divorced tie-dyeing vegetarian mother stretched and cracked their necks, waists, legs or feet at every opportunity,

I'd never seen anyone do that before; it made my teeth grind. They fed me what they called "pulses" in every hue.

My new friends often doubled as my servants, partly because our servants had been my first and only friends, partly because my friends enjoyed the odd sensation of security that came with the vocation. So I never paid for drinks, drugs, food, school or rent. I wouldn't have if I'd stayed home and it didn't occur to me to think about money. And so I remained a foreigner, because profit ran America and I knew nothing of it. I never integrated. Instead, I soon decided that the only *honorable and honest* mode of existence was that of an outsider. My foreignness liberated me from tedious local mores and controls and put me at ease. Most Americans were people who felt like outsiders anyway, and all this alienhood suited us all well.

Only our teachers' ardor for me confused and disheartened me: I wanted to be (here as) an outlaw, not a prodigy. The exception was the Driver's Ed Quasimodo, a bear with egg-white eyes, big porous nose and pickled skin. After bombarding us for weeks about v.d. and the mucusy innards of our genitals, which was unaesthetic and offensive enough, he switched to cars and made us sit by him in a vehicle with no wheels and let him guide our hands on its shift-stick or open the hood and inspect the greasy offal that made his stationary car "move." I refused to examine the inner organs of inert tools. He could not prevent me from graduating for not being a mechanic, I argued. A homeric battle blossomed between us, which daily gave me the chance to show off newly acquired expressions— "waterbelly" "pussywhip" "spineless fart, you wear kneepads," "hump your fist"—proving I'd mastered the art of metaphor in my foreign tongue. I no longer had to turn to the wall for meaning when told "You're off the wall"; I knew that "high" did not refer to height nor "cool" to temperature. That fight got me expelled for a week and made me feel vindicated. I was finally "with it."

I went to the prom with Daimon, who planned to enroll in art-school and marry me. Americans always tried to marry me: I looked like I needed an owner, someone to be responsible for me, if not reform me. I wore an unprocessed-leather dress with big holes around the belly and thighs in you-Jane style to the prom, and went barefoot as I was "training" my feet for a life of no possessions. America permitted and, I thought encouraged, that sort of behavior. My feet had third degree burns from the May asphalt. Daimon—blessed with a memorable name, ample love handles and an excess of sincerity, all of which mutely reminded me of home—picked me up in a white tux and Rolls, gave me an orchid, which I told him meant testicle, and took me to the Met to see *Medea*.

I'd always loved *Medea*. Savagery has always fascinated me because it wasn't inherent in me. Brutal good health, quick physicality, unwavering resolve, icy revenge, true belief, they were to me like the glistening riches a poor man could never hope to possess. Because none of it came to me naturally, for a time I would give myself to any man who dared burn the back of my hand with a cigarette in the street, or used words like "nookie" and chewed up vowels, or could lift me up in one hand. In the American wild, my sense of intimacy became prelingual.

But I never forgot that my brain was my sexual muscle; I never took a ruler or a weapon to bed and never thought that anything but death was destiny. The disparity between what America promised (Canaan) and what it delivered (drugs) excited me, for being so resonantly biblical. Back home, for generations of nonCommunists, faith in America and its vast future and its miraculous power for individual redemption had been the last great religion. But I hadn't come looking for opportunity or emancipation or salvation. I had come to pay tribute to reality. I had come to redeem, not be redeemed. And I thought I knew how: in bed.

America showed me that sex was the one universal language I could depend on. Sex was the only true democracy: everyone fucked. We all, rich, poor, white, black, converged at the libido. I slept with different sorts of men in the same spirit I tried out all 31 ice-cream flavors: as part of my education. Sex was the shortcut to understanding a geography. So I always located my desire not among those already sampled but solely among those I had not yet met.

At that time my dilemma was: "Everything corrodes me, yet I can't keep from touching everything." My desires always turned against each other, so that I came to realize I could, without too much conceit, prefer to fail. Otherwise, I kept worrying, how would a monologue ever end?

Lauren Fairbanks

from <u>Cyber-Satined Sorbet</u>

Everybody Has a Penis; Only Girls Wear Barrettes. I am getting weird.
No, Just Suicidal With a Loaded Gun. To What Degree Are You Wallowing
In It?

Runway is a different business. Enter ass twitching. Hah. Let loose
on a great design. My favorite forever-booked model runs her own pest
control business. I have a Nazi helpmate named Sky for pre-runway
organization and crucial Polaroid taking. His attitude is such that he
thinks everybody, no matter what race or walk of life is saying this (in
muttered tones) "Are you one of the goyim to whom we stink because
you look down on us or one of the goyim to whom we stink because you
look UP at us?" He has it needlepointed on a pillow in his office. That
little adage or whatever...seems to keep him hating everybody and
everybody hating him, so a weird mutual respect abounds juxtaposed
with pure desire to get the job done. Painlessly. Fast. Nobody is carping
at position. Hierarchies are no problem in this organization. Acceptance
of the super celestial. Ubermensch. Ironically, he IS the one who stinks.
His question for everyone is "When was the last time someone looked at
you and sang 'You are the sunshine of my life'?" He's knows me well
enough to trick me into thinking I'm truly going mad. Does things like
put my backpack in the fridge. I'm onto him. We're working out the
kinks. He's a wundercorset kinda guy. Limps like that because he's from
northern Ireland (they have Nazis too) and took a bullet in the knee as
punishment for a crime. Yes he is the proud owner of Hapsburg chairs.
Original coromandel upholstery. Dull gilding. I do think every home
needs a red room of coziness. Where only red foods are served. He's cold
and I'm warm. He calls this customized phone sex ring with what he
calls the three major subgroups; hermaphrodites who possess one testis
and one ovary, male pseudo hermaphrodites who have testes and some
aspects of male genitalia but no ovaries, and female pseudo hermaphrodites who have ovaries and some aspects of male genitalia but lack
testes. He needs to talk with these people on a regular basis. I don't
know what it says about his sexuality let alone his physiology. I'm not
prepared to discuss that but it shows an open side to him people may not
see in the workaday. It's not a two-party sexual system any more.
Reinventing my warmth. I may not be from Argentina but it is where I
have been *comfortable*. Yes, it is a tattoo bracelet above my tee shirt line
on my arm. Pretty as finest lace. Finest kind. I can hear the southern

screamers now in this moment of silence. I think I like the bay winged cow birds more. Warble warble. Excuse me. Decisions must be made.

The trunk show is tomorrow. Get that one something to carry. Tall Poppy Syndrome. Gesticulation or lack thereof is everything in a moving model. Earthbound clothes with a blast of fire. Circus. Epilepsy-inducing signs of life.

Do you need your 30,000 mile auto inspection yet? There's this deal where they marry you for nothing if you bring in your rust-bucket. This repair shop I frequent. Couples reaffirm their vows while they wait. Quick and easy. I'm thinking PHOTO SHOOT. Can you picture Oreo, the poor child really did have a wedding like that by the way…picture her beauty in my wedding regalia at the car repair? I know she retired. Which rock star is she attached to? I was looking at what I thought was a current magazine the other day and I saw her. It was five years old. The absolute nuts. They have one size fits all tuxedos and wedding gowns but we would get a Vera Wang effect going…upper east side does petticoat junction. When your mother is the youngest daughter of a warlord in feudal China…. How's that for a gene pool? We'll have a Sheer Illusion low-cut-back slinky wedding dress (I call it "Isis,") juxtaposed with greased wrenches and laced up wenches. Sometimes I feel like one of those spirits living in an ancient threshold. When people in all rudeness step on me…they must be educated…it is discourteous and unwise.

My trip? Sensational! I took my mother to Dunkin Donuts to answer queries about baby-sitting duties in my absence. Vietnam is one huge notoriously screaming message pool of fashion. Only sultry, reasonably-priced place remaining. They make jewelry out of war-era Zippo lighters. Yes to these shots from the final shoot on Ham Nghi Street and yes to the Reunification Palace layout. We used aged US Army helicopters. See this one? My favorite bar is in the left-hand corner. "The Apocalypse Now." Retro retro. Every character still smoking pot, listening to the Doors as if the lives of future generations depend upon it.

Bored with African shoots. Stalking the wild thing up rocky mountainsides and camping in huts of straw and stinking camel hide. Obvious to all, I need Nam. Everyone is thirteen again. Wild things stalk the bar in sedentary fashion. Wild things drink Le Blue Ribbon and wait…for you. Africa has been done. Don't leave me impressed with your own erudition.

Tehran? Where the party dress code is layers and layers of basic black?

Did you get the socialite proofs back? Always very dressed. They spot every repeat from last fall's collection. Yeah use this picture of Miss Georgia 1966 stuffing flyers from her polka dot golf cart. Polka dots are of polish origin? I'm thinking the word polka. Were polkas Fergie's demise? Excellent. Used to be a print model. Is this the warehouse? Exclusive designer discount clothes? Listed socialites wait years for an invitation to take a job here. *Looker* southern glamour gals refresh me. Big clothes, big jewelry, big hair and horse teeth. Regardez! Regal overstated polish. We capture them "at play" in this "closet wonderland." So what if one pays to use the closet? Who cares if their social security numbers are a mystery to them? I want this shoot worlds away from understated New York. Try a "mature" women's magazine. Don't let them jump my idea. Call Mimi. Thirty years ago when the stag line neared the Boston deb. line, lean bony confident horsiness got picked. I have a theory about that. They wanted handsome male heirs. Horsey women equal handsome men. The female heirs have all the money so the beauty doesn't have to be there. That would only complicate matters. Don't you find things complicated enough?

The "horsy set" outlets need more picture hats..."prayin' and drinkn' ensembles." Ours travel well from church to cocktails. More cows than people some places. Blow ten more rolls of film on that. Until you get it right. They are a tricked about and heavily festooned bunch. They wear brunch clothes to brunch in, lunch clothes to lunch in, tea gowns at tea time and certainly cocktail dresses for dinner. Lunching. Yes yes yes to furs. When you go to Houston, you don't wear black Chanel and minimal makeup. Unless you want to be a minimalist, tinted green, urban Martian. I go to Houston a clothing designer and return a shoeshine girl. It is a humbling experience. I am humbled.

Style—it's about being in a foreign land. PEOPLE are not runway models. Models are freaks lucky to find work. Like basketball players. In order to earn the right to walk around on the street you have to blend. Very few in black or beige. Clothes versus woman. Think parasols and nose bangles. Isn't Marshall Field's doing body piercing now? Seed catalogue gardening equipment is rounding off the many worlds of "accessorize." Waifdom? Over to the degree anything is over—always remains in tiny pockets. Hippies are out there. Punkers are out there. Pockets I said. Spiky crewcuts and long sheer spaghetti dresses over tee shirts. Get yourself a gold Chanel chain and casually lay your mineral water on your Stair Master. Then you have SAID something. Maybe something political. Something serious. Year of the willfully banal accessory. Think porkpie hat. That? That little number's part of our line for the summer hockey fan. Up until this point, the *warm weather Hockey fan* has had very little to wear. Aficionado. Excuse my weather vane. The key is you can't be afflicted with peculiar or long-suffering product loyalty. Style is not "Oh I wish I had on that dress."

When one is working in fashion and by that you and I mean "style," the old adage is not true: "Woman is a misbegotten man and it is said inferior." St. Albert the great or no. What if I can't wait until Saturday? If I'm being ordained a Catholic priest Saturday? Caught it from my new England ancestors. Wager you to be descended from a few of those yourself.

There is no serenity in my work. Over-scheduled and sleep-deprived. Go to Dallas if you think Houston hair defies the laws of physics. The rubberized silk mini-dress is a sham. Devastating in its extremism. Budget copies beat the original to the stores. Exact copies. Knockoffs. Affordable "interpretations?" A photograph snapped at a fashion show in Milan, faxed overnight to a Hong Kong factory, is seconds away from being turned into a sample. Fedexed next day to a New York showroom ready for the retail buyers' preview…. One biggie gossip: Regent to the rags trade has blown the whistle on the smelliest carping family secret in the fashion industry.

I knew yours would be the strong defense that Ready-to-wear doesn't masquerade as the real thing. No secret. Moles. Don't tell me about moles. I used to be one. Do the haute couture and ready-to-wear companies ask within…*Are we overpriced? Do we give value? Do we inflate prices to cover outlandish fashion shows and advertising?* Excuse me for interrupting my own train of thought—but we are very rich. I say that a lot. Very rich. Enough to go around. We do a show once in five years. I happen to be all ears.

Write this down before I forget. I have an idea about flyers to the suburbs. Assume they are fat meat eaters. Size twelve and up. Then assume they're not…technoburbs have changed. Skinny women run families and hold down two jobs. In terms of fashion, I ask you…are we talking bestiality? Only time it IS appropriate. Eaters and eaten. Such a thing as "a little" bestiality? The thought may never be completed…write it down anyway. Our last ad campaign was really a coloring contest for adults. Do you realize how many adults color with crayons on a daily basis?

Christian curios? What we loved was: everything red. I find myself with a tremendous lack of feeling…I have an extraterrestrial indifference towards poverty and wealth. "It's so poor" will be the supreme compliment for this collection. *So poor. So foreign. So extraterrestrial. So ecclesiastical. Indifferent to pleasure or pain.* Yes, the Darwinian spectacle tees happen to be going like hot cakes. The "may God infinitely love you" tees are gaining. We're international. When I say I want heads askew shoes askew, I may get a poor translation like "Broken shoeless melted head…" and I can work with that…. Before it gets too hot. Before we are too hot.

That was Urania my biographer. Don't hang on to verbatim statements I have made. I never said English men like plain women. But think about it. Appalling. If she tells you she's never been to the Right Bank—she's full of it. I heard her quote "I'm a Left Bank kind of"…Yes, I saw how he popped in. He tells me my clothes move out of the Chicago Boutique "very cheerfully." And tells others I've led a good scatological life. It's boring to talk about yourself. That is the definition of a bore. He may talk about me.

Read all about it! Why should fixations slightly Irish in name be left out? Krishna that great sales organizer will be the underlying theme for our usual blue and white striped cruise line. Write that down. Where's the red lacquer screen? What color are they? I want WHITE parrots!

Telephone. MMMhmm. Soft and draped. Large concentration on chiffon. Swatches. Marketing for both petite and missy. Our prayers have been answered! Take me to the top of the world and cover my portliness in gray and brown Fendi fur.

Maybe she wore hats to hide an awful nose. Taken in profile of course. Think Ingratiation with the great. Martinet the second. My first print of import. Chestnuts with the horseshoe silks. Who didn't know about her childhood chestnuts? The rich and horsy still buy it. It's a staple now. My purpose, without smelling like bug spray—was to break into one woman's subconscious. I like to think she didn't realize what I was doing. Far from probable but fun. My Aunt was dressed there in the thirties. Dressed by her own glorious hands. Wasn't Swedish so we didn't have to consider her love of suicide. I cried for two days when I saw the picture of Kurt Cobain aged five in the *New York Times*. Beauty walks with us. Snuffs itself. Beauty IS the power to snuff itself. God help us all. So I douse myself with perfume and get on with the rest of the blessed day in a coven of dry bats. Perfume as mood-altering wonder. Sure to think of it again when I have the time. The whole point of fashion is to work towards a man-made beauty as if you had not received beauty at the outset. Many are handed it and know not what to do.

Back to the insanity of the rejected one. The late great? She would never admit. Her father the peddler. Her half-sister the legitimate. We're talking indomitable peasant spirit and patience, patience, patience. How she loved to sit and listen to the garbage trucks. She worked like an artist in a northern light. *You and everyone.* How did she go from peddler's daughter to top hats, tiaras and so so very dry martinis? Some would have you think it was whomever she knew.

I beg to...No no no. Rip it apart and begin again. She had a former Dynastic Emperor painting silk in a back room. The immense control of his brush, was sadly, not echoed in his rule.

Her sense of the present. Period. The fabricated present. Wasn't ahead of her time—she WAS her time. Her time became her. Embodiment. Crucifixion is the ultimate in bad fashion reviews. No one needs to tell you when you're there. Feel the nails going in your hands and feet. Blood over silk. The illustration worth the wait. I don't care how long it takes. Queue up. Queuing up in Paris is worlds apart. It's usually something grand or delicious at the end of a Paris ligne. Oxymoron? Okay then Chanel diaper bags plus Gucci combat boots is an Oxymoron. Sounds like the length of a skirt. Mini Midi Oxi Maxi.

My work space? Is it *Architectural Digest* again? Tell them it's "after the fashion" of a mall rat Romanov tomb. No I don't mean a bloodied hole in the ground. Think earlier Romanov. Brain Drool. No wonder you wait endlessly for an invite.

My solution to any problem has always been—redecorate. Second solution—find someone's closet to rummage. A way out of every funk. Funk and Judy. Some people do chocolate. A limited amount of space is preferred. Superbly baroque. Empty fuchsia rooms soon metamorphose into NO MORE ROOM AT THE INN. The moment of creation. What I desire for myself or others goes straight into the collection. My jewelry bespeaks ceremony and splendor. Plainest of sack-like clothes. My single Maoist trait. What is your single Maoist trait? Sometimes I need to go to England for a damp spiritual fix. Yes, don't forget tabloid nudes at break-fast with tea and digestives.

Objects reach out to your inner life. A bourgeois nervousness comes over me when things are moved. Gotta let the cats fetch the field mice swimming in your pool. Objects? I want them to be far removed from the daily chores of the pioneers. That type thing. Give me a break. Keep your broken rusted farm equipment. Sell it to a restaurant. One man's decorative art. Let him frame it and hang it. Let us attend to it and marvel at it, perhaps worship it as we fill up on steak and salad bar. Surf and turf. Don't get me started on atrocious fabrics in other words, clothing designers as Interior decorators. Bring in the fabrics and it's a loss. A house—IS not a dress.

Excuse me. That annoying woman is on the phone again? Hand it. I know which "mole" you're talking about De De. I refuse to buy it. Yeah. The female supremacist who hangs with the "stripper for God." Writing their religion, so, if it's all right with you, maybe I should give them A DAY OR TWO. Their dad was the guy conducting six cello-playing nuns and sold out Carnegie. He was a genius. You think NUNS brought in the crowds? The girls do good work for me. They bring me naked bodies with checkbooks. I'm talking sellout. You don't even know what a checkbook is. His little darlings are my little darlings now. Some tireless people whoring after my things...My workers are my things! People here are champions. Morph artistes. So what if they wear seersucker suits from the boys department of Brooks Brothers, Atlanta? So what if theirs is a vacant never orgasmic joylessness.

I have been criticized for seizing moments too zealously: the Armani moment, the Helmut Lang moment. I bring a department store quality to couture. At times I'm a waterer and spreader—a *sprinkler.*

Excuse me but we've all done our share of moling. When you forget that every clown wants to play Hamlet—you've lost every iota of opportunity to comprehend my standards. You are forever tiptoeing down stage to confess what's wrong with me. Copper confused with rust asides. Over? Then pack it in! Traveling carnie. Why must I be consulted when any man has a lyposuction? Lumpectomy without the lumps. Let's be American and lump off body parts in a stress-free manner. That woman is impossible. I don't like to raise my voice!

Imperfect body parts your bag? We bought the Body Scanner. All possible models measured three-dimensionally from head to toe. Scanned. When we narrow our choices down, we pull out the complete measurements of each chosen model for that particular show. We will scan model's bodies (even models are not the perfect size 4) in order to make the clothes fit to perfection BEFORE not during runway. No more pinning and adjusting during show time. Stress buster. The $20,000 pays for itself.

My advice? Stay away from the dry cleaners. Do you like this fabric? MMHMMN. Precisely. The wrinkles are woven into the fabric. Saves on ironing time.

Take women out of undergarments. Would you have women go backwards? My heroine. Lose your heroes and you're lost. Didn't want to be the Duchess of Westminster, BECAUSE, she would say, Haven't there "been so many of those? But there's only one Coco Chanel." Total agreement. Refuse to get into underwiring and pumped up lingerie. Cotton tee shirts and briefs. If it's comfortable—you won't keep grabbing at it minute to minute year after year. Decades of graying, molding cotton.

Real beauty starts when beauty you were born with—ends. Volatile business. Come to me when you want to experiment safely. I started to tell you about Grandma. She exemplifies this ideal. She has fulfilled her desire to quote irrelevant, badly conducted, fraudulent polls. Pollster fantasies complete. What prey tell, is wrong with that?

I DO intend to be called "HER BEATITUDE." By that, I mean my days of lining up for port-o-potties, are over. Something to do with my Grandfather being the great Walrus hunter out of Greenland. My blood line allows me to wait hours and hours and hours for nothing. Handy in modern society. My karma is so good—something always happens. Has a hand-sewn sound to it. A designer's object may be to sell the mother, the grandmother and the daughter at once. Beats driving all over town. "Up" colors are more helpful at night. Always consider whether or not you will be viewed in artificial light. Want to personify a walking mud pie?...Don't wear browns and grays at night. Of COURSE silver is different. To be well-shod is crucial. I'm taking the nostalgia, love and romance out of my clothes while fear, loathing, anxiety and rebellion remain. When people tell me *I'm the Keeper of the People's Memory*—what's a gal to do? Never my goal! Thrust upon me. Every culture's fantasy world. Delve into it. Excavate. I am not a super star. I AM my customer, but do PAY me like a superstar.

Sportswear means dressing in pieces and parts. An American invention. They were looking to dress suburban women. If you've got a city, you've got a burb. We're talking blazers, trousers and coordinated separates rather than couture ensembles. Just cracking my toes. And the all ears world is my podiatrist.

I wear this jade bracelet every day. An estimated hundred years of everyday wear refines the shape of a Ming dynasty piece. Strive for perfect balance. Maybe I can get a good twenty years of striving toward perfect balance before handing it over to my heir. My son.

What happens when this body cult we're going through right now, is over? Can you think that far ahead? Beyond the tip of your breast implants is where any designer must live. No farther. One is as good as subsequent collections. Remain time-stuck in your last, and it's "so long Charlene."

Bankers are willing to bank on the security of a husband-wife team. Something to that in the rag trade.

Don't forget "Showing versus shipping." Yes remember most of what you see on the Runway is never manufactured. It may look good on paper, but when you drape material and play with it—a dress materializes. I accept the shell of an idea on paper. Never scripture.

My simplicity shocks this rococo baroque world.

Regrets? I regret not sketching. In a fashion utopia I would sketch then hand it over to one slave or another and they should return with a dress or some such we could take from there. As it is I do a lot of time consuming cutting.

Yes I did mention him. We still work together. It's actually better after the divorce. Kicked him out with two banana boxes filled with belongings. Definitely old school. Very European which has as many advantages as disadvantages. He and my boyfriend are simpatico. In fact we all live together for the sake of my son and sometimes it's a goddamn boy's club. I walk around banging my head whispering "Who and where am I?"

My husband...my ex...knows any garment "start to finish." He will sketch, drape, cut and sew. We approach differently. We each have complete veto power so we both upthumb anything which moves to production. Here he is. My glowing center. Notify me if he drones on. Our marriage? Marriage can only work if each of you forgives the other for being the opposite sex. No time for this? Perhaps later. He will catch up with you another time.

Armed and dangerous, shall we prepare to beat adversity today? Let's outlast our substance. Let's ogle and assault. Always remember and never forget "Nobody needs anything." If it's Cyberglitter you're selling, everybody has to want...what is it? Cyberglitter. It's all such a willfully odd kick in the pants. Really. Without much doffing of tricorns, and just short of radical nihilism, how does one get to the point where one's fashion house is expanding on three continents with equal rapidity? My house practically invented the faux-leather babushka for the nineties. Credit me. There are no pockets in production shrouds.

We're not talking toothless Russian babushka. My days of being the bicoastal-based wife hitched to someone else's outdated fashion, are over. These are fluid omnisexual improbable times. I'm thinking rural piety and I'm thinking the opposite. Oh God. I look in the mirror and think I'm fifty so this is the face I "deserve" already. The place. My hair used to be ginger. Small? Rotund, speckled and bespectacled? Salsafied locks. Dyed red hair and darkened lids. Miss Emily D. dyed her hair red. What shade? "Fire-In-The-Firehouse When the Dalmations are Being Walked," blast of color. Clairol. Art scribbled on backs of paper bags. Even the lace is "period." I bring my bangs down to my lashes. Softly. "Integrity" is so a color. Is not. Is so. Color of my lipstick. Vacuous, head up and proud of it. My badge. Badge of vacuousness. One brief ecstasy: the opening and closing of a flower. Style not "Fashion" is my life. Collective achievement; a people, a place and a time. We hoped "spending pilgrims" would fly over our town and throw pennies. Pilgrimage.

My work is subverted by artistic mimicry? And what of it? It's about the workmanship. Responsibility to the crafts people. One and oneself should be saved these aggravations. Nine parts desire. Didn't "even poorer than I" Hemingway wear bust-a-gut khakis? Clam diggers? Corduroys? He invented innerwear as outerwear. Pronouncements and images. I have no moral problem with it. Mind you, my tendency is to have very little moral problem...with anything. Today has a mind of its own refusing to be the tomorrow you worried about yesterday.

Then in a moment of delirious sensual enthusiasm and merciless southern light, I Married a man of compelling vagueness—Noriega's right hand man. He wore preppie shorts, no socks and loafers. That toes-adorned man with a ring on his second toe. What to call the second toe? Cute little Band-Aids and goose bumps. Considered himself vaguely married. What jocularities! Blames me...says I, the aggrieved wife, "served meals rejected by Ethiopians." Once in his life if he had his own idea...

Thought myself Josephine Verstille Nivison Hopper more than once. Sweaty sunbelt market convinces itself my religion is "Reform Demonic." How many marriage-related man hours SPENT attempting to get the attention of an expensive specialist like that? Try marrying a man with his eye on someone's clock who thinks a mood ring an excellent engagement ring and knows NOTHING about THE drugs. If there's a picture of you with Noriega in anyone's possession, make sure you know nothing about the drugs! Eye to the clock of another. I'm fresh out of time to dress for a 40s film. Sequences and hidden bitch stitches. My aptitude is for cultivating friendships with people who **matter**. Yes to themselves. What else is there?

I was riding. He was smitten watching me. When I finished and was resting in my dressing room, he entered, wearing riot gear suitable only for dodging bottles. He picked up my nail polish and began, on bended knee, to paint my nails. Everybody had a good time. Everybody saw the sun shine. A curse and a compliment come out exactly the same in the ruling class. It's a wash. Was a black-clad assistant with a clipboard. I have a noirish near-Kabuki face. Eye to clock. No thank you please don't marry me either. Life's a long dressing room hallway where we all dress for a 70s sitcom. Outfits designed for bargain hunting. Funeral-going.

One of those "take your own photo" booths adorns the main vestibule of my house. Where Haight-Ashbury meets Silicon Valley. Don't ask them to pose for a photo shoot. I won't say urinary squats are mandatory. My house is filled with the best people. I step outside and point back to the house saying "We've got some 'fly' people in there." Drum roll and buildup for fly people. Jean Harlow satin.

No, it's not an isolated swatch of wallpaper hanging there. Inspirational. Merely. I'm using it. Having been raised surrounded by Auntie's hanging china plates, my wish was for the suspending wire to wear out...facilitating their being dashed to the ground. Dash me to pieces. In the distant future, find me shoeless, in a kimono (pocketing a pocket size Raid can) in the act of serving tea. Or find me post "pouring out" duties. At this very moment, I'm out of time. My bedroom is hung in shantung silk dyed "Lanvin blue." Feel free to look for the perfect shirt dress in my collection. I draw the line here. You will not find impeccable safari jackets over silk skirts. I also draw the line there. Sit with me as I quietly, urgently, draw the line. Kneel with me.

Visions? Like, an accentuated waist? Models as pagan goddesses? My life is a provincial Hopperfest. Desolate and bleak enough for you? Forever smoking a cigarette in my fake satin slip in an under furnished Cape Cod room...neon flash is a lone starshine up from a subtle nether world...like past days of sewing white lace dresses with red rubber underlay. Astonishingly quaint. Does it bring to mind the Guatemalan saint scraping his knees from one church to another? Churches were not seconds but miles apart. The Blessed Hermano Pedro. His scabs are preserved. Insured for millions. Good works can be aggressively sexy.

Think serious visions which occur at historically stressful periods. They occur in clusters. Think Lourdes. Gaining weight at every meal. Film noire shadows. Like gentlemen's agreements. "But we had a gentleman's agreement" he was overheard whispering or gurgling as they whisked him (feet-dangling) away. That noise...from inside his body. It sounds like ten she-devils pounding on his tubercular breastbone. Asking me to do anything so strenuous as think? My destiny. Renaissance velvets. Reminds me of the Christmas that would be appropriately worn-through Bavarian. Blues and burgundies. Branded leather trim. Hairshirt-looking sweaters. Regality. Excavate me. Begin my demise. *My* clever idea to grow breasts at age eleven. Such a clever girl. The din of the Oompa pa band drowns us out and makes napping *tres difficile.*

When people come into one's home in clusters, one is too polite to investigate which designer was chosen for this particular impromptu occasion. One simply would never stare at the basic black. How rude!

And yet you do. And glean it All. A distinct lack of fashion show pressure remains at my house. Each individual is asked to pose and yet MY REALITY (a good reference point) is that, **they** pose for themselves. Upon departure, each sitter is given one Batman goody bag brimming with the pictures. Am I the perennial rememberer whispering "a curse and a compliment are the same?" No—I examine and critique their fashion sense. Alone. Sans ego. Visuals-apparent. AFTER they depart. And from the little people, I learn. Your query: "What if they depart in a manic hearse?" A legitimate conjecture. My driver secretly waits for me in a broken down Volkswagon wearing indescribably old clothes. Black priest's robes with snuff...like...confectioner's white sugar down the bib. The front passenger door remains broken. Please excuse me while I back-seat retire to facilitate his chauffeuring me. He's in front. He's in control. Likes it broken. So do I. We like it broken. Broken signifies character. I will be mistress of my craft. Bead me on the bias. Cyber-satined in sorbet hues.

Brian Gilmore

Anybody Trying to Fade?

By 9:00 A.M. the third floor bathroom at Calvin Coolidge Senior High School smelled like cigarette smoke. Two crap cans inside the latrine lacked stalls for privacy and were stuffed with coarse brown hand towels which had been clogged there for weeks. Windows covered with grime were cracked open to alleviate the dense foul odors which seemed to never leave the room, and the florescent light fixtures above on the ceiling only worked sometimes.

Von McSwain eased into this reek. Into a semi-large circle of impatient young directionless black boys like himself kneeling or crouching and smoking passively on Newports. Von didn't smoke. Carting no pen, pad, or books, Von was skipping first period again and not thinking about it for a second.

Von found his ace boon, Rick Clarke, from way back to their elementary school days here too. Rick was a regular. Von used to tell him that first period for him wasn't Algebra like on his class schedule; it was Casino Studies. Von tapped Rick on the shoulder and momentarily broke his concentration on the two green squares with the white dots which rotated magically across the stained bathroom floor.

"What's up Von, baby," Rick calmly answered slapping him five, "I knew you would be here, man, I was just tellin' everybody that my boy would be here soon and then the real shit was goin' to start happnin'." Von looked at Rick cynically. Rick had already turned his attentions back to the game but kept talking to Von and watching at the same time. "You gettin' in, man?," he whispered in Von's ear, his eyes locking in on the action going on below, "come on Von, man, get in this shit, man, I got a feelin' that we gonna hit this shit big man, and you know about my feelins' man, you know they don't be lyin' to me."

Von smiled and pulled his pockets out depositing lint on the floor in front of Rick's overzealous face. "That's no problem," Rick said, "no problem at all." Rick reached down in his pocket and pulled out a small roll of bills. Fives. Tens. Twenties. Even a few fifties. Stank smelling moist currency stacked neat in his pocket like a deck of cards. "Here, man," Rick whispered again, "when I nudge ya' that means to start drivin' people in the game with a side pot." Von gripped the bills tight and eased in closer to Rick in front of the dirty simulated tile casino board. He tuned into the game in front of him.

A frail, dark figure shook the small green dice emotionally and tumbled them from his fingers smoothly like marbles. Homeboy was spinning the cubes magically like they were part of his hand. Everyone called him "Night Train" on account he did everything so fast. Ran and walked fast. Rolled Dice like those cubes were lightning. Even use to read fast when he did go to class, but those days were over forever. Rick winked and grinned at Von one last time as he found his spot and got ready.

"Five by three, baby...five by three," Von heard Night Train chant in the circle in a rhythmic cadence. The crowd burst into a volley of curse words almost as soon as the dice toppled to a halt.

"Look at that, Von," Rick murmured, "Night Train cleaned the pot out on a damn eight. Ain't that some shit?" Rick and Von had known Night Train for years from sessions like these; they knew that he came with money and sometimes he seemed to be able to tell the dice what to do. Those days you didn't want to be in the game. They also knew Night Train talked alot of shit too.

"Any faders," Night Train called out instantly shaking the dice boastfully, "anybody fadin...what's up?...all yaw'll niggas broke or what." Night Train slowly got up to leave the room.

"Right here, Train, Rick daringly called out. "I got you."

Night Train clutched the dice he had just won with tightly and pulled slowly on a Newport he had just lit. He looked at Rick surprised and grinned his brownish teeth. He blew out a cloud of gray smoke.

"So...you tryin' to fade, Rick," he called out, "I guess I'm gonna have to take yo money with yo dice. These is yo dice, right?"

Rick shook his head yes. A smirk on Night Train's face grew longer immediately. He wore a dark blue New York Yankees baseball cap with a bent brim, and a pair of wrinkled tan khaki slacks littered with grease stains. He eased back down into the tight bunch smiling slightly. His dark skin appeared somewhat ashy, and his face was drawn and it looked as if he hadn't slept in days. He looked coy in his demeanor. His unpolished black, wrinkled Florshiem loafers were cracked and dried out and looked like they hadn't been polished in months. The T-shirt he wore had a faded picture of Malcolm X on the front smiling but looking serious.

Night Train kneeled back into the game and took one last drag on a Newport before he plucked it behind him and out the open window. The crowd of directionless black boys pushed in tighter; they knew if Night Train was rolling, they might be able to get paid. He had that kind of respect.

He began shaking the dice hard as he stared into and locked onto Rick's pupils. Spiteful eyelids of greed trying to force Rick to blink. Wonder what would happen if a seven came spinning out onto the floor. Rick didn't worry about it. Hadn't happened yet.

His hands shook and snapped. The dice hit the tile, spinning rapidly on the dirty, crowded bathroom floor. The crowd seemed to grow closer and loom slightly over the tile casino board as the dice spun. Rick did not hesitate his moves. His hand stamped down on top of the dice before they stopped and slapped the rotating small blocks to the side

"Gate," Rick said loud. All eyes locked in on what he had done. Night

Train looked coldly at Rick and smirked.

"That ain't gonna save your money, nigga," he uttered, "it's all mine, you can gate all night, but Night Train is gonna take all your shit."

He began shaking harder and chanting out a cadence almost in unison with his deliberate jigglings; "FOUR BY THREE, BABY...! ...FOUR BY THREE...!"

Again the dice tumbled from Night Train's wrist, and again Rick cursed them with an impulsive slap before they stopped their rotations.

"GATE UM," Rick screamed again as moans of disappointment and disenchantment frequented throughout the ever expanding crowd.

"LEAVE THE FUCKIN DICE ALONE, CHUMP!", a voice yelled from the back,"YOU GOTTA PROBLEM OR SOMETHIN?"

"NAW, MAN," Rick called out, "YOU GOT A PROBLEM? YOU DON'T LIKE IT GET OVER HERE AND BET, NIGGA !!"

More bettors gathered around and started throwing money down against Rick. Night Train collected the dice and began again. His rhythmic words even smoother, his talk in unison with his movements.

"You gonna let the dice go this time or what, nigga," he uttered, "we ain't here to watch you slap dem muthafuckas."

"Roll the fuckin' dice, man—it's my muthafuckin' loot," Rick told him.

"You mean it was your loot, Night Train's here to clean your ass out." He lit another Newport and inhaled deeply as he shook the dice furiously. He chanted cunningly, "come on, baby, ...FOUR BY THREE, BABY...FIVE BY TWO..., any one gonna take Night Train to the water..." Out they came spinning in a flash on the shabby looking tile floor gleaming as they rotated. As they slid to a halt, Rick's eyes lit up in shock. But he knew what to do.

"ONE BY ONE...SNAKE EYES," Rick screamed, "MY BILLS..." Rick gathered up part of the pot on the floor and dropped half back down to get Night Train to cover him with another pot. The stakes were growing larger.

"Go ahead Train," Rick told him, "roll..."

Night Train's face reeked with infuriation, but he began rolling again, harder than ever. "It don't matter, nigga, I'm gonna get that one back right here." But again as the dice fluttered and flashed on the dirty restroom tiles, Rick commenced to "cancel" them out with a sharp slap and a hasty cry.

"GATE," Rick uttered again.

"LET THE DICE GO MUTHAFUCKA!" someone in the crowd screamed. "STOP GATIN CHUMP!" shouted another.

"WHOSE FUCKIN MONEY IS THIS!" Rick screamed, "YAW'LL WANT TO BET, THROW YOUR MONEY DOWN!" Rick nudged Von to begin driving the side bets up, "Now Von," he murmured without looking towards Von.

Acting quickly, Von pulled four or five guys into a side bet. Money rested in the main pot between Rick and Night Train as well in the side pot amongst Rick and a group of new entrees who had just come into the room who thought Night Train was going to get them paid. It was prime time. Just as more bills hit the floor, Rick watched patiently as the dice struck the ground hard and spun to a stop. He didn't slap the dice this time or say anything.

"Eight!" screamed Night Train, "my favorite point, now your yellow ass gonna lose your muthafuckin' shirt."

Night Train shook the dice like a tambourine. They poured out of his hands again a few seconds later but Rick cursed them again by slapping them to the side and gating the roll. People again screamed from the back, but Rick told them to put their money where their mouths were. More money hit the bathroom floor.

Night Train didn't hesitate, didn't even squint this time, he was too obsessed with victory, with winning, with the end result he had come to know and to love in foul smelling quasi casinos like this one. He quickly snatched up the dice and shook hard. The beat of his voice rose.

"Come on, baby, eight...give me an eight, baby...send Night Train to the water."

Von began chanting his own cadence as he watched the money in the side pot he started continue to swell. His words were just the opposite. "Eights bring sevens...," he boasted, "eights bring sevens."

Rick smiled at Von who was now just as deep mentally in the game as he was. All eyes were on the tile floor. Night Train balled the dice up and kept shaking his fists. The crowd was hot, humid, clogged with tension and testy smoke. "Four by three," Von injected as he continued his habitual varied cadences, "four by three, right here."

Night Train's hands vibrated crisply. He shook harder and stared with a brashness that exuded from his body. His frail arms looked rubbery, almost unreal. His face was strained fully into what he was doing. Out flung the little green dice as his fingers popped concisely. He released the squares onto the tiles. The dice spilled out of his hands and an ocean of eyes focused on their gyrations. The crowd of directionless black boys loomed over top forming a human cavern above the small grimy tile arena. The dice spun for an eternity, bouncing, rocking, finally in a final flash of bright green spun to their end.

"SEVEN, MY MAN," Rick shouted joyously as they stopped, "CRAPS !...YOU LOSE BIG MY MAN..."

"SHO NUFF," barked Von, "PAYOFF!," he shouted as he gobbled up the money sitting in the side pot. Rick did the same with the main pot.

Silence immediately gripped the cool bathroom. Bettors cussed and plucked away spent cigarettes. Faces racked in disappointment and despair. Disgusted risk takers dissipated slowly about the room leaning on walls awaiting some release that they had not gotten in the game. Von stuffed his pockets. Rick stuffed his. The dice lay still in the middle of the floor. Night Train was alone still kneeling down in front of the dice. He picked the dice up and reached in his pockets and pulled out a small roll of bills wrinkled into a clump.

"It's your roll," Night Train muttered towards Rick, "you won, your dice…" He was coy towards Rick in his invitation.

Rick looked down at Night Train defiantly. Their eyes met in a cold stare again, piercing through the cigarette smoke and blocking out everything else in the room. Rick did not move. He stared at Von. Von stared back with the look of indecisiveness on his face. The green dice glittered on the floor in the room. Rick stared temptingly at the white dots on the sides of the cubes. He picked them up and began staring at the dots even closer. The small round specks seemed to turn into dollar signs telling Rick to "come on, man, pick me up and lets' roll." He looked away.

"Yea, man," he cynically replied, "I would stay and roll with you cats, but actually, I got to make it to English class, so if you don't mind, I think I'll take a raincheck, I does want to graduate. I can meet y'all back here at lunch time or out on the yard somewhere and we can finish this shit."

Rick started walking towards the exit aggressively, but was interrupted by Night Train's voice piercing and echoing violently off the walls.

"YOU AIN'T LEAVIN WITH MY FUCKIN MONEY PUNK…! ARE YOU CRAZY?" he shouted, "WE AIN'T GONNA LET THESE YOUNG PUNKS LEAVE HERE WITH OUR MONEY—ARE WE FELLAS?" he yelled spinning around and giving the crowd of young black men an ultimative look. Night Train stood up to block Rick's path to freedom. A group of gamblers equally as upset moved behind him frowning. "I SAY YOUR BEST BET, RICK, IS TO PICK UP THE DICE AND START ROLLIN' LES YOU TRYIN' TO GET JUDO STOMPED!"

Von and Rick briefly stared at each other and the gathering group of gamblers. Their eyes met. Their minds met. For that one brief instance, their thoughts were mutual, Rick's mind was inside Von's, and Von's mind was inside Rick's. Now that Night Train's aggression and passion for victory seem eternal, it was clear that it was a no win situation. Quickly the two of them took off towards the door. Rick tried to rush out first, but was quickly grabbed by several of the young boys in the room and jammed against the wall. Von jumped forward to help, but felt bones and cold flesh crush up against the side of his face. Von went crashing between the wall and one of the toilets. His face slid in a mixture of dirt and water on the side of the commode.

"YAW'LL WASN'T TRYIN TO LEAVE WAS YA !" Night Train snickered, "…CUZ WE STILL WANT OUR MONEY ! AND WE GONNA GET OUR MONEY IF WE GOTTA BEAT IT OUT YAW'LL NIGGAS." Pinned up against the wall by at least three larger figures, Rick was helpless. Von was almost still by one of the cans trying to ease up unnoticed.

"MAN, WE AIN'T GIVIN' YAW'LL PUNKS SHIT…," Rick yelled back defiantly, YAW'LL LOST YAW'LL SHIT ON THE UP AND UP…" Von felt wetness around his nose. He reached up and rubbed a nostril. Blood dampened his fingers. He looked over and saw Rick in a lock, he saw Night Train standing in front of Rick shouting rabidly. Von didn't move, he had to wait until the right opportunity, the right time. Night Train paced in front of Rick. Just as his back was to Von's, Von made his move.

He leaped up and smashed a fist into the side of the Night Train's face and carried the entire weight of his body into him. It took Night Train hard to the floor. As he collapsed, Von was on top of him throwing a succession of wild body blows and facial bricks. The three holding Rick rushed and jumped on top of Von and began kicking and stomping him from on top. Rick joined it, and began throwing wild blows on top of them. The entire bathroom area was a circle of confusion: bodies flying to the left and right. Blood gushing out in squirts. Screams of pain and agony bouncing from wall to wall like their voices. Shoes jangling down on top of ribs and backs, meeting faces, balled flesh plastering jaws and cheekbones.

Suddenly, the bathroom door flew open and several of Calvin Coolidge High School's instructors ran in and broke up the rumble of bodies. Von's nose bled, Rick held his side, Night Train's lip was split, while others nursed their own wounds. Each time they snatched somebody up, someone else would dive back into the bunch and began punching or stomping.

Before the teachers had a chance to write down anyone's name, everyone leaped up and dashed out in the confusion. Doors flew open and slammed off Coolidge High School's walls loud and recklessly while they all escaped towards the safety of the streets.

Rick and Von sprinted down the stairs and huffed and puffed out the school until they were uptown several blocks. They checked the streets for the bathroom crew at each turn, at each change of block, at each unseen corner. They broke sweat until they were exhausted and only then, only when they were unable to go on with their escape did they stop and savor their small victories.

For minutes they didn't speak, their lungs heaving wildly, their torsos lurched over in batterment from the aftermath of their winnings. Rick looked up at Von leaning on a fence and pulled out the green dice he still had and shook them artfully. Crazily, he spoke to Von.

"Yo, Von...," he heaved between breaths, "...lets' go up Ralph's Carry-out, they be always be ready to roll in the back alley behind the joint...high rollers with big money, man, what'd ya say?" Von's face racked up in an instant frown.

"Hell no, man..." Von heaved loudly, "...you got a gambling problem or something...we almost got our asses kicked just now...and thrown out of school for who knows how long...and you...talkin' bout gamblin' some more. Fucks wrong with you." Rick caught his breath some more. Didn't frown at Von either. Knew what Von was saying was bond, but he had another agenda.

"Come on man," Rick said finally standing up and breathing less, "look at all that money you made. And like I said, I gotta feelin', watch this." Rick stopped by a curb and sat. Rick shook out the green dice they had been using in the game only moments before. They rolled smoothly out. A seven came up. Again, Seven, again, Seven, again, Seven. Every roll was a seven.

"Well, so what?" Von asked.

"Watch this." Rick then took the dice and rolled them a couple more times, but this time he slapped the dice around on a few rolls. He then let the dice go on the next roll. Eight. He slapped the dice around again. Back to seven. Von looked at Rick like he was crazy.

"You see what I mean man, these are my uncle's dice man, my crazy ass uncle who be gamblin' all the time. They some type of trick dice rigged only for certain numbers. All they roll are mostly sevens and eights, mostly sevens. My uncle says all you have to do is slap them a few times and they'll switch to eight. Then you slap them one time, and they'll go right back to the sevens again. Can't lose man, I already tried them in about five different games, it's just a matter of gettin' my dice in the game. Guys figure when they start and they hit like three sevens in a row and win that the dice are alright, but little do they know, that's when I start gatin' like I did after Night Train won on that eight to add some variation, then I really take over."

Von looked at Rick smiling as they stepped up the pace towards Ralph's and more money. Von picked up the dice and tried it himself. No doubt, it went just like Rick said. Sevens, gate, Eights, gate, Seven, like clockwork. Von smiled too now that he knew what Rick's feelin' was all about. They walked up to Ralph's and saw the crowd huddled around the back.

"It's just one thing Rick, I want to ask ya'.

"What's that?"

"Rick now that I began thinkin' about it, what about them snake eyes back there, how do you explain that shit?"

Rick paused and grinned. "I tell ya' man, I just don't know where that shit came from. I picked up the money, but when that showed up, I almost pissed on myself, that shit was not supposed to happen."

The two burst out laughing as they began walking towards Ralph's Carryout and the next set of unsuspecting suckers. Von was in this again. The sweet clamor of uncertainly echoed off in the distance and that familiar cadence of wager blanketed the streets in a joyful hymn. When they reached the back of Ralph's, Von and Rick looked at each other and smiled. The faces were familiar here, but they weren't gambling right now; they were waiting to start a game. Rick and Von stepped in like giants with Rick shaking his dice.

"Anybody trying to fade?" he announced holding back his grin and watching as several young black men stood up and began pulling money out of their pockets. He looked at Von and smiled.

Jaimy Gordon

Bug Motels on Mission

You could go buggy from boredom in the bughouse, if you weren't buggy already. But at least from fall to spring all of us Bug Motels from East Six went to school. We really went, almost the way normal teenagers get on the bus and ride to school. And yes it was queer going to Girls' Classical from the loonie bin, and even queerer to go from Girls' Classical back to the bughouse every afternoon, but everything about a ritzy dreambox hospital like Rohring Rohring makes for strange combos.

A little yellow schoolbus just our size picked us up every weekday morning on the traffic island between trolley tracks at the Broadway entrance. If Mr. Nurse's Aide Reginald Blanchard was the one sent to watch us off, and usually he was, we'd be smoking down the line of us like five twigs of kindling, while behind us loomed the ruby brick hospital, frilled with black iron lace like the fin de siècle society matron she was. Then the bus pulled up and we were off to our separate lyceums, Park School for Bertie, Mount St. Agnes for O, Faith Bible for Emily—I was the only one in public school, since Merlin wouldn't have me think myself so grand, not even from the bughouse.

And at 4:45 we were all back on the traffic island, with tall red Reggie firing up our Luckies again, bending down the row of us with his lighter like a mother bird loaded with worm purée. And as we eyed that swanky Dunhill, inlaid with pearls and engraved not RB but LMcL, obviously cadged from some female ex-patient for favors large or small, we thought uneasily of all the ways Reggie wasn't like a mother to us, for, all things being equal, he would rather please you than thwart you, but he had his price. Now he let us smoke, backs to the wind, while he turned up his own collar, and when we were through he delivered us safely back to Rohring Rohring, sixth floor, east end, the Adolescent Wing, and, wherever we had left it, our mission.

Even when you live in the bughouse life needs a mission. Especially when you live in the bughouse. After all, here you've got no field hockey team, no terrarium for your reptile collection, no Broncos Marching Band, no Future Lawyers of America. We called ourselves the Bug Motels because we were a rock band, but we hadn't gotten around to learning instruments yet. Junk food couldn't be a project here. This wasn't some tough camp where you got a candy bar a week when you turned in your laundry. We had pocket money and charge accounts, two restaurants, a snack bar and a gift shop with a six-foot-long candy counter in the basement. We rolled in malted milk balls, canned potato sticks, cheese and peanut butter crackers, pretzel rods, you name it. For a while we had the use of the doctors' tennis courts in the afternoons, huffing around the sunless courtyard in parkas and gloves, but then it got too cold even for us. We needed a doper to refine and complicate our appetites and godzilla gave us Bertie Stein, not only an experienced dope fiend but a mastermind. Bertie funneled us into the Manhattan Project, the H Bottle, the Big Blue Bomb.

You know that quaint sort of old bomb that falls, like it's raining lipsticks, out of bulky white airplanes in *The World at War*? Under the main hospital next door were a huge pharmacy and the fabulously rumored morgue, but Rohring Rohring's eight stories sat on a warehouse, an underground dump for big stuff, distillation urns and sterilizer boilers and 100-pound drums of industrial cleanser, and royal blue Size H cylinders of laughing gas that looked just like those bombs. It was one of them, fixed nicely next to its twin H of oxygen in Robinhood green on a cart like you'd use to bus a cafeteria, that souled our mission.

Bertie Stein was featherweight and restless and sifted about the corridors of Rohring Rohring all day long in roachlike silence, slipping through cracked doors if he found any, trying every lock and tuning his junkie's x-ray eyes on blank walls and dead-end corridors. In this manner one day he saw a silver cart loaded with nitrous oxide roll off the third floor elevator and take its place, as though such things happened every day, in a row of rolling bins of soiled linens, standing there as they always did until some dutiful flunky wheeled them over the catwalk to the laundry chute in the main hospital. Bertie crawled on his hands and knees between laundry bins and from the moment he goosenecked up for a closer look at that cart with its copper tubes and gauges and mixers and regulators, the funny gray enema bag of a gas reservoir dangling down and the dear little red clown's nose of a mask with two horny valves sticking out of it, he had to have one for his own. For our own. And pretty soon that was our mission.

He reported to the Bug Motels: "The nature of this gas," drawling it out farcically, *gazzz,* "is a cartoon with the picture gone. You know, like, Tom the Cat falls through the roof of the opera house and bounces around the orchestra on his rubber stamp head, hee hee hee, gets spitted on a cello bow, sucked up a flute, digested by a bassoon, ha ha ha, tenderized by a marimba mallet, and finally he gargles the tenor's high C by swinging from his tonsil, ho ho ho, except there's no picture so why am I laughing. I'm laughing cause I weigh nuttin and I got these pink and blue bubbles popping in my veins. And now I'm crying cause I just tasted the tragedy deep in the pillowy fizz. Good stuff you're gonna say. So how could such good stuff be legal for totally square tooth mechanics? Cause they're gonna torture you anyway so you'll never know you had any fun, but we'll cop us a tank before our teeth are aching." The picturesque logic of the bughouse—how could any self-disrespecting Bug Motel argue with that?

Bertie you see had three traits which made him a great maestro of missions: all that Stein moolah, a mind bent on one thing only, and no fear of the consequences, so that if someone had to take a fall, why shouldn't it be Bertie? And that's how he had landed on the funny farm in the first place, by juvenile court order. He had seen the inside of every crumbling smelly youth joint in Maryland and the District of Columbia, and at least had breakfast there before his parents fished him out, over and over, and redeposited him in Rohring Rohring. This scary exposure had only hardened in his dreambox the wish to be changed from itself, by any substance obtainable.

For a week we had been sending Emily down there five times every afternoon in a bin of dirty hospital gowns to scope the landing, since at (presently) 75 pounds she made the least dent in its canvas bottom. Of course she couldn't roll herself off the elevator much less back on to it. She had to peer out through holes we had poked in the side for the ten seconds the elevator doors were open, while up on the sixth floor we pushed the down button frantically to summon her back to East Six before anything funny happened. "*Bombs away?*" we'd whisper in code into the bin of pale blue bathrobes and sterilizer towels, when it reappeared. "Nuh-uh," she squeaked back every time from her nest. And on like that for six days and then on the seventh the elevator came back empty. "Uh-oh." Sumpm funny *had* happened. We looked at each other and shuddered and ran down the hall to play Ping-Pong. We had to look innocent—and besides, Dion pointed out, for once we had just the right number for mixed doubles.

"Three to two, my serve," Bertie hollered, so the whole bughouse would believe in our alibi. "Is she dead?" O whispered. "Who da hump knows," Dion said. "It depends if she went down the chute head first or sideways," I whispered back. "Sideways...ooooo," O echoed in her spooky-flute voice; you could tell from the queer crook of her chin she was picturing Emily stuck between the third and second floors, with her head wedged at an uncomfortable angle. "Say, does it hurt to be paralyzed?" I asked.

"Aaanh, she was only 75 pounds away from disappearing anyhow," Dion said, "she wants to die, ain't it?" "She was waiting for the birds to feed her," I said, "least that's what she told Dolores, who told Reggie, who told me." "That's a very beautiful idea," sighed O, "that Emily is a saint, I'd never think of nuttin like that." "Ya know, certain girls love death like I love D.O.A.P.," Bertie observed, "like O here—you can tell from the eye makeup. To her every day is a funeral." "Just cause you have to die before you get to wear makeup, Hebrew school creepo," O sneered, spookily. "I don't care if I do die. That's why I'm here," Bertie bragged, "and I won't be wearing makeup either, I'm getting smoked, man, cause I figure I'll be 98 percent tetrahydrocannabinol by then."

"Aaay, don't worry, da stuff looks good on you," Dion told O, "lady-like, I mean, Koderer don't wear no black on her eyes, and she looks like Oliver Twist. In the movie, ya know." "Ursie's queer," Bertie explained. I froze and O gasped. "Get fukked," she said loyally, for she was a friend of mine, and as I was wildly in love with her I had curbed every sign (I thought) and was still a * Unbeknownst to her, as proved by the gasp.

"I wear a little clearasil over da zits now and then," Dion said, "but nuttin on the eyes. Nino don't recommend it." Nino was his tailor. "I wonder if they'll put any makeup on Emily," O worried—meaning on her little dead white face. "Aaanh, Emily was a strange looking bird at best. Makeup wouldn't do nuttin for her," said Dion. "I think Emily was cute, in a ugly sort of way," O almost sobbed, in her spooky-flute. [Whap!] "Ace," she added. O had a devastating serve. We volleyed on gloomily.

We had played three whole games—by now we had just about given up on ever seeing Emily alive again—when they rolled her onto the ward on a gurney, trailing white linens like a dead infanta. It all looked like a weird dream: Dr. Hamburger and Dr. Beasley running behind like footmen, or pilgrims, in tunics of elfin green. The last of the day slanted through the tall windows of the dayroom in banks, forming six mirages in the shapes of pyramids. As her body passed through them, the dust, like shrimps and scorpions of pure light, made way for the princess in worshipful agitation. The turban of gauze on her head pushed her face up at us, her open eyes glimmered drily in death through the mashed lace of her eyelashes—but then she blinked and smiled a little.

"What happened? What happened?" everyone asked, and we ran along side the gurney too. "Oooo my neck. It was kind of fun. Ursie..." I bent down to her, and she whispered: "...they think I tried to kill myself..." She giggled. "So what else is new," Bertie panted, and I jerked his ponytail and stuck out a Ked so he fell splat on his face. "...and listen, Bug Motels—*bombs away*," Emily said in code, "Big Blue on three...just standing there..."

Dr. Buzzey (Emily's friendly but futile dreambox mechanic) met Dr. Beasley and Dr. Hamburger, the medical residents, in her doorway. Then her private room sucked in all three, along with a coupla nosy nurses, Hageboom, if I remember right, and Mursch, and the door flapped shut behind them. Fluorescence streamed from its little square window. Somebody clicked shut the louvers. We stood there staring at the nothing of it.

"Ursie," Bertie said, tenderly pinching his nose to make sure it wasn't broken, "get down to three before they move that thing."

"Me!" I said. Bertie after all was my height, had subsisted on tablets, syringe squirts and aromas for five and a half years and was skinny as a yeshiva boy from Ruthenia. "I weigh one twenty-five," I argued pointedly, knowing his own weight couldn't be over a hundred. Even O was fatter than he was. "But girls aren't as noticeable for being up to sumpm," he said, an insight which didn't quite hold up in the bughouse, but I was pleased that he clumped me with *girls*, it meant my cover was working. "And if the bomb is a heavy motha," he went on, "who else but you can carry it?" He had a point there. Now you see how Bertie got to be a mastermind: He knew his henchwoman, just which body part was headquarters of all her vanity, and mine was my muscles.

So I said yes but I stuck at going downstairs in a canvas laundry cart as long as some unknown, unbribed nurse's aide was still on the loose on three, zealously dumping laundry bins down the chute without even checking them for mental patients. "And besides, we got no cart," Dion reminded us. It was true, Emily had been launched from the one laundry bin we'd purloined. We were stuck. But all at once Emily's door opened a brilliant crack—I caught sight of Dr. Beasley leaning down to her face like a strangler—and the empty gurney popped out. The linens on top of it had been whipped into peaks and gulleys, alarming as a meringue pie. Forty seconds later we had a new plan. Bertie had been thinking: *Big Blue...just standing there,* Emily had said, which sounded like that H, big as ya motha (Bertie's charred old doper's eyes glowed like furnace doors), wasn't even on a cart—so we needed all the muscle we could get.

Bertie faded around the corner, came back in a minute with two surgeon's tops he had pinched during some other caper, two pale green blouses with only a few smears of sumpm liverbrown and crusty down the front. He handed one to Dion. "Cheese, cool," Dion said, and waltzed off down the hall with the thing. "No, man, keep away from that mirror!" Bertie called after him but Dion was already turning into his own room. "That's the last we'll see of him," Bertie sighed, and it was. "Hey, what the hump, I guess I can push the thing by myself, it's got wheels. Okay, girls, climb aboard." O and I stared at each other while Bertie pulled his own green top over his head. It was big as a bank lobby on him but the smears of ancient gore and baggy fit looked touching on his haggardness, as though he were a boy genius, out of med school at the age of twelve, whom dissection of dead bodies had shocked out of his growth. I mean he looked plausible in a certain way. Fact was even Dr. Beasley and Dr. Hamburger looked kinda babyish, big-eared and simian in those green smocks. And by the way, what were they doing in there with Emily so long, I wondered, truth-syruping her? Bertie must have had the same thought. "Is she stand-up?" he asked, squinting at her blank door. "As a fuk in a phone booth," I replied with false heartiness, watching O from the corner of my eye. I saw her heart beating in the faint blue fork under her temple. Would she scream?

"Okay, you two, lie down together on this thing and I'll wrap you." She didn't scream. She was wearing a pilly pink orlon V-neck sweater, sumpm only a drapette would wear, a black bra but no blouse under it and the V down almost to her pupik. And so it came about that O and me, the Bogeywoman, lay body to body, or more specifically her lovely head stuck out the top and my bulby nose was pressed to the washboard of bone between her momps, so that I almost swooned for real from hyperventilating while Bertie tucked and patted and sculpted us, under that froth of used sheets, into one improbably thick beauty. "How do we look," I muttered, for an excuse to move my lips. "Don't talk, it tickles," O spooky-fluted. But at least she didn't say don't breathe. I turned my chin up a little so my breath was mossing her throat. "Calm," said Bertie, "you look calm," for O always did, and down we went to the third floor landing with Bertie pushing.

Of course every hair of me waved like a sailor at the nearness of her. She was the *shikseh* oxymoron personified, she was the highest girl and the lowest girl and nothing in between: She was a drapette but also Mary Heartline of *Super Circus,* she had that public gorgeosity, she could be famous right now, a star, a TV star at least, and at the same time she was that sullen teenage underbitch calling you a jew, goading you in her peroxide hair and trashy clothes, then beating you up for looking at her funny. She reeked of the last cheap perfume tester she had boosted from Read's, probably *My Sin.* I felt my heart budge against her and knew she could feel it too—like a mole under a tent floor. But then, was I right? she swiveled the tiniest bit, toward me not away, and my lips were quivering like a rabbit's in the gulley between her momps, kinda folded into the dunes that swelled out of her bra and actually quivering, I would just need to stick out my tongue—and all would be lost lost lost! She might even knife me. I composed myself. I stayed where I was. I was almost happy: I was on mission, but at the same time I was a snouty she-cub who'd fallen asleep at the teat and woken up again in sweet milky darkness. Then suddenly her hand pressed the back of my head, her nuzzy pressed my forelip and I knew she'd let me do whatever I

The elevator doors shuffled open and Bertie sang, "Fuk me, it is an H. Holy godzilla, look at that motha."

And I peeked out of our sheets at the thing. It sat on a stainless steel dolly in a row of dowdy linen bins, a Nike among Miss Muffets. It had been many times slicked over with paint but still had a rough, psoriatic crumb to its blue enamel that made me loath to touch it. It was like sumpm left to rust in a marine junkyard because it might explode—and yet it did resemble somebody's mother: five feet high, all the power in the bosom and shoulders, some sort of undersized glass-faced gauge where the head should be—a meter instead of a dreambox, isn't that just like a mother? Well what do I know, never having had one since I was eight.

"Come on, Ursie. O, you stay put—make like you're paralyzed or sumpm. Perfect." Bertie and I stood side by side, looking down fascinated at O's big eyes wide open and fixed on the ceiling—two Caribbean portholes ringed with stove black, in each of which a blind dab of fluorescent light floated. "I do a good coma don't I," she said, and we both jumped.

Bertie grabbed the H around the waist, tipped but couldn't lift the thing. I laughed. "Okay, Koderer, you do it," he snarled. Then panic whited out his face: "Cheese it—the Regicide!" And suddenly the H was rocking like a drunken bowling pin on its heel. Bertie dove into one laundry bin and I took the next one down the line, and pretty soon we heard the swat, swat of Reggie Blanchard's tennis-racket-sized white rubber-soled hospital loafers on the linoleum.

"Lady O! How ya doing. You be down here scouting again for that doper cat? What did that eight ball ever do for you?"

Comatose. Not a blink. Oh, a drapette of the highest principles was O, stand-up to the final hour, a stone stoic even though we both knew that Bertie would have swapped either one of us, or both, to the hoods or the cops in a minute for eight ounces of Saigon gage or anything else really hard to get.

Our Reginald was an artistic looking tea-colored negro whose beautifully molded lips had ambiguous and unsettling punctuation marks at the corners of them. He wore a little W.E.B. Dubois goatee as sharp as a tack, and his poison-honey eyes were cruel. I mean it was the way he saw the world. Really he'd rather save you than sell you, but first he checked the price.

"What's your hustle today, sweetheart? Coma! All dummied up! Ain't talking to the Reg! Ain't you the one," he saxophoned. "Old O, if she can't say sumpm nice, she don't say nothing, is that it? I hear you! Been had your messed up brain taken right out, huh? Well it was nothing but trouble anyway. Tell you this, sweetheart. You the best looking empty they ever had up here, you know that? And as I know you are a schooled young lady, down with all games, and I desire a word with you, Ima give that coma my special cure—scope the gangway first, make sure nobody ain't coming— okay now Ima turn that coma over to Doctor Blanchard for his patented guaranteed coma process—"

Things went quiet, too quiet, and, since my present laundry bin had no peephole, I had to periscope up through the twisted towels and damp pajamas to see what was going on—and got an eye free just in time to see the dirty dog lying on top of her. His pelvis flowing like wave theory, he wasn't exactly tickling her. No zippers down, though—not yet.

With my record I bet you think I jumped right in there on top of them, punching and kicking. Well, I was a Bug Motel now, and not only a Bug Motel, a Bug Motel *on mission*. I stayed put. Over Reggie's shoulder, O narrowed her eyes at me warningly, and I obeyed. O half growled, half giggled, and finally she clawed Reggie's back with her black raspberry fingernails. "Hey, Lady O, there you is. This coma is defunct, you cured, I Dr. Reggie done cured your bug-eyed self, or was you shucking the whole time? You? Not you! But anyhow you back with the living. I missed you, baby. Now sit up. Gimme some sugar."

O sat up with a sigh and swung her legs side-saddle off the gurney so her gold lamé ballet slippers dangled. She patted her big hair, curled back her bony shoulders, planted hands on hips, pointed her nuzzies professionally and said: "Hey Reg. What's uptown?"

"Welcome back, baby. Nothing much. Same old three-six-nine. Say, what yall crazies looking for down here on three? Wyncha let me take kay it for yall? I wear a white suit but I ain't the heat. I knew you from the world, don't forget that, sweetheart. What was you prospecting for?"

The Blue Bomb stood fifteen feet from them, but Reg had no interest in dentist doap.

"You," she said. "Unh-huh. Huckly buck," Reg said, pleased just the same. "Let's you and me go somewhere. Outasight," O spooky-fluted in his ear, and her scuffed-up gold lamé ballet slippers plinked onto the linoleum. He forgot about our mission. "Hey, baby, I hear you," and next their assorted big and little soft shoes slapped away together down the corridor. I surfaced among the towels in time to see Reginald poke his keys into some door marked no admittance halfway down the hall. And the two of them disappeared behind it.

I wished on Reggie Blanchard all the violent deaths of Pennsylvania Avenue whence he had come. I told you before, he'd sooner save you than sell you, though he looked at the price-tag first. But here he was, a royal, well anyway a royal flunky, fukking a mental peon—for an old-time street hustler like himself he had no mercy. He didn't think O could be harmed by doing it in a mop closet. And neither did O. I smelled sumpm greeny brown and swamp rotten in the whole deal, but after all, we were in the bughouse. To be mentally hygienic or even nosily parental was just not done among the mental patients, and especially not among the Bug Motels. Besides, fukking on her feet, for small change or even in swap for that good old dreamboxoline, in barroom toilets and back entrances, was O's official problem: *she had to stop thinking of men that way*. We Bug Motels had a hands-off nose-out policy towards all official problems, and as for what we really thought—we didn't think it.

It did flash on me that O was about to peddle herself in a broom closet *for us*, the Bug Motels on mission: that is, just to clear the coast for a giant tank of laughing gas—and I resolved then and there not to sniff one sniff or laugh one laugh of the stuff, at least not until O forgave me for letting her. Then again I never believed for a minute that O might not forgive me for letting her. And another thing: none of us, not even Bertie, put that old dreamboxoline—by which I mean assorted dreambox oils, drops, gasses and powders—higher on the list of daily necessaries than O did, although she herself might go easy on the purple dots or the mushrooms—never on the bottle, however. Already I could picture her holding that red clown's nose of an N_2O mask, with its nostrils-of-pig outvalve, to one of our faces after another, while she swigged from her own little half-pint of peppermint schnapps. The feast of sumpm for everybody, that was what O liked when she was Mary Heartline, that and the clear swill she was swilling, vodka or schnapps, kong or moonshine, whatever one of her boyfriends had organized for her that day. Now she was Mary Heartline on *Super Circus* holding out those goldfish bowls full of moolah to our fat fists, only the pennies nickels and quarters had turned into laughing gas, and never mind where she got it (really she had to stop thinking of men that way.)

Well, anyhow, from here on, with O and the Regicide taken up elsewhere, it was easy. Though the thing must have weighed 200 pounds, all I had to do was tip that great mother H up against the gurney while Bertie held the cart rollers in place, and hoist her with one big hoist, and tuck her in, and climb back into bed with her. In the dark, under the covers, she was buxom and stately and cold. She had no nipples to her iron bosom, she was wearing a funny hat, and I had a feeling that just when I needed a girl more than I needed life itself, I had traded in my lovely O for a bust of Queen Victoria.

Karen Elizabeth Gordon
from The Disheveled Dictionary

We interrupt this alphabetical free-fall for a visit to a bordello.

Jonquil, a vivacious, ratted-haired blonde in high school, had turned into a nebulous, though still wanton, introvert by the time she'd finished with Descartes. Her professor, preoccupied in those days with ethics (and brimming with perspicuous insights, fatuous hindsights, sagacious sound bites), could not take his eyes off her knees during his lectures, and was discomfited with lascivious thoughts. How might he lead her into tenebrous chambers with a thousand pillows and drifting, silken light-beams, then expose his tendentious intent? He would propose a preposterous night under the town and throw off his donnish gown! The truth is, Jonquil was way ahead of him on this one, and was already setting up on her own! What had become of the gregarious wench of old, with her nail polishes, raucous laughter, flashing eyes? Quoting Diderot, "My ideas are my trollops," she opened a brothel of Platonic love where fetching notions, scantily clad and fatally attractive, drove many a young man out of his mind and into Business, Pre-med, or Law.

catalepsy

Playing captive audience was no longer her cup of tea, after her long session, with her long legs, at the Eagle Café, where a perfect stranger had harangued her into a catalepsy of enthralled listening and left her in a senseless (but enlightened, he thought) heap (the legs folded quite easily: it runs in the family, as this line-up of her uncles attests).

cognoscente, plural cognoscenti

The gathering was indeed formidable: a collection of idiot savants holding forth on their specialties while the cognoscenti of contemporary literature skulked off to powder their notions or cowered on couches and passed out on porches among their muted allusions.

coup de grâce

Swooping in for the coup de grâce with an "Et tu, Brutus?" was an avenging angel who did a bit of Shakespearean acting and mercenary soul-snatching on the side, and sometimes muffed his lines.

diffidence

Often, these malevolent winds from Trajikistan bring euphoria, buoyancy, even manic surges of energy and diffidence; but then, the horrific second phase sets in, and frenzied acts of impertinence and aggression tumble from one soul to another, till even the most sanctimonious citizen has beheld the loud hound of darkness thrashing about in his home.

famulus

The Walpurgisnacht revelers included a talcum-powdered, timorous banshee; a white witch strapped to an ergonomic plowshare; an enchanted donkey with chattering teeth; and a famulus looking very out of sorts in oversized madras shorts.

fantoccini

COMMEDIA DELL' ARTE SCENARIO

Cutting a woozy swath, Arlecchino enters and traces suggestive arabesques in the air ambidextrously. Ursalina stomps out like 6.4 on the Richter scale. Alarmed, Pantalone skids onto the stage with his fantoccini in fur coats. Burattino gives him a big smack and hastens to demystify Goldonio's departure by producing the compromising fan, by now battered to splinters and silken tatters. The puppets squeak "Ciao!" but Pantalone says "Not yet, my angelini," and brings out his concertina, at which they tenderly cover each other's ears and settle down for a painful sinfonia disconcertante. Colombina prances in pushing a pram and munching a panettone. Out of the pram pops Petrouchka with some guidelines for perestroika. All hie their colorful bodies and language to a caffè on the corner and knock back a few espressos till the train to Rome arrives and they can settle down to some very serious business: stealing wallets and laptops. White collar crimes are their favorites.

genius loci

Dear Loona,

Just a quick post card (those are some of the famous cascades of Azuriko, which by now we've left far behind—although not before tossing one of my earrings into the one called Das Knaben Wunderhorn to insure a musically talented child: local tradition, and the counsels of my god-mother Constanza) to say that rather than dallying our honeymoon away in Trajikistan (you were dead right about the genius loci there), we betook ourselves to the next country west and are now (after difficulties at the border) amusing ourselves quite bestially in Lavukistan (good thing we got our visas for here, too; that "just in case" mentality has always been my saving grace) and will be home in twenty days. As for Trajikistan, there was a conference on labyrinths at the Hotel Flambeau, and they'd brought in an architect from Hotel Mostar in Paris to completely redo the corridors. Talk about genius loci! I divined the presence of the minotaur in the depths of the hotel—the pantry, I suppose, wolfing down continental breakfasts (inapt verb, but too late now) and nuzzling the scullery maids hopelessly in his thrall.

Bye for now, thanks for the poltergeist—such an original gift, and I wish we'd brought it with us, as it might have come to our assistance in Trajikistan.

—Laurinda

in extremis

"Are we talking in extremis here, or is this just a social call?" the baba asked The Grim Reaper who appeared quite suddenly on her t.v. screen and beckoned her with his scythe toward the cinerary urn she had intended for Nestor Telemachus.

internuncio

"I'm no mere internuncio, honey, " replied The Grim Reaper to the baba playing for time, "I'm the message and the messenger, and if you don't clamber into that urn—and I mean pronto!—I'm tucking you under my cloak."

juggernaut

an overwhelming advancing force that crushes or might crush everything in its path; an inexorable destructive force; also a belief or institution demanding or eliciting blind or destructive devotion

Arriving at "former employment, previous positions," on the apprenticeship application, Jonquil cast one confounding glance at the king's portrait before responding in her most adamant, steady hand: "a gentle, unflappable navigator on the waterways, a juggernaut in town."

loquacity

Our interlocutor having quite flummoxed us with her deadpan, coy delivery and recondite replies, and our loquacity having in any case run its course and left us exhausted (we were utterly at a loss for words), we agreed to take a break for a day, a week, a year from this elusive enterprise of talking back to the sphinx.

nefarious

The most nefarious beast for miles around was Deux Chevaux, a hoodwinked tomcat who lived in his mistress's handbag and sprang into action whenever she let him out of it. The handbag, it behooves me to divulge, was made of various animals Deux Chevaux had clawed to death in his ferocious, precocious kittenhood.

nostrum

"You see, what I was seeking at that time, Nada, was an elixir for my Weltschmerz, a nostrum for my shaken confidence, a salvo of accolades from Spoleto and Vienna, and a pair of hairy arms to grab me in the cloakroom while I was rummaging about for my wrap," prefaced La Zermattress, hoping to soft-pedal the humiliations she was about to expose.

pander

"That Bible-Belter panders to the sleaziest hankerings and tawdriest afterthoughts when calling suckers and sinners to his brimstone sheepfold padded with pornography and penitential dollars."
—The Lambkins of Dreadmore Valley

recumbent

Torpor in the Swing is one of the most unmoving novels of recent times; the protagonist does little but blink and languidly turn the pages of her soporific best-seller, *The Wretch of Lugubria,* which we are obliged to read over her shoulder aloud to her while her soubrette massages her feet.

succès d'estime

Flaumina Untergasser's Sumptuary Outlaw collection was the succès d'estime of the season, but her emerald bustiers, ruby stigmatas (bracelets and anklets worn not on the wrists and ankles, but on the palms and the soles of the feet,), diamond swizzle-sticks, and seven-inch gold collars were dismissed by Severo Trobalini in the *International Herald Tribune* fashion supplement: "Fools rush in where angels wouldn't be caught dead."

Illustration Sources and Acknowledgments

Rikki Ducornet: flying, flowing sphinx for *loquacity*, printed with permission of the artist, who is also the author of several miracles.

Jim Harter: *Harter's Picture Archive for Collage and Illustration.* Copyright (c) 1978 by Dover Publications, Inc.

Olja Invanijiki. The image of the nefarious beast, Deux Chevaux, from *Knjiga o Olji.* Knjizevne Novine, Beograd, 1984.

Ernst and Johanna Lehner: *Picture Book of Devils, Demons, and Withccraft.* Copyright (c) 1971 by Dover Publications, Inc. (For *diffidence* woodcut)

Eleanor Hasbrouck Rawlings: *Decoupage: The Big Picture Sourcebook.* Copyright (c) 1975 by Dover Publications, Inc.

Cathryn Hankla

Charmer

Carol thinks of the relationship as an inoculation that took, raising a festering scab. And after the healing is complete, the scar will protect her in the future from ever...from ever being so stupid again. She tells herself that everything could have been different if Steven had explained the meaning of his tattoo instead of merely displaying it that first morning and leaving her to her own imagination, something at which she was adept but which rarely coincided with reality.

She remembers how daylight, streaking suddenly into the bedroom and over his chest that first, bright morning, set his tattoo on fire. With each rise and fall of his breath, the coiled, indigo snake undulated, feigning a strike.

Other mornings, once their weekend routine with each other was established, she watched Steven's chest and the outline of his body, as if it, too, might change into threat. In the end she couldn't tell who had changed more, Steven or herself. Perhaps it was all a matter of perception. Steven's tattoo coiled at the center of every revolution that sent them spinning farther from each other, eventually into new orbits, yet it had been invisible to her, a surprise.

That first night she had run her tongue over his chest and nipples in the dark without knowing what was beneath her touch. He climbed onto her quickly and she was ready. They made love the way starving people approach a plate of food: they stuffed themselves sick because it might be taken away.

She didn't know the source of his hunger, only that her own sprang from two years of celibacy after losing someone she continued to love. The mixture of longing and sadness had killed her libido, permanently she thought. But just long enough, as it turned out, to ambush her on her first date with Steven. In bed, they had everything in common. Even so, she was surprised when he called the next day, his voice filled with not love but assumption.

"So, Carol, what time do you want to have dinner?"

"I already have plans," she lied.

"I changed mine."

"I can't." She wrapped the cord around her arm.

"I cook a mean steak," Steven said. And for a second she thought he'd said he cooked a mean *snake*.

"I don't eat red meat."

"Coulda fooled me."

"Arrgh."

"You set yourself up. I'll grill chicken instead."

"Oh, all right." She could tell he was planning to spend the night. "What the hell," she said. "Come on."

Steven showed up carrying his tooth brush in the back pocket of his jeans and two bags of groceries. His dog walked right into her house behind him and sat down on the living room rug after a few, tight rotations. Steven and his dog were so sure of themselves she almost believed them. But it took three weeks for Steven to tell her his age, twenty-five, ten years her junior, born in the spring as she had been. Since he told her in bed there wasn't much she could do with the information at the time, except account for his stamina. She told herself she'd end their affair the next morning.

At eleven they were just eating breakfast. It was Sunday, after all, and she'd fallen into the habit of feeding him an enormous breakfast of bacon and pancakes, coffee, juice, and seconds. Following the feast they fell back into bed for round two. After more oral sex in twenty-four hours than she'd experienced in the five long years of her marriage, she couldn't tell Steven that it was over, even if she'd remembered to. It would have been bad manners, and anyway, he made her feel everything again, well, everything except love, and who needed that at this stage of the game. There was something about too much of a good thing that converted her intention of saying "enough" into new bouts of pleasure. It felt like the right trade-off for two years of misery after Art had left with Vickie. She had to stock up before the next cycle of famine. Steven was willing.

She figured at the outset that this relationship was unsuited for the future, although there was no single reason for the feeling and it wasn't based on anything Steven said or did. He was bright, an "ad man," he said, working his first job out of college and doing well. That they had met at a bar was an accident of fortune not a sign. She'd had a hard day in retail, the only job she could get after having stayed home five years pretending to care about the Junior League and flower arranging and her husband's career trajectory. She stopped in at a bar in a strip mall where she'd never been before. As it turned out she'd hit the young professionals' hot spot of the season. She took a stool at the bar, planning to blend just long enough to enjoy one drink. And there sat Steven, hunched beneath an Australian rain hat, his conversation piece.

It wasn't as if she were old enough to be Steven's mother, she told herself. It was as if Steven's mother were only seven years older, though, which put her at forty-two, and younger than some of Carol's friends. Oh hell. She'd just make sure Steven never met any of her friends. He didn't seem interested in anything but sex and food anyway. When her friends called it was easy enough to say she was keeping warm during the winter with a wonderful man she'd met. They were a little too happy for her, in fact. Had her misery been that blatant? Nevertheless, a fling was a fling until proven serious, and fling material didn't have to be marriageable. She was safe, but only until she began to wonder if she wanted to be.

When they went for a hike one Sunday morning in late April, she knew another phase had begun. The hike had been Steven's idea and he'd announced it the night before so that they had to go to bed early, and they slept. By nine the next morning they were a half mile down the trail and way ahead of lovers of the kind she and Steven used to be. The weight of her fleece pullover—a gift from Steven—felt perfect. The lightly scented morning air said spring, but it was still crisp and clear. Steven strode into the lead and after another quarter mile the trail started a slow ascent. They were heading up to St. Mary's falls, a popular spot that provided just challenge enough after a winter of horizontal sports.

All morning the winding trail sent them fording the stream bed. No sooner than she'd hopscotch protruding rocks across icy water than they'd run into another place where the same ritual had to be repeated.

"Oh hell," she said, after the fourth careful balancing act, and plunged through the water in her boots.

"Your feet are going to get blisters," Steven said.

"My boots are supposed to be waterproof."

"Beware the gap between advertising and reality."

Steven carefully removed his hiking boots and socks when he ascertained that he could not ford this time. He stuffed the socks inside the boots, tied them over his shoulder, and stepped into the freezing water.

"You could always carry me," she said.

"You're too...*soft* as it is."

Was she hearing him right? Did he say she was too fat? She glared at him as he tip-toed toward her through the water. He laughed, and it sounded forced to her. She splashed on ahead, up the opposite bank, and attacked the trail, leaving him to catch up after he got his precious socks and booties back on his feet.

Steven tapped her shoulder. "You're practically running. See those jack-in-the-pulpits? Mayapples over there." Steven pointed.

"I'm working up a sweat, Eagle Scout."

"Oh," he said. "I hope we brought enough lunch."

They tramped on in silence. Steven fell back several times as he contemplated the wild flowers. Carol lowered her head and ploughed forward. Her breathing had started out shallow—she'd felt winded after the first half mile—but turned deep and regular, as she hit her stride. It was true, women were built for endurance, not for the sprint. As Steven came up close behind her she could hear the nylon day pack swishing against his wrinkled work shirt with each of his steps.

"Carol," Steven said. "Let's stop here and sit by the river a while."

Steven peeled off the trail and she followed him to an overhanging rock. They scooted out to the edge and dangled their legs over the fast water unfurling below. The white noise of the water soothed her and she reached over to take Steven's hand.

"I'm sorry I've been grumpy."

"That's okay," he said. "I'm Happy, or is it Doc?"

It took her a minute before she clubbed him with her open palm and let herself be enfolded for a deep kiss.

"I like your medicine, Doc." She felt his hand slip between her legs to rub the place where the seams of her jeans met. She wished his effect weren't so instantaneous. Her feet weren't all that was wet.

"I want you," he said.

"Here?"

"Here and now, on the edge." Steven pressed his tongue into her mouth and himself against her. She felt his knot and desire surged through her. The rock was hard and cold but comforting beneath her as she pulled off her shoes and soggy socks, leaned back and wiggled out of her jeans. Light filtered through leaves and through his fine hair as he leaned over her. He had untied his boots again and pulled them off so he could shed his pants. The rest of him was in shadow but once he lowered himself she felt how solid he was, like the rock beneath her. Everything felt real, whole. And then, she remembered.

"Did you bring anything?"

"No. Do you want to risk it?"

Did she have a choice, she thought? Her body was dissolving into a puddle at her center. She wanted him, and before she said anything he was taking her so fast that her spine was being bruised against the rock. She couldn't help it, she gasped in pain. He flipped them easily, and she moved at her own pace on top of him, brushing her breasts against the snake tattoo. She cried out several times and kept moving on him until he caught up with her.

"We're crazy," Carol said afterwards. "I finally worked up a sweat."

"I think it's okay. I seem to remember from sex ed that it's unlikely at this time of the month. You're almost *due,* aren't you?"

An odd choice of words, she thought. It surprised her that he paid such attention. Self interest, of course.

"Yes," she confirmed. "In the next few days."

"It'll be all right, then," he said, as though he had the final word on nature. And maybe he did; he was already rising again. She stared down at his penis, frowning.

"Your charms," Steven said. "I can't help it."

"Like you need encouragement."

"I'll follow you anywhere."

"Don't humor me." But Carol wasn't going to waste the moment. She turned onto her stomach and felt him push against her. She pictured the snake on his chest uncoiling, sheathing itself with her skin.

✳

There's something about the inevitable that always happens: day into darkness; abstinence into passion; and passion into punishment. This time it took about a month after the cliff experience until she was more than half certain that the transformation had occurred. Still, she hesitated to tell him.

"What's been wrong with you? You keep turning away. Have I said something?"

There it was, her opportunity, the opening. "No," she said. "We both did something…"

Steven looked at her. "Oh my god."

At least he was quick, she thought. With Art she'd had to spell it out with a magic marker: I'M PREGNANT; she left the note on the refrigerator. What kind of magnet had she affixed to the note? A bunch of bananas.

Then the obligatory, "Are you sure?" Steven asked, in the voice of every man alive and sweating.

"My breasts are turning into bottles. I'm surprised you haven't noticed."

"I might have, if you'd let me near you in the past month. But now I understand. Damn, we must be the dynamic duo. Only once without protection—and zap, zam, zowy!"

The script was changing. He seemed almost gleeful. Where was Art's incredulity, the "it's your problem" side step?

"If you're seeing someone else, now would be a good time to confess," Carol said.

Steven flashed at her, almost speaking and then closing his mouth in what appeared to be genuine hurt. "How could you say something like that?"

"Oh, I don't know," she said, wounding him with the open sore Art had left. "Maybe it was something you never said."

"I do love you, you know. I just thought you…you wouldn't want to hear it." Steven reached for her and she drew away.

"How can I believe you now?"

"Because you know you can. But you've never said a word about how *you* feel. It's okay with me. I know you were married to an ass hole before. It's going to take some time, but I'm willing to wait."

Carol couldn't answer, admit that the tables had turned. For Art she had an abortion she didn't want, and for Steven? How could she now do the opposite for the same bad reason, to please someone else? There was more at stake in pleasing Steven, another human being, a human heart that would have feelings she'd forgotten.

"I can't go through with it."

"We don't have to get married right away."

And to think she had thought he was quick. He was unwilling to admit her logic, but he would, he would thank her later.

"For Christ's sake, Steven, you're only twenty-five."

"I'll be twenty-six next month," he said, proving his youth.

"And I'll be thirty-six."

"I know. So what?"

Was he listening? "What are you suggesting, exactly?" she asked.

"I think it's obvious. I want the baby. I want you. I want to marry you, but if that's too much to ask right now then I'll live with you."

"Why do you have that stupid tattoo? It gives me the creeps."

"It's about self-mastery. I had it put in one of the most painful places for a tattoo. This is my life; I direct it. I am the snake coiled at the center."

"I can't do it," Carol said. "My life has never been about me, and if I have this baby it never will be."

"That's not true. I'll help you."

Carol tried to imagine the two of them caring for an infant. The two of them holding, changing, feeding an infant. She saw herself heavy, round, slow, unable to earn a living and unable to flee, and Steven backing away from the swollen monster she had become. By the time she gave birth she'd be lucky if she even knew his address. And if she married him? Chivalrous of him but no guarantee. But the more salient point was that she didn't want anyone's help right now—she'd had enough broken promises for a lifetime, enough of waiting to see what the other person wanted, felt, would do—and caring for a baby took at least two. She didn't know if there would ever be a right time for her.

"I don't want your help. The part of me that could believe you are true is gone," she said.

"But you can't just—like it never happened."

"It is the only thing I can do." She laid her palm over his tattooed heart in a gesture of comfort.

Afterwards, it was impossible to say who left whom, only that each had been betrayed and thereby reduced to an agent in a chain, a catalyst for pain: Art hurt Carol; Carol hurt Steven. Whom would Steven hurt? In time someone new would recoil from Carol's pain, this wound inside Steven, beneath the figure of the snake.

David Haynes
Senior Will

Maria sat in the last row, by the windows, the fourth seat back just where there was a crack in the linoleum, a camel-shaped hole peeled open and dark amber-colored, revealing ancient adhesive now as smooth and as polished as the rest of the gray and beige checkerboard floor. Mr. Staples had let them pick their own seats on the first day of class and Maria chose her usual one, not in the back where the black boys and the real troublemakers sat, but a few seats up from there and off to the side where it was unlikely she would ever be called on, or noticed at all, as far as that went. All the seniors had to take an elective English class. You could pick from Rhetoric, Advanced Composition, The Contemporary Novel, or just plain Senior English. Which was her choice. Those other courses were for college types. They were known to be a lot of work and all Maria wanted was the credit. Mr. Staples was focusing on American junk.

No one had ever called her a prize student. Many teachers at South High made it clear to her that academics did not seem to be her strong suit. They called her lazy and unmotivated, wrote her scolding notes on the backs of her papers which accused her of not using the mind with which she was gifted. She'd do much better work, they said, if she spent more time paying attention to the lesson and less time watching the clock. As a matter of fact she did choose her seat not only so she could be inconspicuous, but also because from there you could always get the best look at the clock, located on the wall opposite the window, and she remembers how while Mister Staples droned on and on about some silly story which maybe had a ghost in it and maybe did not, the second hand on the clock above the chalkboard hardly moved at all. It was so slow that she had to stop watching it finally and put her head down on the desk.

Staples was an odd character, she always thought. Old-fashioned, like something out of one of those foreign movies, or like one of those fussy men on those English comedy shows they put on channel two during the late news. But he was black. He always wore a suit—a nice suit—and he would walk up and down the aisles often, almost as if he were on patrol, hands behind his back, delivering his sermons about this or that. She didn't follow the words, only the soothing sound of that voice, which resonated as if he were built like a massive organ, rather than slight and narrow, as he was. She would ride the rhythms of his speech, her heart keeping time, calming her to just this side of sleep.

Behind her, her boyfriend Josh, who back then was just a big goofy looking kid with sandy blond hair down to his shoulders and buck teeth (which she loved,) sat bolt upright in his desk. He balled up bits of paper in his fingers and flicked them so they dropped down the neck of her blouse. She picked them away and swatted at him and tried to ignore the nasty-sounding laughs from the boys across the way. He looked so innocent back there, Josh did. That was his cover, really. Dumb as the day was long, and he knew it and she knew it and so did Mr. Staples and all the other teachers, and the deal seemed to be that as long as he sat quiet and did not disrupt and made at least some effort to get the work done, they would give him D+s and C-s, and at the end of his required time at South he would walk across the stage with everyone else, be handed a diploma and be gone. She'd wanted to tell him to lay off the paper wads, but she had been afraid to call attention to him, had not wanted to get him into trouble. In twenty minutes it would be noon, their lunch hour, and he would be done for the day and off to his DECA job at a garage over on University Avenue. Any behavior notes might threaten his status in the program, so she turned toward the window with her head still down and adjusted her body in such away that she could catch his eye. She gave him an evil look, and he looked back at her, his yellow-green eyes smoldering in the way they had done all last summer when they'd sneak away to a secluded part of the beach out at Fort Snelling State Park. He raised his eyebrows in a way she thought was nasty and silly and sexy all at the same time. He would stop now, she knew, and she eased herself back around facing front.

"Miss Bonner," Mr. Staples said to her at his desk after the bell. "A minute of your time, if you will."

Josh stood in the door, waiting.

"To your next class, Mr. Jessup," the teacher ordered.

"Hurry," Josh mouthed at Maria, and he walked away, but not before directing at the teacher, who was a bit shorter than him, a look full of benign disdain.

"Have a seat," he offered.

"I got lunch," she said, nervous. It was October and this was the first indication she had that he even knew who she was.

"It's my lunch, as well, and I'll only take a minute of your time. You may sit, if you like," he repeated. She stood. He fished through a stack of papers and pulled out one on which she recognized her own handwriting. The assignment had been to write about some poem by some woman named Emily something.

"I put a D on this," he said.

She shrugged.

"You don't care?"

"Not really," she lied. She shrugged again.

"You can do it over if you want. I can move you up at least to a B."

"Why?"

Mr. Staples had laughed. "Because you want a better grade? Because you want to do your best? You tell me."

"I don't have a reason. I'm not interested in that poetry junk."

"You surprise me, Maria. I guess I read you wrong. I expected you were more ambitious."

"Well, I'm not," she said. And though she remembers it being hard, she had stared him down. He was a black man with intense dark eyes which sparkled almost as if he were laughing even when he was not. He did not blink and did not look away.

"What will you do with yourself, then?" he asked

"What do you mean?"

"When you graduate. What will you make of yourself? You seem to be fairly carefree."

"I never said that. I said I didn't care about this stupid assignment." She had smirked when she said this and had tried to sound as tough as she could.

"Fair enough," he nodded. "Pick your own topic. Write about something you are interested in."

Maria remembers feeling boxed in when he said that. She remembers that what she really wanted was just to be done with the whole damn episode, but with his fast talk he had backed her into a corner where now she had to do what he wanted—which was more work—or look like a fool. "I don't have anything to write about," she said.

"Write about your honey back there," he'd said. He had been packing his briefcase, tossing in criss-crossed piles of papers as if they were bricks.

She flushed and dropped her eyes at the mention of Josh.

"That's your boy, am I right? That Josh?"

She nodded, still avoiding his eyes.

"No shame. Do me a little paper of some kind about him. However it suits you. A poem. A story. A song. I guarantee you a C," he said. He clicked the briefcase closed and offered her the door, which he locked behind them as they stepped into the corridor.

"Unless it's too hard for you," he said, over his shoulder, walking away.

✳

Maria finds the essay folded into the same page of her South High School yearbook which has Josh's senior portrait on it. His hair in the photo cascades to his shoulders in golden waves the way the boys wore it back then. Meeting the camera, his bright eyes shine out from smooth skin which predicts none of the ravages of fifteen years of alcohol and slave wage scut work beneath every worn out beater in the city. The essay is handwritten in the neat Palmer-method script she had learned so well with Ms. Anderson hovering over her shoulder back at Groveland School in the third grade. Across the page the cross strokes on the Ts line up as perfectly as soldiers marching across a field, the loops of the Ls and Bs and Ds rise off the line, each a proud standardized whorl. This is what she remembers most about the essay—the pleasure she had had sitting there at the kitchen table in the apartment on Minnehaha Avenue crafting the final draft in her very best hand, and how she had tolerated not one blemish, cross out, or noticeably uneven stroke. The trash can next to the loud old refrigerator had been heaped with balls of wadded up paper so it looked like a pile of snowballs ready to be thrown. She doesn't remember that she wrote all of this.

JOSH: A ONE OF A KIND PERSON

Not every girl is lucky enough to meet a guy like Josh Jessup. I was one of the lucky ones, I guess. I will tell you about how we met and a little about why he is so special. I can't tell you all the reasons he is because I would be writing forever.

I met Josh when we were sophomores and we had a class together. The class was Science and the teacher was Mr. French. For one class we had to go to the lab and work on experiments. We had to mix stuff together and if it was blue it meant one thing and if it was red it meant something else. Mr. French gave everybody a partner and so I ended up with Josh. I had seen him before and thought he was kind of goofy looking but I didn't really know him. We mixed the stuff together and wrote down the answers. He made me read the instructions and write in the workbook, but he did all the mixing and pouring. We talked a lot and it turned out he was pretty friendly. We would see each other in class, and then he asked me out and we have been together ever since.

What makes Josh special is he is a kind person. He does not say mean things or hurtful things about anyone, and when he seen little kids in trouble in the street he stops to help them. He has a sick grandma on the East Side and he is forever going over there to check in on her and see does she need anything. He is not the sort of guy who when he is going with you is also chasing after every other girl in school. I would not put up with that, so it means we have a good relationship. He does not do too well in school, but he comes everyday and tries hard. I help him with things he cannot do too well and try to encourage him. Even though he has trouble in school he is good with his hands and is learning a trade. He is very proud of his work and will have no trouble getting a job because he is good at what he does.

I cannot wait until we are finished with school. We are planning to get married and spend the rest of our lives together. We will live in Saint Paul and I plan to work for a while until we start our family. Josh loves kids and would like to have as many as we can afford.

To summarize, I feel privileged to have a boyfriend as kind and as loving as Josh. I only wish that all girls could be as lucky as me.

She smooths the paper against the edge of the yearbook. She rolls her eyes and snickers at her own optimism.

"Didn't you hear the bell on the damn microwave," he shouts down the hall.

She lays the yearbook on the closet shelf and goes to dish up the casserole for Josh and the two little boys.

✳

She had handed the essay to Mr. Staples a week after he approached her about doing it. He hadn't spoken to her again about the assignment— nor about anything else, for that matter—but he did look at her more often now when he stood at his desk lecturing or when walking the aisles during discussions. At least it seemed to her he was looking at her more. Maybe he had always been watching her and maybe she had been so busy watching the clock that she hadn't noticed. Whatever: now he would catch her with those twinkling eyes and somehow the hour went by faster. It seemed easier to pay attention and to follow where he was going, to figure out what all these old-timey stories and poems were about.

He gave her a **B-** on the essay, and he wrote her a note. He told her that despite the sentimentality, he could tell she had put a lot of herself and a lot of her time into the piece.

She should have looked up sentimentality. She really didn't know what it meant, whether it was a bad thing or just something he didn't like. She did not look it up because she was side tracked by the last sentence on the page. In parentheses he had written: *Are you sure you want to marry this guy?*

He handed her the essay in class just after he gave them an assignment to read a story about some guy who murdered his girlfriend and buried her in the floor. She had read his response and then in her shock had folded it quickly and stuck it in her notebook.

"What's that?" Josh asked. No one else had been handed anything.

"Nothing," she said. She had planned on reading him that essay on their way to the homecoming dance. It would have been perfect. She would read it and he would know how much she loved him, and why, and they would have a perfect romantic evening. Now, there was this ugly question scrawled in bright red ink across the bottom of her beautiful writing.

"Some extra credit," she said.

"Do some for me," he whispered, his voice husky with innuendo. And then he began to complain about how hard the words in the story were. Mr. Staples signaled for him to be quiet.

"Wait for me at the lockers," she told him at the end of class. She lingered at her desk until the rest of the class had exited, then approached Mr. Staples.

"Why did you write that on my paper?" she asked.

"The B-? You worked hard. That's worth something in my book."

"About me marrying him. That ain't your business." She stared him in the eye and pushed down the emotion in her voice.

The teacher pursed his lips, prissily she remembers. "I'm sorry," he said. "You are absolutely correct. None of my business at all. Please, forgive me." His eyes were lit up in a way that felt to her like a challenge.

Even so, she relaxed. She had expected him to be harder than this, more confrontive. She felt brazen.

"What's wrong with him?" she asked.

He stopped packing up, got a sly smile on his face. "I thought we just agreed that was none of my business."

"You already put your nose in it. I want to know."

"Fair enough," he said. "You may consider my query as a thought provoker. Nothing more."

"Think about what?"

He nodded toward the door, picked up the briefcase and started with her down the corridor.

"If this is really what you want. That's all."

"What's wrong with him?" she asked, dogging him, stepping around in front of him, persisting. "What gives you the right to judge a person?" she asked.

He stared at her for a minute. "My question was for you Maria. It wasn't my intention to criticize your young man. He's..." and here the man had hesitated. "He's like a lot of the young men around here. Seems like a decent sort. Good enough and hard-working. You young women come through here and so many of you, the only thing you think about is catching one of these guys as if that's all you were put on earth for. Every one of you sounds as if life were always going to be happily ever after. Then you come back ten, fifteen years later full of regret. I always wonder if anyone ever asked: are you sure? Is this really what you want? And I wonder if it would have made any difference. So I'm asking you: Are you sure you want to marry this guy?"

"Yes," she said. "Yes I am." And she walked away toward Josh, waiting as faithful as a big pup, down the hall by their lockers.

✳

After supper, after she has washed and put away all the dishes, made the sack lunches for tomorrow, and while Josh is sprawled on the couch with his six pack and the boys have gone to bed, she pulls down the yearbook and turns to the teacher page. There is Mr. Staples, looking much the way she sees him in her head. Well-dressed, a shit-eating no-teeth-visible smile dominating the picture. She wonders if he is still the same—if he is even there anymore. On the dresser is the invitation to the fifteenth reunion of her South High class. She can go back and see if she wants to. She turns back to her own picture. Then she stands in front of the mirror. She is not the same, but not so bad, really. She's long since cut all the wings out of her hair, and her face is certainly fuller. And she would never get into that scoop neck dress again. But she could walk into that Radisson and feel pretty good about herself. She goes out to show the invitation to Josh.

"We got our reunion coming up," she says.

He belches. He is watching the cop show with the fat guy and the thin guy. She doesn't know if they make it anymore or if this is just a rerun.

"I think I'm gonna go," she says.

He pops open another can of beer.

"Should I put your name down?"

He gets up and pushes past her to the bathroom. Finished, he saunters out around her, zipping himself up, suppressing some disgusting digestive noise, letting the sound sputter from his lips.

"You're serious about this crap?" he asks. He scans the flier and tosses it on the floor. "Fifteen bucks. Shees."

She retrieves it. "I think I'm gonna go. I'd like to see some of the old crowd."

"Such as? Who you gonna see that you don't see in line over at Rainbow?"

"Some people left town, maybe. I haven't heard from Sherri in a while. Some of the old teachers even."

"Yeah, right." He sucks down most of a beer. "Look: spend your money if you want. Me, I don't need to go down to some hotel to have a bunch of folks look down on me."

"We got nothing to be ashamed of."

"Yeah: a grease monkey and a grocery store check-out girl. We're living real high."

"There's people worse off than us."

"And they'll have the good sense to stay home, too." He dismisses her with his hands and goes back to the show.

✳

Maria was pleased that, despite her standing up to him, Mr. Staples still showed her respect. He still caught her eye, still made it a point to try to get her engaged in the discussion. In the spring they read this play by some guy with a state for a name about some girl who never left her house and finally got one pathetic date who didn't even like her. This was just after Josh finally got her a ring, a real ring, one that told everyone—even people like Staples—just how special he thought she was.

"Your reaction, Miss Bonner. To the play," Mr. Staples prompted.

Maria had been lost in a reverie, staring at her ring, imagining the ideal Como Park wedding, with a dozen bridesmaids and a train on her wedding gown a hundred feet long. This diamond might be small, but it was real and it meant she was getting married, and because he loved her, too, not because they had to. It was the real thing.

"I…uh," she began. "I thought it was sad. That poor girl stuck up there all alone without a life."

"The poor girl's name, Miss Bonner?"

She had no idea. She had been letting what little studying she did slip as of late, ever since he gave her the ring, on Easter, and though she had skimmed most of the words, she remembered nothing much about the play, certainly none of the names.

"Rose, isn't it?" she says. She remembers something about roses. There was some snickering in the room.

"If you wish," Mr. Staples smirked. "Is it this Rose's fault what happens to her? Her isolation. Her loneliness?"

"Who else's fault would it be? My stepdad says you make your luck."

Mr. Staples had laughed, she remembers, and had moved the discussion on elsewhere.

"Nice ring, Rose," he said to her, on her way out the room at the end of the period. Josh had already run out ahead. Since he'd given her the ring he seemed to have the need to put some space between them, to not always be around her, hovering. She remembers not minding.

"Is that the chick's name, or what?" she asked.

"Look it up," he said, nodding toward the textbook. He grabbed her hand and hoisted it. "So, this is the rock I've heard tell of."

She stretched her fingers daintily.

"I'm blinded," he said.

"It's what we can afford." The cash had actually come from the sick grandmother on the East Side, or at least a hundred dollars of it had. The other four hundred was financed at the jewelry store.

"When's the big date?"

"This summer. We're keeping it simple."

"Still got a few months to change your mind, then."

And she had laughed. "You don't give up," she said

"My dear Rose: I've been in this business for twenty years. Every year they show up with the rings and the babies and the eyes full of hope. And just as many show up five years down the line. The Love Boat's sailed, they're fat and miserable and they're all trying to figure out exactly how it happened and what comes next."

"There's no baby here," she said, patting her perfectly flat stomach.

"A blessing, to say the least." He looked her over as if he were a car shopper about to make an offer on last year's model. "I'll make you a promise," he said. "When I'm an old man and I run into you in Dayton's and you've long since left this guy in the dust, I promise I won't gloat."

She shook her head and walked towards lunch. Gloat: he'd never get the chance.

✳

Josh snores beside her in the bed. He is warm tonight. Sweaty. She wonders if beer can get into your sweat, because if it can, it has. That's just how he smells. He isn't a bad man. Not like some. He worked everyday. Worked till he dropped, but he did not like it, she knew. And there was so much they wanted from life which was so far out of their reach. Their boys, nine and eleven: they couldn't imagine there would be a way for them to go past high school, and Jeremy, the youngest she could see had already begun to figure that out, had already developed this cool, why-bother attitude toward his studies, that same attitude she had worked so hard herself to cultivate. The oldest, Joshua Junior, was smart enough, but so many other kids had the advantages. Books that she could not afford, and trips, and camps, and educational toys. And, and, and. If he stayed with it he just might make it, might get that scholarship and make something of his life, and thinking of that already breaks her heart a little, because she wonders if that does happen to him, if he should be so lucky, will he walk away from them, turn up his nose at them because they were ignorant and poor and hadn't done better for themselves.

She takes down the yearbook again and pages through the pictures of the young men and women they knew so well. Mostly alive, she believes, because there has been no war to erase them. This one is a carpenter and that one is a nurse. That woman works construction now—she's been seen out on I-94 in her orange vest, tanned and bulky. There are plumbers and teacher's assistants, and many of them, like her, are still checking at the grocery store, or on the line at some job they got while still in high school. Look at them all: so earnest, so proud. "You have not failed," she tells the faces. "You done good!"

On Saturday she will wear her gray and white striped dress, a very tailored one she bought just for a special parent's night at school so her boys would be proud. A hundred and fifty dollars—a half weeks salary—and it was worth it because the boy's had clung to her all night like she was a queen.

She turns to the back of the year book, to the "Senior Wills." Recorded there, all the hopes and fears that her class left to the ones coming up behind them. A quarter is fixed to the page, under a yellowed piece of cellophane tape. Mr. Marvin Staples has signed his name right underneath it. She's almost forgotten why, until she finds above it, faded and smeared, the cryptic will, buried amongst the hundreds of others. "To Rose," it says. "I leave twenty-five cents for the call when it's time to get out. M.S." She peels the quarter from the page and drops it in her purse.

More have turned out for the reunion than she expected. They are packed in the ballroom, and it is as if she is wearing fun house glasses—every face is fatter or fuller or thinner or has changed shape, and they are all smiling and they hug her and tell her how she hasn't changed one bit.

"Neither have you," she says, and she giggles at each little fib.

There is Ronald Alsop who she had that terrible crush on in junior high. He is a little round around the middle these days, and is still smoking, just as he was out on the corner during eighth grade. That stuck up Cindy Stevenson has put on weight. Serves her right, but she is happy and shameless. She gives Maria one of those phony Hollywood embraces people do on TV, complete with the smacks in the air by each ear.

She spots him over with the teachers. He is talking with some younger men she has never seen. His trimmed tight head of hair is now peppered with gray, and he looks a bit stooped-shouldered. She approaches him.

"Mr. Staples?" she asks, her voice weak, tentative. "Do you remember me?" She covers her name tag with her hand.

"Is it Rose?" he asks, and she can tell he really believes that this is her name.

"You called me that," she says, surprised at how pleased she feels that he has called her up out of the past—even if the past was a warped one. She drops her hand revealing her names—maiden and married—written in different colors of pastel marker.

"Oh, Maria," he says, shaking his head, dramatically. He extends his hand to her. "It's good to see you again. How are you?"

"I brought you this," she says. She has already fished the quarter from her handbag. She drops it in his hand. "We're still married," she says.

His eyes look away as if he is searching for someone. Then they come back to her face. He takes her hands between his and shakes them. "Well yes, of course, darling," he says. "Of course you are."

Cynthia Hendershot

Heads

My face in the mirror, they tell me, point, but I know it is not. My body as I lie on top of my lovers, my hands spreading across their chests, but not my face, not my head. They gave me someone else's.

The streets are silent now, the bodies swing slowly in the breeze, their bulbous eyes covered with black cloth. I step out covered in a black cloak to go looking for my head. Sifting through the baskets, head after head, some still warm, muscles still moving, I raise my candle and look, but among all the heads—young, beautiful faces blackened by death—mine is nowhere to be found.

Back home my husband greets me, concerned. He caresses the hair on that head and I tell him to touch my breasts, because I know they are mine. As he sleeps soundly next to me I rise, sneak outside to meet a lover, an executioner.

He is pale, silent as he leads me to a hotel where we register as husband and wife. We stand naked before the long mirror, our skin silky in the dim candle light. He kisses my cheek. It's not mine, I whisper. He holds me close, presses his penis against my clitoris. That is mine, I whisper, a faint laugh in my voice.

I lie with my head on his chest. He smokes, caresses my ass gently. These are crazy times, he says. I lift my head, look him straight in the eyes, will you help me find it? He stares at me stone-face, his hand resting on the small of my back. You see so many heads, I continue, maybe you could find mine. He pushes me away, rises, dresses, walks to the door, be glad you have one at all. He slams the door. The face is blank but my body still cries out for him, I float disembodied, scattered through veins and arteries, while that head rests heavy on my shoulders. I bang it against the headboard.

The streets reek of dead flesh as my husband leads me to the doctor. As I sit in the waiting room twisting my hands my husband whispers to the doctor, the doctor nods. I see them conferring about my insanity while this head weighs heavier, I see my executioner lover at his filthy work, his mind fixed on my naked ass smooth beneath his blood-stained hands.

When I talk to the doctor I deny everything. My husband stares at me curiously in the dining room as we sip burgundy. I'm quite cured, I smile, placing my hand on top of his. Outside screams pierce the dark night like explosives. I squeeze his hand tightly.

The next day I smash all the mirrors in the house, invite another lover over, caress his cock, make him come all over the sheets and all over my belly. When my husband gets back I am standing naked in the bedroom. He touches me, smells my lover on me, inspects the sheets. His face turns mauve, I notice, then I fall back on the bed laughing. He walks up to the shattered mirror, his body split in the disjointed lines. He smashes it again, cutting his fist. He comes toward me, smears his blood on my breasts, then he leaves.

In the cold night air I find my executioner sitting beside a lime pit, his breath reeking of vodka, his clothes blood-stained and black with dirt. I touch him on the shoulder. He stares at the face confused. Beneath the mask of this other face I am burning for him, I am expanding in my ribcage, ready to burst all over his filthy body. He lifts my skirt, rips off my underwear, enters me, and in the thick, decaying air, my body rises, leaving the head thrashing on the dirt, leaving my lover hungry, clawing at it as it slips through his fingers.

He leads me back to his cold room. You can stay here, he says, pushing his face close to me. I nod, tell him I will send for my things tomorrow. I scan his sparse room, the dirty glasses, the black hood folded carefully and placed on top of a faded photograph. I set it to one side, look at the photograph, then look him in the eyes. A woman, he shrugs, I loved her, she did not love me. I stare at her cruel face, the delicate lace encircling her throat.

When my lover returns the next evening my fine dresses are spread out on the bed, the single mirror in the room in shattered, and I am holding a razor to my throat with one hand, caressing my cunt with the other. He backs against the door. I want it off, I scream, coming, falling back, crumpling black silk. He rushes toward me, throws the razor on the wooden floor, covers the neck with caresses. Don't leave me, he whispers, while undoing his trousers. I need you, whoever's head you are wearing. Before he enters me I ask him to cover my head with his executioner's hood. He does and as we merge I love him, my body free from the other person's head. My warmth glows, a neon ribcage beneath thin, white skin. As he comes he tries to remove the hood, but I take his hands, place them on my breasts. Beneath the thick, black cloth the face stares straight ahead, impassive, unblinking.

When my husband finds me I am lying in the dark in the executioner's room, waiting for him to come back. I have been drinking his vodka and am now staring at the wall. My husband walks in, lights a candle, comes toward the bed. Why do you hurt me, he asks. I look at him, my face angry and blanched, it is not mine you know. I was executed and they gave me another woman's head afterward to heal me because they knew I was innocent. I am not a criminal. My husband falls to the floor. In the dim candle light I see his face is emaciated, his hands are shaking. Come back, he says, poised on his knees. I can't, I sigh, I need to be here with the executioner. He covers my head, he looks only at my body. My husband stares at me helpless, I'll help you find it, let's go look. I rise, put on my cloak.

He leads me carefully through the icy streets. The suspended bodies are blue, their clothes ripped off, blue breasts, blue toes, blue penises, but the heads are covered. He leads me to the baskets, he sifts through them until, overwhelmed, he vomits in the gutter. It's not here. He moves up behind me, breathing heavily, your head must be rotted by now.

You will have to live with this one. No maggots in eye sockets in this one. He laughs wildly. Please come back, he whispers, squeezing my hand, squeezing it until bones pop. I can't, I say, running, sliding, back to the executioner's room.

The next morning as my lover is leaving, he places a box on the bed beside me. This was left for you, he says, kissing my exposed breast before leaving. I turn over, go back to sleep, my back pressed against the box. When I wake up, I open it quickly, curious, a gift from another lover, a hat, surely. Inside the pretty white box done up with pink ribbons is my husband's head. I scream, throw it across the room, take out the envelope at the bottom of the box. *This is my last gift for you,* the note reads. I crumple the piece of paper, throw it into the cold wood-burning stove. I pull at the hair on the head, take the razor and chop off the long blond curls, throwing them into the dead fire as well.

In the snow-covered streets I stop a young man with a cherub's face and ask him to take me to a hotel. He nods, takes my arm firmly. In the cheap room I remove my cloak, show him my shorn head. Do you mind? I move close to his body, start unbuttoning my dress. Can you love the body without the head? He nods, confused, yet aroused, I see. Please cover my head with something, I touch the bulge in his trousers. He rips down the cheap lace curtain, ties it around my face, pushes me on the bed, rips the layers of undergarments, loves my body, his hands never touching the head once. I'm leaving you some money, he says, to the cold, expressionless face beneath the lace. My body still wants him, still feels him deep in its corpuscles, his scent, his voice, his gentle touch. My hand reaches out for him, but he has already gone. I bundle up in my cloak, gloves, buckle my shoes, leave the money on the dresser to pay for replacement of the mirror I smashed, smashed when I saw the shorn head and haunted eyes reflected there.

Back at the room I light a fire, take the head, throw it in the stove. The stench of burning flesh fills the rooms, my lungs. I feel the gorge rise in my belly, fight it, digging my nails into my arm, drawing blood. When my lover gets back, he lights a cigarette, places it in my mouth, unlaces my corset, kisses my belly, my thighs, pretending not to notice the other man's scent. He covers my head with his hood, carries me to the bed. You can love my body without the head, can't you, I whisper. Yes, he murmurs, his head between my legs, his tongue teasing the lips of my cunt. It is not mine, you know, I say, in-between moans. I know, he says. In the room still reeking of burned human flesh, my body triumphs, taut, sweat-covered, engulfing the executioner, my laugh echoing in marrow and blood, the face still as death beneath thick, black cloth.

Jamie Holland

Healing

Usually at this time of the day Tim is deep into meditation. He starts on the floor, Indian-style, slowly eating rice cakes from the bag. He closes his eyes and, in his mind, concentrates on the rice cake—the styrofoam texture, the beige color, the wheaty taste—until he *becomes* the rice cake, floating steadily against the blue sky, like a surreal painting. In this state, he is at peace. And whatever makes him feel at peace, the doctor said, can't be all bad. But Tim, he warned, Don't underestimate the trauma. Rape is not your everyday occurrence. And then he said, *Time.* He said, it'll take *time* for both of you to resume normal activity.

Tim has been trying, though, for three weeks—since he came home from the dark room and found Sarah curled up on the wood floor shaking and naked—to resume normal activity. He does freelance "street life" photography like he's always done, but being behind a camera bothers him now, the fact that the second he peers through the lens he enters someone else's private world. He no longer wants the responsibility of seeing what he sees. Last week when he brought the camera to his face he saw not the kids in the alley jumping rope but the scene he cannot get out of his head, the one of the three men in tuxedos on New Years Eve, their jackets tossed aside, taking turns on the girl who lay limp like a puppet, red formal dress hiked up, legs spread so far they could split.

Tim never told anyone what happened that night four years ago or how he, from the slit of a door, watched it happen. He pushed it all down into another place, figuring he would never have to retrieve the memory.

Breathing deeply, he watches his chest rise and fall. He closes his eyes and tries to relax, but they don't stay shut—they drift around the room, straight up to the ceiling and around to the flowery wallpaper. There are bright pink roses in the design that remind him of the roses on the cake he bought for Sarah's birthday party two months ago. After their friends left, the two of them got in bed and fed each other the last piece as if they were bride and groom.

Sarah's key turns in the lock and he jumps up and greets her in the doorway, not with open arms, of course—just an eager smile and probing eyes wondering, Well? Are you any different today? Are you ready to embrace yet?

"I'm really beat" she announces. "The restaurant was packed again."

He slides her bag off her shoulder and sets it down. "I made dinner," he says, hopeful.

"I just want to rest." Her long hair is tied back in a braid but little ringlets friz around her hairline, softly framing her face. He takes the braid in his hand and brings it up to his mouth, kissing it lightly. It is as close as he comes to crossing the line of invasion.

"You smell like…, like…" he closes his eyes and, with his hand, gestures like an Italian, "spaghet*teeni.*"

"Funny," she says and walks toward their bedroom. He follows her through their apartment, she in high heels and he in bare feet. His feet make a slick sound as they come up from the floor.

"I couldn't meditate again," he says. He sits on one end of the bed.

"Maybe you're all meditated out." She turns around so that her back is to him and takes off her white shirt, exposing the purple bruises on the sides of her rib cage that are now yellowing in places. He winces at these as always, a nausea uncoiling in his stomach. Over and over he has tried to picture exactly what happened that day—piecing together the fragmented clues she has given him: the slam of the door behind her, the thick hands, the black jeans, the reek of stale sweat—and all Tim sees are enormous fingers discoloring her skin, then the image bursts into a kind of frenzied rage.

He can't stop thinking of how the pictures he was developing the day of the attack didn't even turn out, how it was actually a waste to stay in the dark room. He could have made it home earlier and clubbed the rapist to death.

She kicks off her high heels, shimmies out of her hose and changes into a long, thin nightgown like she's been doing every day now since it happened. She plops on the bed so that she's at the opposite end. "God I'm hot," she says, fanning her face with her hands.

"I'll go swimming with you," Tim offers.

"Just let me lie here a while," she says.

"O.K." He looks at her feet, which are swollen from the heat. On her nails there is pink polish but most of it has worn off so that you can see the tips of the nails. His eyes travel up to her face, to her long blonde eyelashes that flicker as she drifts into sleep.

He does this a lot now—watches her sleep. The doctor said she is fully recovered—physically—but what matters, he remembers him saying, is "what's going on between her ears." Sarah almost smirked when the man said this. She wouldn't even let him sign her up for a support group.

"I hate those group things," she had said to Tim on the car ride home.

"How do you know if you don't try?" He thought he had sounded like a father but at that moment it was clear to him why parents always said it. "Look, I'm just trying to help," he'd said. He reached for her shoulder but she moved it so quickly that his hand landed instead on the seat.

"Please" she had said. "Would you just not touch me?"

✳

Tim gets up from his end of the bed. He lays his hand across her forehead.

She turns on her side, curling into the fetal position. Her face is smushed against the pillow, her mouth puckered like a little girl's. Her nose is hard and almost raw on the tip from being sunburned so often. He thinks it's ironic that she spent so many summers being a lifeguard. It's hard to believe that she was once the one who saved people.

He goes out to their small balcony and sits down. The heat hovers like a heavy wool blanket, and immediately he begins to sweat. A stream drips down the center of his back and it reminds him of the way Sarah's fingers used to trace his spine at night, tickling his skin like a crawling spider.

Now, at night, there are no spiders on his back. There are nightmares about people with no faces. There is strong black coffee in the morning, one or two of Tim's phone calls to her each day, during which Sarah tells him how tired she is or complains how "blah" she feels.

"Come home then," he says. "Let me take care of you." *Let me make it up to you,* he thinks.

"You don't understand," she always says. "I can't just leave like that."

And then they hang up and he waits. He jumps when the old woman who sorts the mail sticks the envelopes through the slot or when a car door slams outside the window. Sometimes he finds himself wandering into their room, just sitting on the edge of the bed. He imagines taking a witness stand in a courtroom, a defense attorney wrinkling his forehead, saying, "You mean to say that you allowed a rape to occur in your home?"

✳

The pool below is packed with bodies in bathing suits. Men play volleyball in the center of the pool, spiking the ball at every possible moment, checking out the women in bikinis. It reminds him of his best friend Jeffrey's bachelor party the other night that was held at a topless bar. Tim left early, complaining of a bad stomach ache, and drove anxiously to the restaurant where Sarah worked. She sat him at a table in the back and he watched while she finished her shift, serving hot plates of spaghetti, fat bottles of Chianti. The men at her tables—was it his imagination?—they eyed her rather seductively—and so many of them were alone. Some even turned around to check her out as she walked away. You could see so little, though! Black skirt to the knees, white long sleeve shirt, high heels. He wondered how they imagined her to look underneath, if they even came close.

Lately, though, it's been hard to call up just how she *does* look underneath. Sometimes when he sees her naked in the shower or in her underwear and bra, that's all he sees—*Sarah naked, Sarah in her underwear and bra,* and other times a sudden craving takes over and he has to turn away to hide it. He ends up in the locked bathroom with the faucets running, repulsed afterwards. Just yesterday when she was lying on the couch reading, though, he felt something much stronger than need or desire—he wanted to be so far inside her that the rest of the world would disappear.

Back inside, their room is stuffy. The blinds are tightly shut and the windows are only partly opened. Sarah is by the bureau reading labels on little bottles and tubes. She has crease lines on her cheek from lying down.

He sits on the end of the bed, watching her at the mirror. She unscrews a cap and dabs liquid on a cottonball, rubbing it all over her face in small circles and then on her neck. Her face is red and splotchy when she finally stops. She looks at the cottonball before throwing it away, then holds it up for Tim to see. "Look how much dirt there is." She tosses it in the trashcan and leans close to the mirror, inspecting her face.

"Let's take a trip," he says. "Just get out of here for a while."

"Yeah," she says. "Wouldn't that be nice."

"I'm serious. Let's just go."

"I can't just get up and go like that," she says. "I have a job. They don't just let me leave when I want."

"Well they should," Tim says. "Considering."

She drenches a fresh cottonball and does the same thing, scrubbing like she's rubbing off paint with turpentine.

"I think it would be good for you," he says. "Good for us."

"Look at all that dirt," she says when she's done. "It just keeps coming."

Tim stands. "Are you even listening?"

"I hear you," she says.

"Well I wish you'd at least think about it."

"O.K., O.K.," she says. "I'll think about it."

Tim walks over to the window. He pulls the string on the blinds and lets them up about a foot. The old man below waters his garden with the long green hose like he does every day. He looks happy down there, Tim has noticed lately, the way the late afternoon sun caresses his shiny head, the way the water flows out of the hose so easily. A woman, probably his wife, appears and hands him a drink, something that looks like coke or strong iced tea, and then she says something that makes the man laugh. He throws his head back and lets all his teeth show. It lights up his whole face.

In the bathroom Tim studies his dotted beard and uncombed hair. He read another article today about rape and this one included photographs of rapists and, underneath, quotes like, "I didn't know her and I don't care" and "Yeah, I'll probably do it again." Some had beards. Several were shaven and well-groomed, even handsome. They look so unlikely, he had thought, then he had remembered the tuxedos, the slicked back hair.

"We try to push down certain memories," the rape counselor said over the phone when he called one day in desperation, "but they're triggered from time to time."

He turns on the faucet and it bursts out in full force. With both hands he brings hot water to his face. He picks up the razor and shaves until every speck on his face is gone. Then he combs his hair and tucks it neatly behind his ears. Before going, he messes it up a little.

＊

When he steps out Sarah is back on the bed.

"I can barely keep my eyes open," she says.

He lays the back of his hand across her forehead. "Just rest then. I'll do the dinner."

In the kitchen, he takes out the containers from the refrigerator—chicken with olive oil and lemon, pasta with fresh tomatoes, hummous—just some of the things he made today. He knows it's too much food for them, but it helps to have something to do.

They sit down at opposite ends of the kitchen table, the plastic bowls of food between them. Halfway through the meal, he says, "I was talking to Jeffrey today. He said he and Kathy have a gun in their house."

Sarah moves the food around on her plate, separating it by colors.

"He says it makes them feel safer just having it around." But immediately he regrets saying it—What is he thinking—that she actually had *time* to reach for a gun?

Sarah slouches back in her chair, and the fork falls in between the food she has been playing with.

"I'm sorry," he says.

She looks at him straight-faced but challenging. "For what?"

"For saying that. It was stupid."

She pushes her plate away.

"Hey," he says. He stretches his arm across the table, reaching for her arm. She leaves both, though, in her lap.

"Talk to me, Sarah." He reaches further, trying to touch just the tip of her elbow.

"Come on," he says. "Give me your hand." Then he hears himself: *Give me your hand!*, its tone no different than *Get down on the floor!* or *Hike up your dress!* and slowly, he draws it back to where it belongs, pressed tightly against the other one, as if praying.

＊

In bed Sarah sleeps near the edge, curled up. She falls asleep quickly, like she has every night since the attack, and Tim lies awake. His heart beats loudly when he first hears her sleeping. It should have the opposite effect, he thinks—knowing that she's safe and sound next to him—but it doesn't. It just means that she has checked out again and won't be back for another eight hours.

He thinks of how it used to be right before sleep—limbs comfortably tangled up in each other's, intertwined perfectly like two pieces of a puzzle. He always fell asleep first, she used to tell him, but now he uses *her* breathing—steady and determined—as a lullaby. He wishes she were doing it purposely, nurturing, like a mother singing her baby to sleep, but he knows it is not intentional. She is far away in her quiet private sleep, in the other world where it is easier for her.

234

At six in the morning Tim wakes up and realizes that he has not even seen her cry. He has seen her sleep, go to work, and come home, but there have been no tears, no signs of a release.

Is this his punishment, he wonders, for not being there on time, for not walking into the apartment a half hour earlier? Is this silence what he deserves?

He looks at her next to him, sleeping with her hands scrunched up by her face, and he wants to scream and shake her until she says something—*anything*—except how tired she is. He imagines the insides of her body tied up in knots, shriveled and rotting, starting to smell.

✳

An hour later Tim stands by the kitchen window, letting the sun drench his bare back and shoulders. It would be nice, he thinks, to be at a beach, basking in the sun, reading a book, throwing a frisbee.

He surveys the surrounding apartments—their sliding glass doors and air-conditioned bedrooms. There are mostly single people in this complex—some couples, or college boys, like in Apt. 20, who everyone knows because of their parties on the weekends. Tim sees different girls coming and going constantly from their apartment, some more than others, but always the stand-bys in their tight jeans and sunglasses. They leave quickly in the morning, trekking across the soft lawn, smoking cigarettes, as if on a shift.

"How many girls do you think they've slept with?" Sarah asked the other morning. They were watching one of the girls walk toward the parking lot.

"Probably 50," Tim had said.

Sarah had rolled her eyes. "You just know the guys are dicking them around."

He had never heard her use that word before—*dick*. She'd said it the way he'd heard other women—friends of his—talking bitterly about past lovers or one-night stands. *Dick*. It was an awful word.

✳

At the table Tim sits with a legal pad and a pencil. He begins to write a list of things to do. It feels good to write, to get a few things in order. The faucet in the bathroom, for instance, drips sometimes when it's turned off—it's another one of those unexpected noises that makes him jump. And the doorknob to the bathroom—it just twirls in his hand when he tries to shut the door. Also the railing on their balcony wobbles when he leans on it.

He thinks of teenagers in Florida on spring break falling off balconies after drinking too much. He always hears about that kind of thing around April. It makes him nervous to have kids, hearing those stories. He thinks about bars in Fort Lauderdale—he's never even been there but he can imagine—loud music, a sea of burnt shoulders, the smell of Coppertone, the taste of keg beer. Strangers losing inhibitions, waking up in random hotel rooms.

He remembers Sarah saying, "How can people sleep with someone they don't even know?" Their first time together, they slept the entire night holding hands. They woke up and she stayed for three weeks. They cooked their meals and washed each other's hair, sculpting mohawks and Statue of Liberty spikes out of shampoo lather. When she went back to her apartment, they both cried as if they were returning to separate countries.

✳

He hears the toilet flush and then the door open in their room. She's getting her bathrobe, he knows. Grabbing it off the hook and wrapping it around her, tying it twice. She is bending down to look in the mirror that is hung too low, inspecting her tired eyes, her cheekbones that are becoming too prominent.

In the bathroom the water bursts out of the spout in the tub. She hasn't taken a bath in a while and maybe that's good, he thinks. Maybe it's a sign.

When she walks in he asks, "Did you sleep all right?" knowing, of course, she did.

"I was dead to the world."

"I'm amazed at how easily you can sleep."

"What do you expect me to do?" She takes a mug out of the cabinet and pours the coffee and some milk into it.

"Do you think maybe you should be talking about it?" he asks. "To me or to someone? Just to get it out?"

"What is this—an interrogation?"

"Please" he says. "Don't get like that."

"I'm not talking to that counselor." She tightens her robe so that it completely covers her chest.

"Sarah," he says. But in practically the same second she is gone, just a swatch of her bathrobe in the doorway, the sound of her slippers sweeping across the floor.

He sits back down, then slaps the carton of milk off the table, whacking it, and it splats on the floor, landing on its side. Milk dribbles out on the tile, traveling toward his bare feet.

"You can't make her talk," the counselor had told him over the phone. "She will talk when she is ready."

"So then what do I do?"

"Be gentle."

He imagines pinning her down, making her cry or scream—anything except sleep. *Gentle.*

✳

He cleans up the floor and stands at the sink, pouring liquid soap into his palms. He tries to ignore that the liquid resembles sperm but he can't. It is filmy white and stays on his hands, still and determined. He lets the water run over his skin, making it slick, then soapy. He stays like this at the

236

sink, comforted by the sun on his shoulders and back, the steady stream of water on his hands.

He pours himself some coffee and looks at the color of it in his cup. He cannot believe how black he drinks it. It's got to be killing his insides. He sits down and reads the list he had started earlier: *Fix leak, Fix bannister, Fix doorknob.* What was he thinking?—he doesn't know how to fix faucets. And he hasn't picked up a hammer since he was about twelve. Maybe, though, he will learn how to do it. Maybe he will do it today. After all, how hard can it be? To prove his point he underlines *Fix* in all three cases.

In the bathroom, she steps into the tub. Tim listens to the quick plunk of her feet in water, like two rocks tossed in a pond.

From the bedroom he calls her name softly, slowly, so that she will not be startled.

"Sarah?" His whole body tightens as he says it.

"Hmmm?"

"I'm going down to get the mail, O.K.?"

"O.K." she says from the tub.

"I'll be just a few minutes."

The water drips slowly into the tub. He can practically see the ripples the smooth water makes each time the drop falls. He stands for a moment, motionless, waiting, but she says nothing more, and so he goes, carefully tiptoeing through the apartment.

He locks both locks, checks them, and goes down their narrow hallway. A phone rings somewhere—muffled—like it's being shoved under a pillow. He has never seen what's behind any of these doors, not even a sliver when passing. Late at night sometimes he hears a T.V. going or someone locking a door, but he never knows who's coming or going.

Behind another door, he hears a man and a woman laughing hysterically—almost crazed. Tim pictures them on a couch doubled over, holding their stomachs, gasping for air.

Downstairs on a table the mail is piled up according to apartment numbers. He wonders where the old woman is—the one who usually sorts the mail during the week. Tim has never really spoken to her except to say thank you but she seems like a kind woman. Her hair is grey and she wears it parted on the side with a small red barrette holding it out of her face. It is the kind of barrette a child would wear and Tim has always found that cute, but thinking about it today, it strikes him as sad—almost tragic.

He goes to the front door and stands by it, looking out. The sky is completely clear. The leaves on the trees glimmer as the wind moves them, making them flutter. Two women stroll down the sidewalk, both wearing long, flowered skirts. One appears to be doing all the talking, explaining something, it seems, while the other one nods slowly. They stop in front of a building and hug. It is one of those full bodied embraces that lasts for too many seconds and Tim turns away, grabbing the mail off the table—a catalog and the phone bill. Sarah will be pleased with the catalog—it's easy reading, visually satisfying. Tonight she'll squint at the tiny print and then drop off to sleep and Tim will place the catalog on the bedside table and turn out the light, listening to her beside him.

Quietly he unlocks the door to their apartment and, inside, hears the water running slowly, dripping into the tub. He goes right to the bathroom door, and, through the slit, sees her in the tub with her head thrown back against the ledge. Her eyes are closed. Sweat beads burst, dribbling down both sides of her face. He tries not to look at her body under the water but he does anyway, and quivers at the bruises. He closes his eyes, wanting to pray for something—*anything*. For forgetfulness. Please Lord, let us forget this, but he hears the countdown to the new year, he sees the girl in the red dress, and his eyes watching, taking it all in.

He lets out a sigh and immediately Sarah starts slapping the water, screaming.

"Sarah, it's just me!" he says, but she is already standing, dripping, with a bottle of shampoo in her hand raised like a weapon. He flings open the door and runs to her.

"It's just me," he says. He wraps his arms around her shaking, wet body, tightening his grasp, making sure she won't get away, making sure she keeps holding.

They stand like this, her in the water, him out, for a long time. With one arm he grabs a fresh towel and wraps it around her. She is mostly dry, though, from him.

Hillary Johnson

Seismatrix

In the year 2095 A.D., the entire surface area of Los Angeles is covered by a thin organic sheath, a noeoponic "skin" that preserves the structural integrity of human constructs during periods of intense seismic activity. Without this dermal prophylaxis the "city" of Los Angeles would literally be reduced to rubble....

I met her at a party in the basement of the Bonaventure slums, one of those spontaneous affairs that seems all the more predictable for its just having suddenly "occurred." Over the years, the party girls have become more and more mimetic of the environment, the random pose, the guffaw, the outburst, every behavior so studiously chaotic. There were, of course, real Catastrophe Artists among them, women who could divine faults and witch tremors, but I, for one, had never met one—until now.

When I saw her standing next to the punchbowl—my future Seismatrix—I have to admit I felt a sudden access of rigidity in my being, and my first thought was, *Yes, here we go, just one more sclerotic assignation in the dark.*

But there was something different about this girl. She had a volatile, birdlike stillness about her. She seemed to move little, and when she did her gestures were invisibly quick, so that her body seemed to shift instantly from one picaresque tableau to another.

"So tell me something about yourself," I said, sidling up to her. She smiled. "People say I have a heart of gold," she said. "That I'm full of pity for my victims."

I might have recoiled, for she looked at me archly. Her face was sharp and nervous, and her features seemed to be molded to express emotions that lay outside of the human range. Her short black hair lay on her forehead in oily, iridescent feathers, and somewhere behind those eyes there were talons, and screeching. The only thing that kept me from running away in fear was the vague suggestion of flight (let me be clear, here: my feelings on this point were both sexual and sentimental). She was my first witch, and nothing like I'd expected. Here was no sanguine voluptuary with jackhammer thighs, but a brittle, fair creature almost hatefully beautiful to behold.

"Would you like to take a walk with me?" I asked.

"Would *you* like to take a walk with *me*?" she replied. She wanted me to collude in my own undoing. My saliva glands gave a kick. I could have said yes, but I decided instead to smile and lead the way, somehow naively thinking that my failure to assent would actually protect me.

We both removed our felt booties and passed out through the Bonaventure's main sphincter, into the silent night. The light from our flashlights made pearly streaks through the sloppy, ionic mist that rose from the city's pores, an acrid nocturnal cloud-forest that was no less beautiful for being basically a form of waste.

The girl was young enough to have never seen a shoe, and her waxy, splayed feet were dyed a paisley red and blue after the fashion of the day.

We left Bunker Hill and slip-slid down along the arroyo, my less sensitive paws losing their purchase in the tiny rivulets of chlorophyllic sebum that oiled the sides of the canyon. The girl pranced ahead of me with something close to gaiety. I thought: maybe I'm wrong about her.

Then she paused, knelt, and began to stroke the greensward like the back of an animal. "Oooh," she said. "It's hungry tonight. Can you feel it?"

So: I wasn't wrong. My date was a seismic witch, the gods were hungry, and I was the handiest piece of meat that had ever lived. How nice. Despite the rather ludicrous level of danger here, I was turned on. I looked at the back of her neck in the beam of my flashlight and thought about snapping it, the sharp sound it would make. Then I got to my knees beside her.

She guided my hand with hers. "There's a fissure under here. I can feel the slight firmness. The lesion is fully occluded. It probably happened years ago."

"What happened?" I asked uneasily.

She ignored me. "There's so much scar tissue out here," she said sadly. "Did you know that?"

"No," I said. When children are young, their parents tell them that there are monsters under the skin, to keep them from piercing it out of sheer curiosity or childish meanness. I believed it until I was almost thirteen, when I finally achieved a certain useful level of pubescent denial about such things.

"Come on, I have something to show you!" She hopped to her feet and traipsed quickly down the arroyo, while I followed slipprily behind her. It was dark at the bottom, the mist was thicker, and the flashlight's beam offered nothing but a pearly rod opaque light, unrevealing. Suddenly I tripped and fell flat out into the soupy well of perspiration at the valley's bottom. She was under me, I realized, her naked skin the same temperature as the earth. She wrapped herself around me, sucking on like a limpet, giving an oozy moan.

"What," I said, struggling, "was it...you wanted to show me?"

"*This,*" she whispered. With superhuman strength she grabbed my wrists. One hand she twisted behind my back, rendering me instantly helpless, while the other she raised high like a pitchfork and then plunged downward to the ground. In my surprise, I didn't even think to make a protective fist. I felt the surface break under my fingers, and suddenly I was up to my wrist in hot, wet matter. Her tongue licked at my ear. "Like it?" she whispered. Still holding my arm, she dug me further in. The more I wriggled, the deeper I went. She let go, and I could not pull out. My knuckles grazed against something gritty and hard. Pebbles? Dirt?

Then she grabbed my other arm and plunged it, too, savagely earthward. I was face down, my arms buried, the wounds geysering up at my face great quantities of limpid green tears, blood and sebum.

"Stroke it," the girl cautioned from astride my back. "The only way to get out alive is to give pleasure."

More or less armless, I began to buck and flip in a most undignified manner. Meanwhile, she kicked me mercilessly. I clawed my way deeper, reaching for handfuls of the complicated sub-organic entrails. An gust of odor escaped from the hole I was making, and the girl crowed triumphantly. It was an evil, hectic smell, made up of superheated vegetable matter, bones, concrete, feces, oranges, blood and clay, a filthy loam. As I kneaded it with my fingers I felt the earth begin to shudder.

"Yes!" the witch cried out. "Yes! Yes!"' She yanked me back by the hair and then plunged my face into the twitching, fleshy maw. She squirmed and kicked and arched, swooning, and then it happened.

The earth sucked harder, and then it shook with a convulsive, lung-crushing growl, followed by an eerie yawn, a lull, and then the worst possible mayhem: a thrashing, seismic howling, the kind of tectonic roar that once leveled freeways, broke eardrums, changed subway routes, broke legs in two like matchsticks. I fell into the opening cleft, drawn down by the earth's gravity into the terrific, crushing softness of it all, through blood and stain and rot and boiling water, sinking toward the bright density of pure magma. I knew I was doomed and I *desired* it, and therein lies the madness of it all, the part I will never recover from: that feeling of insatiable lusting terror.

And then it spat me out again. I awoke in the night, my naked cheek pressed to a sward of cool, unblemished green not far from Arco Plaza. How I got there, I'm not sure. I never saw that girl again, or any more like her. I think about leaving town, even send out resumes from time to time, though sometimes at night, when I lay my hand upon the city's silent skin, I feel the tissues swell and I hear the faint rumblings of my own apocalyptic desire, and I know that I will never, ever leave Los Angeles.

Dennis Jones
Alti Plano

Pilot looked at La Cumbre and held the baby. "The Peak," Heiberto called it as they drove out to the point where La Paz became mountains. Pilot was alone now. The child was still. He didn't think Heiberto was in on it—not the way the porter carried on about the Americans. Prince Edward and The Virgin. The fucking Americans. Pilot had flown them in from Santa Cruz, and now they had taken him for seven hundred. Burned. Plus the baby. Pilot looked at him through the layers of dirty blankets and wondered if the kid was sick, or maybe dead. He had not moved at all since Pilot took him in his arm. No coughing, no breathing. A lump that opened his eyes once for a slow second as if disturbed in mid-benediction and closed them again. Prince Edward and The Virgin weren't coming. The temperature dropped with the falling darkness. Fucking lousy Americans.

✳

They would not shut up, the couple from New Jersey. Pilot had tried to ignore them and fly his plane, but they were too loud. An enormous man and his thin wife—arguing. They began shouting once the Cessna lifted away from Santa Cruz. The engine-thrum filled his ears, but he heard them.

"You should have given it to him," the woman said. Pilot checked over his shoulder and glanced at the woman. She looked out the window when she spoke as if shouting to the clouds.

"To the priest?" the man asked, his cheeks pressing his eyes closed as if he was very sad for her. "He was crooked."

"He could have helped," she said. The wife kept her shoulders turned from him. Pilot thought she might squeeze through the round window and fly off.

"Father Octavius," the husband barked and shook his small, smiling head. "Who knows if he was Catholic?" He was fat, Pilot saw, huge. A domed stomach bulged over the man's crotch. He crowded most of the seat from his wife. Sweat poured from his jagged hairline into a heavy black beard, wild and untrimmed.

"He knew where to look." The wife's thin nose touched the glass of the passenger window as her voice trailed off.

Pilot noticed the woman's height when he helped them into the cabin. Her chest sat high in the seat, an exact opposite of the husband. Pilot banked the Cessna along the west face of Mount Illimani to prepare for the landing in La Paz. They were silent as the mountain grew in the frame of

242

the cockpit window, and the plane slipped into the darkness of the peaks. The sun cast blue shadows across the snow and the Cessna's outline blurred into the sides of the rock.

The plane broke back into the sunlight and Pilot nosed the plane down on final, radioed the tower his tail number again, altitude and headings, his speed. The controller's English was not perfect, but Pilot knew him. Behind them, the mountains spilled white again from the summit well into the base. The woman gasped as they made a lazy arc onto the alti plano, the high plain of the Andes.

"Show us where to deposit checks we don't have anymore, the priest would have," the man said.

"Beautiful," the wife said, ignoring him.

*

He could just leave it. Pilot had no obligation to the baby, or anyone else for that matter. He had practiced this before. He left for Vietnam and did not come back. A three year hitch and then gone for good. The length between the contemplation of the act and the act itself did not matter. The end result was the same: a ripped wallet photo at the bottom of a metal foot-locker. Cuban cigars in wooden box on top of it. Priorities. When he thought of his wife and daughter now, they were like vague cities in a country he once lived in. Recognizable but unfamiliar.

Pilot cradled the child in his left elbow. He kicked a rock and hummed to himself, the stone clapping down into a ravine. The wind drowned his melody, but he knew he was making music. He should have never started this, he thought. But Heiberto wouldn't shut up about the Americans. Heiberto just didn't know when to shut his fucking Bolivian mouth.

*

The couple took over the entire third floor of the hotel and made the porter run for everything they needed. For three weeks the husband and wife drove Heiberto ape shit. "Fucking royalty," he muttered in a slow Bolivian accent as he smoked with Pilot outside the hotel. After a week, he took to calling the fat one Prince Edward, his wife, Mary—The Virgin. Heiberto climbed the walls when he told Pilot about them. He squeezed the cigarette the American offered between his knotted fingers, blew the smoke from his mouth as if he was lifting weights.

"I warned you," Pilot said. When he helped them down from the Cessna, the husband told him to take their bags out front. Pilot looked at him—two round aviator lenses over a tense smile. Pilot filed flight plans and did not carry bags. This was why he insisted on cash up front. He wasn't their fucking bag boy.

Once, Prince Edward had loudly informed Heiberto and anyone else in the lobby of all the things Bolivia lacked. In broken English Heiberto listed them—consomme, arugula, feta cheese and pine nuts, braised lamb chops with a mint chutney—and Pilot listened. The chandelier, *particularly,*

Edward had said, galled him under the circumstances. A replica of Carnegie Hall's lighting fixture, hung from the high-domed ceiling of the hotel, enormous and provocative like a hanging, crystal heart.

"You have that," Prince Edward boomed, his face broken into pained folds and pointing at the cut glass, mammoth in the full sun light, "and no lemon torte." He was operatic in his need.

Heiberto threw fake jabs, cigarette still in hand, towards Pilot's face as he told the stories. He was a welter-weight. Could have made the Golden Gloves in Madison Square Garden. Heiberto told Pilot how it was: Prince Edward said "jump" and he expected Heiberto to ask "how high?" He learned the phrase from a Marine guard at the American Embassy.

"*Pendejo*," Heiberto said and spit a black bit of tobacco onto the street. "Pilot. What is how you say, consomme?"

"Broth," Pilot told him. "Chicken broth, sort of."

"Why he don't just ask?" Heiberto said. "Fucking Prince Edward."

"He doesn't speak Spanish."

"*Spishh*," Heiberto spat again, face smashed into a disbelieving smile. They watched the small cars chug past the hotel and turn up the road towards San Francisco Cathedral and The Witches' Market. The bald wheels raised a dust that hung yellow all day. Heiberto wanted to hit something—his forearms braided into muscle—porter's cap pushed back off his shining head.

"Are there no babies left in Bolivia?" he asked.

Pilot knew full well there were. He could take them to a dozen places. They could go to any barrio on the way to the airport, stop on the alti plano, walk behind the wire fences and pluck one, easy as an apple from a tree. Dollars worked best. Pilot could have driven them on the road from Cochabamba, through all the busted towns of the Chapare jungle, talked to the campesinos at the coca market in Sinajota and made a deal in the plywood hut that said "hardware store" on the front over a worn picture of the presidential candidate. Easy. But the road was too crude for Edward, too much dust—it was the end of the dry season, August. They had to fly, and anyway Edward never asked. Americans never ask.

"Maybe," Pilot said looking back at Heiberto stubbing out his cigarette, "but not at their asking price."

✳

The baby's eyes opened. Flat, black stones and watery. Pilot knew the couple would come for him. They wanted him to get the kid. The baby stared at him. The Virgin had looked at him too, Pilot was certain, her eyes damp and helpless as the woman from the orphanage held up her pink hands. The couple sat in the hotel lobby. She *did* mean to look at him, Pilot was sure of it. Maybe he drank too much pisco. The breeze whistled in his ears, the kind of wind that tires, makes clean sheets more welcome at the end of the day. Back in the hotel he was sure the look meant something. The Virgin turned from her husband, her cheeks swabbed red with

244

emotion and their eyes locked on each other. Frozen in stark consideration, Pilot thought he knew her for that second, that she needed his help. He pulled his jacket around his neck, blew warm air into his free hand. She *looked* like she was asking for his help in that one moment. Damn. The baby closed its eyes. Pilot's arm grew tired. He couldn't stop thinking about The Virgin's eyes. Were there ever better explanations?

❋

Pilot disliked watching the couple negotiating the adoption. He'd rather be in the hangar working on his plane. If the hotel had takers, he flew to Santa Cruz twice a week, other places on demand. He liked the Santa Cruz run, because the town was at sea level and reminded him of Miami with its long avenues centered with cement and grass islands, rows of clean bars with cold beer, small casinos in the hotel basements. Pilot struck a deal with Heiberto's boss to charter tourists between the capitals, take them up at a cut rate and blind them with the light of Illimani's vast white face. He ferried jungle trekkers out to Chimore, brought mountain climbers up from the tropical zone. Pilot ran an occasional fishing group to Titicaca on the border to bring home huge lake trout packed in ice bags. Prince Edward and The Virgin were his last passengers. The dry season had ended. Two weeks of rain grounded him, and there was no sense flying in bad weather.

He drank pisco and lemon in the hotel bar, the strong Peruvian tequila racing straight to his head and thought about some other place than La Paz, as he watched Prince Edward and The Virgin sit out in the hotel lobby.

The woman from the orphanage reviewed their options again. Pilot had seen it a dozen times or more, maybe closer to fifty. If not these Americans, others. Braids tightly threaded behind the small woman's head, business-like. Silver strands frayed into her round glasses, and thick wrinkles notched the corners of her mouth, as if the weeks of telling the royalty the bad news—that there is nothing, nothing that can be done—had taken its toll. Prince Edward and the Virgin nodded, thoughtfully. The woman held her legs tightly together, a pile of manila folders on smooth thighs. She looked down at the files. Pilot knew what she would do next. She would tell them that there were a few remaining options and raise her hand quickly, because she did not want to discuss it then—"*por favor* think about it." When she turned her brown hands up, the palms were the color of sea shells.

And then The Virgin turned her head and looked straight at Pilot.

❋

Pilot sat. He placed the baby by his knee and lit a cigarette. The wind took the smoke away quickly. Heiberto couldn't have been in on it, Pilot thought. The Bolivian needed him. If only for his cigarettes. Pilot knew this was all bullshit, of course. Even Americans like him, those that ran with the locals, took what they could get and kept running. Pilot had no friends in the world. Why would La Paz be any different?

Anyway, Heiberto didn't see the look she gave him, the starter gun for this mess in his hands. He just drove Pilot to La Cumbre with the baby on the back seat. Pilot had sat in the passenger side and watched the *cholitas* waddle home from the market, bright knitted shawls pulled tight over humped backs. Dusty bowler hats perched on braided heads. Bolivian Charlie Chaplins. Heiberto took a four-by-four from the hotel motor pool and started east, climbing in a long, crowded loop from La Paz along the narrow roads that cut the foothills and mountains.

"It will be safer for this there," Heiberto said, "to do this thing." The Americans had no luck and decided to stay a week longer. During the cigarette break, Heiberto said he wanted Pilot to talk to them, kick Edward's ass. But Pilot had said no. He should always say no.

"They are your guests," he had said. "Don't you want to show them the high regard you have for all Americans?"

"They want too much," Heiberto said as if he felt sorry for them.

"We can fix it," Pilot said. Heiberto stopped throwing jabs.

"Let's walk a little," Pilot said, and they did. This was hours ago when his ears did not burn with cold and the mountains were further off. The baby sniffed. Pilot looked at it in the dark and stubbed out his cigarette.

✳

They had walked to the Witches' Market, wandered down cobblestone streets jammed with small-time jewelry stores, one-counter food stands. The Indian women sat in small groups, marking the entrance to the market with their dirty, bright dresses. Pilot looked at the meat stands, blood running off cutting boards into the street, rows of gutted fish with mouths closed tightly. He was the only American. Heiberto kept walking until they reached a table of half-filled liquor bottles, Johnny Walker labels covering Bolivian corn liquor.

At the next corner a bare-chested man stood as a snake coiled beneath his armpit and across his chest. He held a leash in his hand. A green lizard sat still at its end by the snakeman's feet, tongue darting absently. Heiberto asked him where they should go and the snakeman pointed to a window over one of the shops. Pilot felt for his wallet, but the man waved his hand. The snake slid to the end of it and around his wrist. The man smiled and shook his head.

"Pilot, let's go," Heiberto said. Pilot looked at him. They were really going to do this, buy a fucking baby. He could stop it right now.

"I know where to get one," Heiberto whispered.

✳

Pilot stepped over the baby and walked back to where he and Heiberto had waited in the truck. He walked further off until he reached a draw that sloped away into rocky terrain. Patches of snow crushed under his shoes as he walked back to the child. What difference did it make now—if she looked at him or not? Pilot had told his wife he loved her long ago, now he did not. He had kissed his newborn daughter behind her tiny ear and whispered that she was everything in the world. Now she was taking graduate classes or dance lessons and was nothing to him.

The Virgin had spoke to him once in the first week, before she looked at him. He was in the bar still. She had walked across the lobby and stood in the entrance as the waiters rolled silverware in heavy napkins, ashtrays clicking clean into rolling trash cans. Pilot watched her in the entrance.

"They're open," he said. She sat down, a few stools away from him, and ordered a Manhattan.

"No luck?" Pilot asked. She stopped running her finger around the tumbler rim.

"What do you know about it," she said. Her face was smooth, no lines beneath her eyes. She wore linen pants and fanned herself with the damp cocktail napkin.

"Enough," he said.

"I can't say the same," she said. The Virgin looked up with her mouth partially open, about to say something, then stopped. She finished her drink and rose to leave.

"If you need a flight." Pilot looked at his hands holding the glass. The Virgin frowned and looked away.

"Surely," she said and walked out.

He was making excuses now as he walked back. The silver light had gone almost black. Heiberto told the Americans about La Cumbre. He said Edward had the money. Pilot picked his way back, a little disoriented until he made the baby out, a loose rock on the ground.

✳

Heiberto got them into the country quickly. An old truck with arched chassis approached and drove past, wooden slats fencing bunches of green and yellow bananas piled high in back. Two stray dogs trotted behind. Pilot watched in his side mirror as the mongrels waited for a piece of fruit to tumble onto the road.

"You don't look at the llamas," Heiberto said. Pilot smiled at him, how he substituted the "y" for the ls.

"You see one 'yama,' you've seen them all." A few of the animals blended right into the hillsides. Daylight fell into a broad grayness and when the llamas moved, they looked like narrow cuts of rock that removed themselves from the earth's face and walked away. Pilot thought that all of the country could break apart piece by piece and wander off, vanish just like him to let the lawyers puzzle over it all.

"Look at them," Heiberto hissed with wonder, nose above the steering wheel. The Bolivian must have seen dozens of them before, Pilot figured, but still the erect beasts with straining necks moved him. "They are given by God," Heiberto said.

Heiberto turned off the road and onto a wide plateau and faced the mountains to the south. Pilot looked around and saw the scattered lights of the outlying neighborhoods glitter, but they were distant as stars and just as hopeless.

"We wait for them here," Heiberto said and jumped from the truck. Prince Edward said they would come. Pilot followed the Bolivian. The land dipped and flattened again. They stood at the edge of the stunted plain next to a notched wooden cross jammed crooked into the dirt. A bed of rocks circled the stick. The base was tucked with wilted white carnations, grimy and old and almost a dozen miniature saints or prophets holding tablets, crosses, a bible and smiling wickedly into the lengthening dusk. Empty beer cans lay on either side. Ribbons and bows hung from the horizontal edges. A crude memorial.

"Voodoo," Heiberto said. Pilot knew he only meant spirits and charms, tokens of meaning for the dead to carry away. Terms Pilot would understand. "Many people die on these roads," the Bolivian said. "Too steep."

"A remembrance then, this?" Pilot asked.

"Yes."

Pilot recalled the group of hikers, two Americans and a Bolivian guide who had lost it on the mountain's western face. He was new to La Paz then. Snow pack had gone soft and they fell—who knows how far?—before they slammed against a stone ledge. He had flown one of the Americans to Santa Cruz for the final flight to Miami. The consul from the embassy had found a decent coffin to place the hiker in and a black body bag. Pilot just flew the man and came back. An easy job. The embassy check cleared.

"When will they come?" Pilot asked. They both were getting cold and started back for the truck.

"Soon," the porter said. The wind blew his hair up in the back, and he pushed his face into his familiar crushed smile. Heiberto walked back to the truck, throwing short jabs and moving in slow boxer steps.

✳

The sun had gone behind the Cordillera Real in the west and the wind swept slow and lazy through the snow fields that wandered down from the mountains. The Yungas jungle was beyond the eastern range, a swift plunge into a tropical zone. Pilot could hitch a ride with the banana trucks that labored down the highway. Or he could just walk it back to the outlying neighborhoods of La Paz. Five miles. The road wasn't that bad, he'd have to worry about some falling rocks, but they were mostly in a short valley on the way out, passing the occasional shack, some slough water, and then rocky foothills.

They had taken him. Damn, he felt bad about it. Stupid—to a point. He picked the baby from the ground. Through his coat, he could feel the heat move through the child, the yellow blanket warming his stomach and easing the thickness from Pilot's chest. He had to choose. He hated choosing.

✳

Heiberto's beeper went off

"They aren't coming," Pilot said.

"I go get them," Heiberto said. The truck smelled like sweat.

"And leave me here? No fucking way."

"Pilot, please," Heiberto said holding up the beeper, "I lose my job."

"They aren't fucking coming." He was getting angry. Mad that he could not run.

"I come back, please Pilot. I come back." As the truck rocked off the plateau, Pilot never thought Heiberto wouldn't come back. He had to come back.

*

Darkness covered everything. Pilot could see nothing, but he felt the mountains close in on him, heavy and sullen in the dark. Heiberto was hours gone. And the fucking, worthless Americans. He put the baby down carefully by the cross, tucked the blanket around the tiny face and neck. The baby could cry all it fucking wanted. Nobody could hear it out here. Not his baby, not his goddamn baby, he said to himself. The stupid bitch had looked at him. A foot-locker picture. The dirt crunched as he moved.

Pilot picked his way off the plateau, rocks fizzing down and onto the road. He walked towards the mountains and listened for trucks.

Lawrence Lebofsky

LAKE MEAD

From his eyes above the cards, you could tell he was fixed to die
  —Jackson Samuel Heath, *Biography of James Butler Hickok*

Stories

Ronnie won eighteen thou in Vegas, bought alligator boots, called his wife said hi hey babe it's me yeah I know I know I haven't called but but slow down calm shuttup already I'm flying in. The person waiting to use the phone, brunette with tapping gold-sabre heels, wraparound shades, gold heelstraps nuzzled in their weave against her ankle, burgundy mouth, the rise from perfect ankle into perfect leg, made eye contact and took him.

She, Vanya, newest and by far loveliest sud hustler at the second old-est freestanding saloon on the Strip. The Famous Mojave Tavern on Las Vegas Boulevard, referred to simply as the Tavern by the clientele, an unfortunate medley of ne'er-do-wells, castouts, a rumored eunuch, the stray junketeer or pack of teens who departs after an awkward lookabout for something else or more. Franz Brundt, a stack of muscled wurst upon his end stool, sipping in undeviating companionship with Fats Nells, across from him at the long bar steely as a wolf considering its kill zone. Between their timberline silence is spread a crew of nobodies you won't note on your landscape but will instead assume into one featureless mass mask— shy as ghosts even among themselves, wordless without the daily updates, sports commentary, drollery, talk of tail, individual beefs or family details or plumb mindless jabber of places where locals gravitate.

That's assuming you notice the Tavern at all, bound as it is on the right by MegaEmporium, on the left by MegaPark, an eight-story garage whose action often spills out in front of the bar, blocking its sole entranceway. New blood seldom pours through, perhaps the wanderer in the midst of his own movie, in which his fall from money and power and grace and sex is embodied by his sudden presence at a corner table. MegaPark's one point six miles of lights inflict the hallucinageria of a hundred-foot high birdcage sparkling with running neon come sundown, nullifying the Tavern's listless string of bulbs, implying weary, raling sighs housed behind the cramped facade. As though the Tavern itself might be a museum or gift shop once dedicated to the inauguration of the aforementioned parking lot, fallen to disrepair now that there are bigger and gaudier lots to visit.

*

Gene Smilin Lips "Greenfeld" Krug borrowed thirty thousand from some fellows in Las Vegas back in 1967. Didn't pay back in in time, got his head shot. Laddie Mazursky had his eyeballs slashed up near where Vanya has her dry cleaning done. The facts on Paul Puller are complicated by countless retellings, but the gist is he owed someone a bunch of money, entered The Flamingo and never came out. Soon after a sandwich named for him appeared in one of the coffee shops—he was a well-liked guy.

The thread is that they all boarded for a short time at the motel where Ronnie lives. He knows their names, the details, where details of the different stories converge, where truth clears space for legend. He understands the nature of the faded stains on a wall...goddamn, he thinks, the earliest high rollers were gunslingers...what atmosphere! He likes to line the floor with empty bottles, likes to bang through the center hall at any hour to vomit in a corner, likes to think he could be mistaken for the ghost of one of these famous dead wiseguys. He sleeps, within him a heart races like a strange intruder, its beats drawn out and devouring of the sounds of restless flies, a rusted fan, a countdown.

*

In her kitchen Vanya hummed, sorted Ronnie's laundry. Last night he'd told her she reminded him of a shadow, and then they had sex in the tub, and afterward to cool them down she'd twisted the faucet and found it dually broken: icy water hard. That inspired this panicked bout of laughter which subsided into screams when she couldn't turn the stream off and they couldn't untangle their individual parts to escape. They finally rolled onto the tiles still convoluted, still howling for no reason, just to howl, then after they started grinding again, then again.

Vanya hummed, skin hot below her robe. She could see them lasting all the way. Stupid given her background some say, but she hid her doubts in the creases of Ronnie's chinos. She hailed from Asylum, Oklahoma, population dwindling, aptly named for, as Vanya put, "It's where Daddy was." When she was seven he lacerated her head with the rock of purification. He developed in her (locked in the closet) an anathema to brown eyes and short fingernails. She endured a decade (skin under a cigarette) of his whims, rations of physical (breath on her neck, like rotten cabbage) and emotional abuse doled at the discretion of Our Lord until one May afternoon her mother, twice county once regional beauty queen, returned from her second self-institutionalization, slit gently her soft palms with a broken bit of glass and ran hollering into the corn. Daddy pursued with dependable shotgun. Vanya grabbed the bills from the kitchen drawer and ran thirteen miles to the depot in her workboots. The bus took her trembling to Flagstaff where she slept scared mindless on a wet bench in a suburban park within a valley of footfalls and bat chirps.

She turned eighteen and caught a ride as far as a tourist outpost near Hoover Dam with a sixteen-year-old in a Range Rover who told her his dreams then raped her five times in two days and left her for the maids. Summarily evicted, bloodyfooted, destitute, she epically staggered the remaining miles, clutching herself as one would a purse when fraternity types downshifted their convertibles to call over. She received second-degree sunburn and hospital meals—three per day—as her Vegas welcome. Scratched herself shaving and faked the resurrection of an old trauma so as to lie on clean sheets an extra weekend, then finally got booted. No one inquired as to her bruises. Two male attendants pushed her into the street.

Into the lavender swirl and, in the way nighttime Vegas amplifies the senses and at the same time blunts them with so much sheer so muchness— so that whereas you hear your name the whisper on everyone's lips, the rustle of wind as kisses are blown on a pair of cellulite cubes for good fate, you soon habituate to the nonstop slot whir at each pull of twenty million crankshafts and the metallic outpourings of winners, the undercurrents of change that whiteout all other sound—she saw in the swish-swish of pointless multidirectional cruising more bodies than she'd thought possible, dolled in tuxedos, in pink pajamas, fans and glitter, a mass moseying in broad daylight at 3:30 a.m. between casinos guised as pyramids and pirate ships and looming pterodactyls awash with a billion balls of light, even the fast food joints lit like two-story novae and, glowing buoys anchoring the swarm on the proud arms of their "uncles"—like enlightened polyps— prostitutes, their impact after two minutes' observance a life lesson; Vanya immediately subtracted twenty dollars from the first out-of-towner stumbling, attempting to walk right and left at once, out of the Riviera.

As she took to the trade, in the middle of it all, the most indigestible moments, she wondered if Daddy might right then just possibly be dying of syph, coughing up the composition of his own throat, raving, lids swollen with acid pus, reaching in vain at the cross into death for his black belt and Fryes. After a four block, three week, sixty-some room apprenticeship Vanya happened to ball a jowly conventioneer perspiring Glenfiddich into a temporary coma and, again with the lowly algebraist's giddiness, minused his wallet off him. Took his shoes. Fled down an alleyway littered with blind bleeding derelicts and held her breath. Searched the wallet again and again but in every case it came to four dollars.

Remembering the trick who would soon be in pursuit, suddenly terrified of having her epitaph be four dollars she stooped through the garbage and winos who wanted to know what she'd do for thirty-five cents and ducked into the most unapparent grotto imaginable, what she took for an abandoned building or outhouse abutting the skeleton symmetry of MegaPark.

"Omigod," she said, "This place stinks like crap."

"It ain't rose petals Blondie," spoke the face above the heaviest set of torpedoes Vanya'd ever seen, "But the Prince of Wales don't seem to mind." This person guffawed as Vanya got bearings. "I'm Minnie. The craphole's mine. If you ain't looking for a job"—she torqued the chords a notch and threw her voice toward "the boys" intent on the wood beneeath their drinks—"I'd scatter, 'cause some of these lambs ain't seen a woman in a real dress"—at this moment a torn shoulder black stretch cheap thing sans accessories, undies, the ensemble not so much worn as lacquered on— "in what, years?"

"Aw Minnie," moaned a sunken head, "Layoff, willya?"

"My boys," Minnie continued, "Must be among the most prolific masturbators in all Nevada, cause I never see no women stayin', and ain't none my boys leavin'. Ernie Pants sits there fourteen hours some days, ain't got no job, never talks to girls.... Hey Ernie Pants, when's the last year you was with a woman?"

"Let me alone, you heifer."

"And it ain't like none come in here. We see it all the time, 'cept they order a water and take off before the ice's melt. Just imagine the conversational gambits. Fine asses on some'm girls too. These numbnuts couldn't get laid in Vegas."

"Aw shut up," said several.

✳

Senses so acute they roar at the vibration of keys scraping through a lock tumbler three rooms away. The first prize winner at the 1985 Halletsville Kolache Fest Bullride removes his penis from the woman and hurdles shirtless through the open window, hanging in midair like the climax of a song, a moment added to time. Slams backfirst into the day's garbage. Jumped by dog, punches dog in the mouth, says There's a shitty way to start a morning. Slinks to his room and lies on the bedsheets avoiding a roach on the pillow and the eyes close.

Alcoholic, Ronnie pieces together a day's events in his dreams, in which menacing strobes juggle skincolored rainbows over a bed that spins, Ronnie's kidneys grueling tiny stones into sewer-destined piles in his sleep, serotonins if he's not too loaded furiously desymbolizing possible meanings, harbingers, white whales. Ultimately returning to the only concepts he instills with any structure: odds, probabilities, and second chances, which only truly make sense when he is losing, unlucky, fading.... What he can accomplish so embroiled, squinting for a thin line of illumination stitched into the air beyond the spectra of waking sight, seems at first dubious.

The Sunday morning dream, subtle as a butt-fuck. "Look, I know Bill B.," he'd said, red webs scrawled on his eyes in neat sequences divisible by four, pupils grayly constricting under a hangover's red pressure. Letting ashes tower before they collapse onto a desk. "So what I'm saying, and what I'm saying I'll say only once, is, I know Bill B. and my name's Ronnie and I'm not gonna say it again. I'm not gonna repeat myself." The repetition, the Morseian garbles, the words sounding all cryptic and Mandarin to Vanya when Ronnie speaks in his sleep.

The shadowy other man in the dream, in the room in the dream, impassive, his shirt too hot for outside the room, outside the dream. Ronnie a shivery pup, sparking cigarettes off cigarettes. The endless repetition. He drops the filter into his coffee, which as usual absorbs it utterly with an unpleasant hiss. "So?" He brushes hair from his eyes; it falls back in place, or out of place. The walls money-green, flashes of velvet catching the eye, themes of suffocation playing in Ronnie's head as he twists besides Vanya in the blankets. "So? Is someone gonna tell Bill I'm here?" The man did not respond. "Because I'm not gonna ask again." Ronnie wiped his brow. "I'm not gonna say it again."

Down to the sweat smell of desperation, the insignia of neckties, this and other encounters get captured stenographically perfect. This particular attention to detail explains the value he places on sleep: It's the key to his longevity. For sometimes in his dreaming Ronnie will glimpse a shadow criss-crossing the ones supposed to be present, that make sense, *belong*. Sometimes an additional pattern cascading at an impossible angle from the flicker of a good lamp that shouldn't flicker will throw the image of...well anything, really, anything Ronnie's dream catalogue can't attach to, can't explain through some fragile linkage with his experiences, unconscious, archetypes, his armaments of defenses, years-old, hours-old, that protect him from real shadows come waking day.

✳

Minnie thought Vanya did a stellar job yanking the boys from their shells. They made efforts to neaten their presences and whispered tasteful jokes. Still, after four weeks they had yet to initiate conversation with a complete stranger or even to make a lewd remark to Vanya, whom Minnie outfitted in suffocating cocktail frill. The Tavern became a practicum of finished manners.

So Ronnie, stepping into the drama about now, concluded that most Tavern souls were pleasant, eager-to-please, at least a quarter queer but who wasn't these days? Astounded by Ronnie's cleanest joke. Perhaps a twinge barren in the luck department. Ronnie the quick study that he sometimes is learned a few dollars spent companionably livened things close to the point of merriment. And Minnie thought a couple of kids in deep heat like Vanya and Ronnie might rub off some of their excess libido on her boys.

The damn thing was, Vanya had begun to wonder if she'd had too much experience to let herself get hooked on an alligator-boots wearing guy. She may have fallen in love with her first nonpaying bedfellow, but she's not removed enough from the past to have forgotten the ways of men. The outfits Minnie provided dissuaded circulation but did not affect Vanya's mental self-portrait: She knew what appearances were. She spoke poor Oklahomese but her upstairs engines revved continuous. Ronnie didn't have a job, had money to throw, stayed out late, way past the end of her rotation sometimes. She closed her eyes in bed and only slept when Ronnie entered on tip-toe with the sunbeam. She had a notion it would all come down.

✳

Here, a different kind of drinking place, where the bowlegged end is the same but the process less watered down, the conversation keener, the Keno machine working, the slots looser the floor better swept. When Ronnie enters, blinking against the unexpected Budweiser fluorescence of it all, he's greeted without the recognition he's used to at the Tavern. He feels inexplicably lighter within the cush support of whitewalled anonymity. Plus, underneath the lightness effect, safe in what appears a family-oriented wetspot.

But no it's a bar, and the 300-pound gentleman picking his teeth at the counter has eyes that drill right at you. He gestures Ronnie to an empty booth.

Jesus, Ronnie thinks, this wog's scarier than the ones who're after me.

The big man settles in. "What, shithead?"

"Well, uh, a friend told me..."

To avoid what would transcribe as a dull, and coded regardless, exchange, we fast forward to later in the day when Ronnie, having secured a second and entirely hostile creditor, knelt into the Tavern, immediately becoming assimilated into an amoeba of boozehounds. Among these luckless shells he felt noble, royalty, evidenced around him by the whoops and handshakes and the old boys closing in like starved piglets to momma until he could smell their individual "usuals." Where Vanya?—He glimpsed her in his intrusive hotel glamour shot waking nightmare, its particulars obsessively amended over time, naked on all fours on a king-size canopy sea of bed, the client rubbing hundreds with new great big Ben Franklins over her backside, ink smearing off the bills, tens of thousands forgotten, casually spilled onto the carpet....I really need a break, he thought. Squinting in the smoke and dry air he thought, I really need something.

All Ronnie needs is to look around. The crimson noses and nonexistent dental work expanding into crooked grins, the unsure huh huh when Ronnie asks Mister Goddenfrey how they hang, the pairs of eyes blinking closer toward a cerebral sundown, a pale yellow sun death like cigarettes on teeth or gold nuggets melted down, alchemized into babyspittle, their animation petering like fading stars from dead cosmologies. If anyone, Ronnie included, forgoes the glass' comfort to read behind the cool sweat brailled on the rows of nodding foreheads, he might trace to the source of most human error.

Vanya and Minnie popped out from the storeroom, into the fray. Vanya surprised Ronnie with an embrace from behind, causing his drink to splash. "Goddamit!" He glared at her, shoulder twitching. Franz tore a belch that made everyone recoil. Ronnie looked at the ice in his tumbler, at his hand half-raised, at Vanya. Minnie staring at him. All of them staring. He turned back to Vanya, something about the sight clearing his head for a decision. "Let's go to the casino," he said.

Streak

Vanya's primary reaction to the streak was anger, as though instead of bedecking her tiara to ankle with baubles ("And it's good jewelery," he said. "It's damned expensive."), Ronnie'd dealt her into bondage to cover a Trifecta. The feeling wavered into a quiet certainty of impending tragedy as a week crept by, skepticism dissolving altogether when Ronnie started bringing designer dresses. Minnie also was impressed. Whenever Vanya showed up in sequins or something especially whorey, she whistled.

"I could'a knocked 'em dead in that, baby."

In fact, after three weeks Ronnie let her open a checking account and provided starter money. He still came home past dawn, but instead of sneaking into bed before the door shut he summed totals on a long sheet of ledger. He left the numbers for her to find.

"Ronnie, I never had a bunny rabbit."

Vanya's bunny had white specked ears that rose two inches and drooped nine. Body chocolate with white spots. She christened him Marshmallow and told him how one day in what's called the future she and Ronnie would have enough stake to leave this desert for someplace where it got cold sometimes and people watched television or read the bible, calmly, to the children before bed. Marshmallow smiled all the time.

The Tavern continued to enjoy its revitalization. *Vegas Weekly* did a short item. Some idea about a nostalgia site. Minnie hired a piano man and a short-term investment counselor. The irregulars crowded into one corner, not seeming to mind the better class of clientele. Newcomers sometimes mistook Ernie Pants for a busboy, and he worked up a good number of freebies off their tips until Ronnie caught on one day and gave him the eye.

"Every other dump on the Strip for years got millions to relocate. I get a parking lot trussed up like a giant canary house right on my ass and not a cent." Minnie fingered a portfolio from Valley Acres, A Living Community and cackled. "Not that it ain't finally payin' off." She watched the augmented bodies of her three—three!—waitresses: Just oldfashioned know-how.

It's Vanya though....Minnie understands, as forty autumns in Sin City have demonstrated that staying ability is the result of good fortune or thievery—and thieves never last. Good fortune in this case a nod not to same-old but new faces, as in that of Minnie's little helper they come to savor. The quality in Vanya that lets the gazecaster feel he owns her, expensively, down to the snowy shoulders. Minnie understands also how it can all be swept away if Vanya leaves or Ronnie plants a seed....She continues to thin the kegs and accelerates her pension contributions.

For her mind, though slightly obscured with whiskeys-for-one and Demerol and just too much makeup, easily understands the poison that characterize the Ronnies of this town, deadly for Vanya, for Minnie's condo near some hot springs. She'd counted uncountable Ronnies in her career, beginning in a strip joint circa 1957, shaking it for a houseful of groping Ronnies. Ronnies disappeared. Maybe they all ended up in the same place, below the sand 100 miles in either direction, body frozen in a rigid lap-dance posture. She wouldn't know. Drop-offs occurred within some specialized time frame outside of witness, under the inscrutable cover of town security.

The short-term effects were obvious enough. Whenever Ronnie dropped in at midafternoon—soused as a lord over what Minnie envisioned his personal fiefdom of secret smut—he'd pull Vanya aside and whisper to her, have a few, jaw over the semantics of vulva with his wide-eyed admirers and leave. Vanya wouldn't be herself afterward. Sure she sassed and seemed to glide—but without the verve, the pyrotechnic jigglings, the trademark excreting horniness that normally hung round her head in a visible corona. Her vanished bounce and fluff soured the taps and amplified each cough and swivel.

"Sweetie, come talk in my office."

"OK, Minnie," Vanya said, sopping spill with her washrag, her face reflected in the new gloss. She managed a smile at Franz and a finger-wave to Fatty—just the sort of wastefulness Minnie had to straighten her out on, those wingless lead-dicks—and trailed Minnie into the storeroom with the two chairs and file cabinet.

"Hon," Minnie began carefully, "How're things 'tween you 'n Ronald?"

"Fine, Minnie." Vanya sensed a talking-to, her answers little counterpunches that echoed in the claustrophobia.

"Because," Minnie said, "He doesn't seem in the best moods lately." I've seen it before, dummy-bun. He stinks of rotting from inside. Of need. Of owing.

"Actually, Minnie, things couldn't be better."

Such the closed book...Minnie had thoughts on everyone, but with Vanya it was pure speculation. "Sweetie, I know Ronnie's got goodness. It's just the sight of him makes you tremble, your eyes are heavy lately, and I get the feelin' Ronnie keeps some rough company." Minnie tired quick of lecture-giving. "You know you come to me and things get worked out? Look up at me, child."

Vanya rose up, meeting the eyes hanging in the pocked and storied face, below the garden of fake yellow ringlets: "Yes."

✳

The casino floor materializes suddenly, elasticates into the funhouse, enter through the dripping mouth. The crowd, in either suits, sweats or shorts, in running shoes or tasseled loafers or plastic thongs, oozes as a single mass from point to point, rebounds between the bumpers, occasionally a fixture breaking off the nucleus to idle at one of ten thousand play stations. Ronnie deviates from the frenzy and spins toward the edge of the floor, gasping from his latest downspiralling confrontation with yet another fucking Korean Twenty-One dealer. At the onset of the streak, which he reckoned with a watery sapping of strength could be referred to now in the past tense, he'd sworn off all Asian dealers except for

Malaysians, whom he'd read had extremely bad luck. But with the streak came the feeling of immortality, that drinking did not lead to drunkenness and so on, and hence he drank more, slid on the Asians a bit, and now new shadows romped headless through his dreams.

A medium-size pig tore across the floor, wove through an aisle of Pokermania machines. A brief comedy ensued in the struggle to capture it. A young woman in a kind of terry cloth half-top and high-laced bubblegum sneaks said, "Was that just a pig went by?"

Ronnie said, "I think it was just you."

"Did you call me a pi-yig?" Shit, Ronnie thought, here's the type to have brothers lurking around the corner with branding irons, who'll tear my knuckles from my skin, with biceps the size of bisons...

"No, I just meant your imagination."

"Oh." She tried this out, apparently to decide whether she should call off the brothers. "That's sweet. I guess."

"Say," Ronnie said. "I just had a win. How 'bout breakfast? I'm Ronnie."

She shook hands, laughing. "So am I."

Creditors

Minnie rationalized. The stranger could be a cop what with those shoes, sneaking in for an on-duty. Or a cab hack. Or a godawfully bad gambler—in which case he's home.

"'Scuse me beautiful"—definitely not a cop—"Is this really the bar Sonny Liston fell down in?"

God bless *Vegas Weekly*, she thought. "None other. December 4, 1961. Never the same after. See here." She pointed at a chipped corner of the mahogany bar. "That's where his head hit."

The man laughed and took a snapshot with a slender camera.

"Hey boy! Din'cha see the sign? 'All Photography is Strictly Prohibited Without the Expressed Authorization of Metro-Goldwyn Mayer Studios, Hollywood.'"

"They shot a movie in here?" The man glanced at a family of flies hovering at the rim of one of yesterday's pitchers, still a quarter full.

"Remember 'Vegas Stripped?'"

"Yeah, but not this place."

"How 'bout the fight scene?"

"Sure."

"Well, when they was scoutin locations, a little man with an accent who smelled like a woman came in and said he was lookin for somewhere they could film a brawl, someplace real shitty where they could, you know, destroy everything. They was gonna pay me fifty thou to demolish this box."

"I guess that makes sense."

"So they started princip, whatsit, principal photography, but after the first day the guy said this wasn't what he was lookin for, that they needed a place that would look somewhat clean before they tore it up. He said The Tavern was, now what was his word, oh yeah: 'dingy.'"

"Then why the sign?"

"Well I go, 'Hey boy, this dump is clean, we've been pickin up after it for weeks.'

"And he goes, 'this saloon is *dingy* and we can't do the scene here.'

"So I tell him that we've just shet down for a week to tidy the place—and we never close sir, never—and if he don't want no trouble from some old friends of mine—I'm old-school hon, case you haven't added your deuces yet—well, he'd better give me something for the trouble."

"Does this have to do with why there's a parking lot on top of this place?"

"That came later. So the guy goes, 'OK, OK, I'll tell you what, you can provide the booze.' So now next time you see the movie, wait 'til the credit lines roll up, and you'll see 'Refreshments provided by The Famous Mojave Tavern on Las Vegas Boulevard.' You can't miss it."

"So you never saw a cent."

"No. They fucked me."

The man drank water. "Wasn't there a Little Miss Minnie at the Stardust in '58?"

"'Twas I."

He roamed an appreciative eye. "May I say you're holding up real well, Minnie."

"And I have the ardor of the people."

He looked heavenward. "Amen. Minnie, when does Ronnie come in?"

She thought: Vanya. "I heard he's been holing up at the Lucky Nine."

The man began filing his fingernails, looking down. Tut-tutting. Minnie watched the brisk small movements as he turned his hands, working them until the edges were smooth, then the cuticles, the file suddenly gone along with Mister Nice Guy.

Well it's just Ronnie they want, she thought. Not worth losing one's shirt over. Or, for that matter, a condominium. She said a number. The man said to expect he'd return within the week and don't be fucking stupid.

✳

Ronnie read his box of bran flakes. Red-eye breakfast. 'Best if used by' followed by a date. *Use?* Fuck. Ronnie thought that was a stupid word choice for a food product.

"Bacon!"

Vanya ran from the kitchenette with an enormous skillet, brimming the way Ronnie liked it, oil popping. He helped himself, mulling the lines on the afternoon's ballgames.

"Ronnie, I need fifty dollars to buy a wedding present for Shelley."

Fudge off. "Who?"

"Shelley at the Tavern." Her Okie bray rattled his teeth like evil little dice. Christ, dice. What in Hell happened last night? He knew he'd feel shitty all day, knew it would affect his decision making. He felt like he'd drunk a pint of blood.

"Who'd marry Shelley? Not one of those fuckoffs at the Tavern?"

"Her cousin's best friend's older brother from L.A."

Inbreeding. Another headache. He had things to do. He had needs.

"I'll go to the bank this morning."

"Oh I don't need it right now."

"Shush. Sit here. No, to the right. Ah...Good. Tell me who loves you."

"You lewd badboy."

He took his time reaching the bank, meandering several blocks out of his way then tracking back, his motivation not so much to make time as to separate from the pain of his own body, to float ethereally, to shapeshift into dust and lose himself in the wind. Invisibility. To avoid the still lifes of shadowy presences, their hiding places only half-revealed in last night's sleep.

He walked into Wells Fargo and withdrew the balance of Vanya's savings. Hell, he'd put most of it there in the first place. Some of it. He stared at the wall clock, a sudden queue snaking behind him.

The Vietnamese—of course, he sighed—behind the indestructible plastic shield flashed him a semicircle of teeth. Ronnie had to marvel at them, their perfect arc, their gaplessness, a single solid enamel row; peering in, the bridgework...impeccable. He shook his head back into the day. "Here you are, Sir. Is there anything we did that caused you to withdraw your account?"

She passed it through the slot in hundreds. He ignored her and stepped into the later morning. Ninety-six and rising. Reflections of the sun taunted him, blinded him. He walked home in the straightest line he could.

The bitch was the more he drank the greater chance the warning shadows would come to his sleep lacking the telling details. The faces became unspecific, shadows in the other sense. Hence there lay the chance he might walk into the wrong someone.

"Oh God. Dee." He caught his balance and smiled like a boy. "What are you doing here?"

She slapped him, laughed, and slapped the rest of the color from his face. A blond dude sporting shitkickers and a blue sheet like some saint sprung from a psycho ward stepped out of the truck—Ronnie wondered how she'd kept up the payments—to her side, with an I-ball-your-wife expression Ronnie wanted to burn off with his Zippo.

"Where's Sally?" Ronnie said.

"She's with my sisters."

"Oh God Jesus."

"I want the money."

"I want it back," he said.

The boy drove his hand into the upper third of Ronnie's face. Swift and measured, the natural order of things. Ronnie fell on his back and convulsed on the sidewalk. He heard Dee's goon whisper near his ear: "I am not unlike a god to you. A bringer and suppressor of pain."

"People are watching," choked Ronnie through a pinched feeling that began in the eyes. Dee kicked her shoe point into Ronnie's groin. And again.

"Maggot," she said. The boy pulled out Ronnie's pockets. He handed Dee the money.

"We're going to go fuck," she announced, her hand dropping down the kid's front. "I want the rest of the eighteen grand. You owe me. You owe Sally."

Ronnie coughed and spit red. "I don't have it anymore." He could have said he'd lost most of it then doubled it and more then lost it back.

The boy grabbed him and pulled him up by the lips. Dee kicked him before he could cover himself. Ronnie screamed.

"Ronnie, do you think that was the right answer?"

✳

An accident near Vanya's place, a red Fiat wrapped boomerang-style around a white limousine, the Fiat owner sobbing inconsolably with his wrists cuffed behind his back as an acne-riddled police greenhorn offers him a breath test, remind Vanya of something from her old life. What is it: objects never intended to meet welded together, forging one larger system that resembles neither? It's not a riddle game but her ninth birthday, Vanya fleeing the consequence of some punishment, creeping into a cave that did not exist until a week prior, the collaborative effort of a threesome of massive post oaks felled by a recent tornado. With some idea about subsisting off sap and bird eggs she concealed herself for two days in a dark blanket. Her mattress the ground slithering. Hungry after forty-eight hours she risked a reconnaissance, sidling after midnight partway to the house when, pinning her like a rat beneath the cold kerosene moon, Daddy's voice resounded Vanya's name across the chill pasture air. She fled, holing up in her brambled rampart another two days. At one point she slept then woke, stomach wailing, stretched, scratched her arm and heard rather than felt the wound split. There, an inch maybe two away, Daddy's boots pointing toward her. So well camouflaged was she that he missed her right then, but she knew he wouldn't the next time, and forced herself awake two more days, not wishing to be captured dreaming. As time passed and each coyote song echoed through her tiny and empty body, each reverberation off her ribs tendering a choir of terrified howls, she crawled to the house, her reservoir of endurance too depleted to either stand upright or care one way about the inevitable beating. Daddy seeing her approach through steaming rheumy eyes nearly swallowed his tooth-pick in his laughter, having spotted her two days before and given her only thirty-six hours to live. He held his tumbler up to the strange speeding cloud cover as if to acknowledge to his maker he'd lost the wager and owed Him one.

She progressed south on the Strip, the right angles of familiar objects suddenly imbued with equivalent familiar nastiness. She was certain she'd feel better if she just screamed: A single wail to disrupt the flux of the crowded streets would right the world in its groove. Probably not. If she screamed here the sound might get overlooked, attributed to the roar of the volcano on the lawn of the Mirage, whose explosion tolls each hour.

The coordinated tapestry of vacationers enmeshed in their marathon human surge, who stop only to pause at the mouths of casinos as if considering the stone entranceway to Jaffa, began to take on certain mob attributes before Vanya's pretty blues. As though these people were heretics who would wait anxiously for a sign from the Deliverer to guide them by an arc of blue electrons to the chosen nickel slot. Many here soley for the shows—a theatre lavishly decked out with all manner of buccaneer regalia; some details lifted from the Portuguese, others Spanish or Marseillean—the crowds acclaim the authenticity. Two lovelies, topless, possibly robots, flank the stage. The conjuror between them swashbuckled in panteloons and a hook-hand prop for comedy element. He produces a hare from his rag, vest and silk triple-coat—the ensemble adds a visual thirty pounds—which he smartly skewers of innards and roasts with backyard dexterity on a metal spear over a portable range before he covers the whole wet mess with his kerchief and intones the spell words and the animal reemerges unharmed.

"Excuse me, aren't you a prostitute?" asked an impeccably attired man with oversized beaver teeth. Vanya felt her hands tighten on her purse, sped her walk, but unable to help herself turned her neck to let the remark's utterer penetrate her line of vision. A mannequin in a store window. Its slackeyed expression intent on the throng waiting for the light to change, hobnobbing in front of cafes, marching single file in and out of revolving doors, a roll of quarters in each inanimate trouser pocket poking sideways like so many ten-dollar erections.

She survived the obstacle course of parked cars, entered the Tavern still involved in thoughts of her tangled hideaway, the face of idiocy her father must have seen as she begged him on diced kneecaps for sustenance, anything. From that day she was to apologize every time she entered his presence for something she'd done. If she'd done nothing punishable, he'd beat her worse for lying.

Anyway, the stranger waiting at the door, for whom it must have been a great accomplishment to squeeze his colossal frame into such a tiny space, said, "Where's Ronnie?"

"I wouldn't know," she said, thinking he's one of the guys who owe Ronnie money.

"Don't singsong me," he said, "You think he'd protect you?"

"Protect me from what?" She really had no clue where Ronnie frolicked until he came in for margaritas around two-thirty.

"Look whore." He came up close, blocking the light and casting across her face a wide black band. "Tell your boyfriend Bill B. wants to see him." Impossibly he stepped nearer to Vanya without touching her. She smelled alcohol, a swanky label they didn't carry at the Tavern. "In fact, tell Ronnie Bill B. knows him. Tell him that. Yeah." There was joy in his face, his eyes backlit with something impish, with something he'd been waiting for the opportunity to speak. "Tell him Bill's not going to say it again."

✳

At two-thirty that day: "Hey Hon. Bill B.'s looking for you." Ronnie provided that day's first real funny, choking up a spray of booze. The guys hooted. They thought Ronnie was a card. Ronnie composed his face and steered Vanya's arm to the office. Minnie almost stopped them: No one had office privileges except Minnie, but she held to a hope that Vanya would wise up and heave-ho the bum.

"Ronnie, what's going on?"

"Did someone approach you? Did anyone touch you?" He held her arm too hard.

"No. Ronnie, what's wrong? Who's Bill B.?"

"He's this fuck owes me money." His fingers worried in the air and he fell silent as though planning his moves on a psychic abacus. "Who came to you?"

"This guy in the garage. He said to tell you Bill knows you."

"Of course he fucking knows me." Ronnie tried to remember the last encounter with Bill's guy, but it was watery, hazy, the details like something picked up subconsciously, from a movie watched half asleep. He closed his eyes. Cold temperature. Round table. He heard his own voice...I'm not gonna say it again...his face spun grotesque so that Vanya said, "What's wrong? Are you in trouble?"

He looked at her. "Bill owes me a hundred bucks. He doesn't wanna give it up, so he sent someone over to scare me. Hey, can I borrow a twenty? I'll pay it back today."

"Are you going to take out fifty dollars for a gift for Shelley?"

"Of course, babe." They French kissed. She pulled back.

"Ronnie, what happened to your lip?"

"I accidently ate some kiwi."

✳

Ronnie cream-cheesed his bagel and contemplated suicide. He whistled the last bit of Muzak from the casino where he'd dropped nineteen hundred in just shy of fifteen minutes. It was all he could do not to cry. On the final hand he'd split, doubled both, turned inward, the dealer's face dissolving, Ronnie's mind filling with nothing. Emptiness achieved, the sound of violins rose up into the agora and swelled, a mountain of crystal melted and spread in an abundance of watery paths. When he came to a fat security figure was shoving him not gently, he had passed out, there was a wall of interested faces, he lifted his head from the felt, the dealer swept his chips away.

He sipped his rum and something as noon erupted at the Mirage. His brain moved on its own train of slow lava. His nails begged for cutting.

Shaky hands. His knife lurched away from the bagel toward the soft web of his inner thumb. As though lured by blood a heavyset man appeared on the other side of the window. Ronnie stopped; his blood stopped. They both stared through the divide, unsure of who was in the world and who was a fish in a bowl. The man turned north and shambled off. The blood ran from Ronnie's hand onto his lap.

He no longer could keep straight the faces of the men who pursued him during the day, whose profiles only marginally corresponded with the close-ups he wrestled through his dreams. A tall blond Italian suit type? a wiry scarnecked Corsican? a nondescript shooter with a day's beard? They all passed the same in the streets without stopping. They all cast shadows of equal proportions regardless of the sun's coordinates.

He corked the wound by pressing it against the pulse of his arm. Left three percent on the table and went home, fundamentally exhausted. Too tired to imbibe. To deal with Vanya. Intending to sleep all day.

He dreamt of Lake Mead. He had never seen the lake himself, so his dream was not to scale, but his estimates were uncanny. He saw the dam and wondered how such a barricade could hold back that kind of volume. Then the lake turned black all over, and sank into itself.

Vanya burst in and he jumped from sleep to attention. She who normally possessed a cool Ronnie wondered at the source of mouthed like a guppy for words. Finally got out: "A man came up to me in the Tavern just now and said you owed him eleven thousand dollars."

I'm going to die today, Ronnie thought. "Was it the same guy?"

"No. He said he didn't even know Bill B."

"That's strange." Shitfire, they're advancing from all sides. Pick a lie.

"Ronnie, your skin is yellow." It was, observed closely, the white-yellow of the lamplights under which a Jack the Ripper-to-be- might slaughter, a beacon seen in that famous mist, through the watery corners of eyes squinting at some shadow of midnight that did not belong, that moved like no good subject of Victoria. It hung from his cheeks like the torn flaps of the revolutionary colors after the clouds dispersed over his beloved Alamo. He looked like shit. "Are you OK?" she said. "You didn't come by the Tavern."

"Oh I'm fine," swerving off the bed, "Just catching a snooze."

"Do you owe that guy eleven thousand dollars?"

"That's a real exaggeration."

"Nine?"

"Nine what?"

"It's like Acey-Deucy. Nine thousand. Higher or lower."

"Listen, V.—"

"Ronnie, where's my savings account?"

"What!"

"There's two thousand dollars gone from my account."

"What the fuck are you talking about!" The trick was to become so enraged she'd have to think it genuine. He'd call the bank and rant until he pulled out the chord. He'd have twenty thousand by tomorrow. He had sure things practically pissing down. "Give me the fucking phone. Give me the fucking phone!" She gave it. It rang in his hand twice.

"Aren't you going to answer it?"

"Hello?" he said. A gritty drool zig-zagged between his shoulders, sliding down and alternating the blades. His wife's voice spoke back. For some sick joke of a reason he had an erection. He felt someone stick voodoo pins into a Ronnie doll with a strand of real Ronnie-hair glued to its scalp. His shoulders spasmed and he fell back.

A dark wood. He pissed into Lake Mead. He did it thinking nothing at all. He looked down and saw streaking out from his small splash a million arcs rippling toward the edges of the lake. Then it was still.

"Ronnie? You there, Ronnie?"

"God." He felt, saw the trickle as reflected through his pantleg. "What happened?"

She was excited, her words arrhythmic. "You answered the phone and went into a shock or something. It was like an electric eel got put on your chest. You jumped around and all and fell and I thought you were dead!"

"Hmm."

"What? Stop mumbling. Who was on the phone?"

"It was the bank."

"Really?"

"Yeah. They were apologizing for their fuck-up."

"Really?"

"Yeah. They said they felt bad because you're so nice."

"In just that short period of time?"

"Yeah. Hey, what did you say to the guy?"

"Who?"

"The guy who was in the Tavern."

"I didn't say anything. The guys took care of him."

"What guys? Leg breakers?"

That confused her. As though it were a question she might answer wrong. And be penalized for it. "You know, the guys. Franz and Fats and Ernie and Izzy."

"Who's Izzy?"

"He's the shy one who hangs out with Franz and Fats and Ernie and Chuck."

"The shy one? Those guys couldn't get laid in Vegas."

"Well they kicked the guy's ass."

When he heard Dee sobbing over the line something backfired like rams butting horns of lightning at the center of his chest. The phone against his ear rose one hundred degrees. As he trembled and wet himself, but before the ripples from his stream subsided a breath from Mead's farthest perimeter, a driveway of light crept from the sky.

"Who did?"

"The freakin guys at the bar!"

265

"No."

"Yeah, soon as he touched my arm they let him have it. They really fucked him up. I think Ernie bit off his pinkie."

"You're shitting me."

"No sir. Franz held his arms back. Like this." Much against his will he let her administer a full Nelson. He broke it away. "Ernie just went insane."

"That's...amazing," he said.

"Yeah. Juice?"

"Sure." She poured it from a carton. He tried to swallow and gagged.

"It's all fucking pulp!" He flung the glass at the wall.

"What're you throwin the fuckin glass for?" she yelled.

"Who the fuck you yellin at?"

"Let me the fuck out of here," she cried and pulled the door. Ronnie grabbed her hair and banked her head off the wall. She said "oohh" and wobbled in the doorway, warbled on the step, fell headways on the pavement. Shook it off, leapt up running. Ronnie stood looking at her then at the hair in his fist. For the first time he realized she'd done it up platinum.

Kept running to the Tavern. A sticker with a woman's head on a whale's body on Vanya's locker. The woman's torso chained to the fridge with the caption 'Manage Blubber.' Vanya pulled her outfit down and stepped into the legs. It clung to her skin like protective sweat. Minnie walked in, saw the sunset yellowing on her cheek and sent her with a charge card to a hotel. Vanya's attempted thanks got lost somewhere deep in crying and she ran in her ittybitty getup out the door but not before everyone sitting in their places like the linchpins of solidity saw and froze in slowtime like a stopwatch sinking in a lake and charting the rate of its descent through endless fathoms.

※

Dee had pulverized her nails with nervous biting energy; she bought fakes she liked and admired the way they sounded on the tabletop.

"I'm sorry all this happened."

"Dee, I'm the one who should be asking forgiveness," Ronnie said.

"Fuck you should. Begging's the word."

"Dee, I beg you to forgive me."

She laughed. Her room cost eighteen bucks a day. It was painted Venus flytrap-green but was comfortable in a caffeinated, predatory way. Where reptiles might live.

"You get me on the phone after two years of nothin. Six hour drive to Houston airport with a five-year-old who can't stop drinkin water. I ask at the counter for a prepaid ticket like you said to and the man looks at me like I'm speakin fuckin Mexican. And that's it. No further instructions. No cash to get home on. Next you'll be asking to borrow some money."

"I can pay you back double." Stale material.

"Ronnie, as far as friends go you suck."

With a straight face he said, "I've tried to be nice. I bought Vanya a bunny."

"Listen to you. You sound like an goddamned idiot. Your life is a crooked piece of shit. I can't believe you're not dead. You're alive, but for some of us it's the same either way."

"Come on Dee." His head sat heavy, bent forward, ready for the gallows. "I'm trying to be good. I'm really trying to be more what you said, a giver."

"A bunny rabbit is not a five-year-old!" She started to cry. "Neither is a whore," she sniffled, sounding of course stupid and wishing that particular melodrama hadn't escaped.

"I think the jig's done with Vanya," he said.

"She's catching on to your, what do you call it, life?"

"Yeah. I don't think she knows I screw either."

"How many?"

"What? You mean fucks total?"

"Ballpark figure since you've been out here."

"Well..."

"Five hundred? Three a week?"

He snorted. "Five hundred. Right."

She laughed too. "The ultimate male. Bet Vanya's some cutey."

"Yeah," he said. "I think she's the gateway."

"You're still having that dream?"

"Just sometimes. Not every night like when I was in jail. I'm still pissing in the lake, only now it's the Hoover Dam lake. The water starts getting waves but they disappear without breaking when they hit the shore. Sometimes I feel like if I want I can just step right onto the water. I close my eyes and take a couple steps and then I'm definitely walking but I don't feel any surface at all and I can't open my eyes and there's this light and then I can finally open my eyes and I'm awake and my heart's fucking going crazy."

"And you think she's the gateway thing?"

"I only have the dream when I'm fucking up extremely. I won't go into the details, but lately I just can't win. I mean I win sometimes yeah, but I lose so much."

"Same-old."

"As always. But the path to the dream is always the one I feel bad about. Like the old woman I scammed back home who sent me her picture so I could stare at it in jail." The face in the photograph about as old as time. "I stared at it when I went to bed every night, and the dream didn't go away until they sprung me and I left the old bitch in the cell."

"Like when you had the dream when Sally was born."

"Right. The gateway's the victim. That's my theory. And with Vanya and now you in town it's like a double whammy. Speaking of which, where's *your* whammyboy?"

"Well..." She reddened.

"Somethin happen?"

"He turned out to be a moron. We had to go to the amusement park every day and ride the rollercoaster then play Wack-a-Mole all night at Circus Circus. Like kids. He'd walk a foot off the ground in his boots and talk about knocking over a fruit stand. No, really. And then it turns out the kid's really a kid, like sixteen." They laughed, Ronnie remembering a couple of sixteen-year-olds he'd known. "Oh, and I'm real sorry about kicking your nuts in on the street the other day."

"Oh don't worry about it. You hadn't seen me in a while." They were suddenly in a small room with a bed. "You can make it up to me." He wiggled his ears and she smiled at him and shook her head, a breeze from the AC ruffling her cornspun hair. They fell to mattress business. And undebatably fulfilled the purpose of this meeting. To watch their shadows crawl the wall like beasts in a dance is to understand what they ever had. Afterward he would dream that a slip of light entered his vision and though he felt the lake lapping gently below his treading feet he still could not open his eyes to witness such a miracle.

✳

It came down to Ronnie's choice. A public place, to talk. He felt the regeneration of calm.

It's not about the money anymore, the voice had said. You embarrass us. We've found your phone number, and your address. You should pick a place.

It sounded like what someone had told Ronnie once about excommunication. After the bad guys mark you yet you demonstrate unusual success at staying not dead, they shook hands and packed you off and terminated the slate. A free trip, one-way, a witness protection racket to keep you safe from your protectors. My God, he thought, this type of deal only happened to the best. It happened to Arnie Ganzetta. Hogan.

Actually, he thought, Ganzetta may have gotten whacked.

He searched for himself in the ceiling mirror, first unsuccessfully. The reason: That thing in the glass was far from his expectations. In fact he resembled a light shitstain where he lay horizontal. At his back he felt a cold filmy residue he was afraid to disturb. A cobweb hung over there, held his eye. Twenty-seven thousand plus interest in the tank and what amounts to agony flares arrowing from his heart through his body (whenever he's not dreaming of Tinkertoy spindle-shadows legging after him across the desert flats, everlooming when he's draining his Johannsen into the lake's silvery nightwaters), Ronnie none the less felt most fortuitous, the erasure of his death sentence in itself the breath of life and all. Thinking this he felt a mint vapor breeze through his frame and flaccid muscles, as though his personal harbored pestilence had been exorcised through the opening of a window only then spotted.

Not that he felt about to trust anyone. So his naming the Tavern at three he thought just genius.

✳

Just shy of three Ronnie stumbled, sober, imbalanced by the state of sobriety, off the street detouring through the garage and past the MegaPark attendant and through the narrow sieve between two fenders and into the bar.

"Hey Minnie," he said, "Where's Vanya?"

"Hey Ronnie, bad hat. She's on her break."

"What? But sh-, sh-, sh-"

"Ronnie, could you s-s-stop doing that? Or maybe you'd rather do it outside."

Ronnie accounted for everyone: Franz, Fats, the psychotic Ernie Pants, a couple moldy hanger-ons any of whom might be the one Vanya called Izzy, in their setting of graveyard predictability.

Three men entered, two simians and a smaller fellow in a salmon-colored suit between them who said, "Ronnie," and it hung there.

Ronnie's head spun. The room moved from silence to silent menace. And Ronnie's ace for this situation was on her break, probably window shopping with a Virginia Slim dangling from her craw just standing there, taking her sweet time…"I didn't expect you until three," Ronnie said to the smaller man.

The man looked at his wristwatch and said, "It's exactly three-oh-three. Shall we get started." Ape and ape two advanced. Ronnie nearly toppled. His upheld palms faltered as a riff of shrapnel dumped from his capillaries into his veins.

"Whoa, I thought we were here to talk." The bonebreakers flanked him, but Ronnie appealed only to the one man.

"Jesus, Ronnie, you look completely like shit. Is that vomit? God you look awful," the man said. As though a doctor and family friend concerned for Ronnie's welfare yet without the professional walls and thus disgusted.

"I could really use a vacation."

The man, having diagnosed, seemed distant and deaf and bored, as if he found everything after the initial register of fear in Ronnie's eyes distasteful among his company. His aides grabbed Ronnie's arms and lifted him.

"Hey!" he screamed, the customers across the room immersed in the split-up sections of a newspaper. "This is a public place!"

"So it is," the man said, looking at Minnie, who just stood there, thinking, This is great, while Ronnie remained suspended and embarrassed with poor bladder control. "Minnie, OK if we take this thing into that office there?"

"That'll be fine," Minnie said, hoping it'll end soon without too much to clean up after. Her eyes did cut downward when Ronnie's wordless face searched her own. Vanya walked in. Ronnie noticed first and shouted her name. Those at the bar were on their feet.

"Ronnie, what's going on?"

"Vanya!" Ronnie shrieked. Everyone looked around in a big eye shootout.

"Ronnie, what the fuck is going on?" She stepped toward him. One of the Ronnie-holders grabbed her wrist with his free hand. Vanya's eyes instantly watered.

"Get him!" Ronnie yelled to the small crowd standing. "Look what he's doing to her." They remained stoic as ever as if for all time lifeless there, suspended in the infinity of indecision. They withheld from the rescue Ronnie'd envisioned with a stillness painful to behold, for their features distorted with the effort to stay immobile and quite a few cried as did Vanya. Ernie Pants hopped foot to foot like an tsunami questioning its own nature before loosing a tidal wave. The smaller man, the obvious leader of the trio, looked at his and all the faces of the bunch and at Vanya's and motioned to release her. She leaned against the back wall, pale and unreadable. Ronnie could no longer feel the area where they held his arms. Fats and Ernie and the rest sat down.

"That was your getaway plan?" Minnie was not sure she could believe it. "I can't get over how sad you are."

The man leading the show assented. "That was a very foul setup. We'd hoped for something at least a little entertaining from a guy like you." This was not said without respect. "And now?" People were reading, quaffing again. Ronnie surveyed this through blurring eye slits. Tears compounded his vision, he considered each face in its own lens, thin, vertical. He silently whispered farewells. In truth he'd liked this bunch as well as any before them. He saw Vanya. He wanted to die with the name of a beautiful woman on his lips, but curiously she made no effort to intervene. He felt he'd done right by Vanya, no matter what anybody had to say. Whatever it was the two of them brought into this world, that thing had to have luminous properties, for he could see a compartment in Vanya's eyes still smoldering with it, and that ember now dies out, and perhaps that is why she seems so sad.

A strange parade began, Ronnie aloft and center. Toward the storeroom. Minnie didn't approve of this but didn't want Ronnie stirring a scene in front of the MegaPark, in front of spectators.

"Vanya." Ronnie slurred, his hair dishevelled. Face stubbled and wet and grimed, looking altogether like an extra late for the Exodus. His clothes flapping things in disarray among his limbs, his mouth a dry essence.

His captors paused to hear her answer. It seemed important that she say something, to bring a proper end.

She looked up. "Ronnie." She did not go on. So all he had to take with him was a face, an expression. A minister eulogizing the corpse in a hole at his feet with a single nod. And what he thought was: I've been cheated.

His head lolled onto his shoulder. They scrunched into the office and the door shut for a minute. Arguing sounds. The smaller man, the ringleader, stepped out and conferred with Minnie. She was pissed. The man left to use his car phone. Minnie sat with a cigarette and warm scotch. Vanya drifted in small increments around the room and belonged at home.

"Minnie, who's that man?"

"That's Bill B."

270

Mead

He felt a soft barrier, like a pass through flesh. Then into this otherworld, where he knew the names of most objects but an everpresent sound that lay in everything told him all was different.

He wiped away a feeling like sleep that hung onto him like a placental bodybag. He looked down at himself. Nude, unetched by scars. His palms spread upon his chest to inspect the irregular heartroll that ultimately placed him in this setting—no gateway, no guiltwagon had carted him—to find it exorcised, replaced with a vibration whose energies pooled near the soles of his feet and extended throughout him, and seemed somehow connected to the odd music rebounding about.

He inhaled deeper than in the past ten years and by the time he exhaled he stood at the edge of a forest. He followed a trail of total curvature as invisibly high trees bent slightly to clear his way. Dense unknown undergrowth carpeted under his feet and to his amazement multiplied. This world was all amazement. An area that first appeared as a tiny silver coin shimmering in dustclouds became a lake rimmed with red valley, the water itself pitched in black like a bottomless inkwell, an extension of the descending nighttime sky. He hiked down to inspect this dark water of the lake he can never remember the name of. It took him a long time and when he reached the lake he had to urinate. His stream forced the barest ripple.

Far off toward the water's boundaries he could see the billion lights of Vegas, a pattern of colorful flags slurred together, embroidered on the horizon into a single distant gold. His eyes adjusted and he realized the lake was blackened by a pinwheel of shadows cast by figures standing a foot from the waterline, completely containing its beaches, Vanya and Dee and little Sally's brokenheart face and those of loan artists and sharpies and elderly shoeshine boys and croupiers alongside the Tavern crew and a small nation of pick-ups—one or two named Ronnie themselves—and pitbosses and folks from Texas, Ronnie's parents and their friends, a few teachers and first and second loves and rhinestoned blondes and their patsy boyfriends all winding up scammed; every arm who'd circulated across his fate-strings, they all cast equal shadows the thickness of a knife's edge, connecting at the lake's midpoint though the sky sat incontemplatably empty of sun. Ronnie tumbled and ducked through bushes without purpose and through entire meadows of thorns and gnashing vines, jackal screams. He never tired but ran until he stopped halfway up a bleached and ragged mountain whose base continued to germinate stones though it's higher than any peak on Earth. As its apex pierced the sky it entered a deep, basking light the substance of which could be explored for eternities stacked endwise. From his vantage Lake Mead again appeared as a precious ointment bubbling from some subterranean deposit, boiling within a blinding indictment of sand. Vegas could be seen as a bright aberration, a gaudy oasis to the northwest. He saw the Tavern interior as a single fleck of gray.

Without his knowing he'd climbed to a valley which lay in a broad mistbowl flush with the strange sound, not quite music but clearly emanating from a source outside himself and drawing closer. He beheld a wonderworld believable only by a child young enough to store his toys in a painted box, one that contains a plastic-headed accordion mallet useful for annihilating such dreamt worlds when they begin to bore. A heat to which he cannot compare other heat cloaked his back and shoulders, approaching from behind and breathing like a great winged myth touching down. No rain hung in a sky polarized blue.

"I've won! I've won!" He bellowed across valley after valley, the entire globe an atom hung lazily on his eye. Strange fourlegged shapes perhaps augmented fawns scattered like a swarm of hornets and came together eons in the distance, dissolving in a black pinhead near the line of earth and sky. This dark pupil bloomed then sank into sand and formed a crater then burst volcanically, spilling something the color of wine. Thus the sight he held formed and reformed like the world forming out of an electric sea, the infinite variations of its oceanography as transitory as human time, the theory of mountain building over milennia an interesting idea disproved. In every direction he saw Lake Mead postioned like a mirror for the sky, as the sky's projector. He stood transfixed by this connection until the temperature consumed him into the skyscape as another blinking nib of light, as much the scenery as the foliage or the dumb creatures eating from it or the wind that changed to perfect larkspur as it passed.

Ben Marcus

Presentation of the Church

He examined, for instance, the airplane. A hang of trees outlined the flattened grass; it is possible that there was bird life while he worked. The trunks were chewed about not by shrapnel, it is determined, but by a dog, or more likely, the children. Let me say that the fissure was not so great, no, but had been introduced onto the wing. An unfortunate affair. The fuselage was shorn of the body. He took the pieces of straw, the cloth, the child's doll. There were glinting, children's trucks in the window of the airplane. A man's refrigerator. The blue glove of an injured animal fluttered from a piece of wire.

The town, then, is annexed to a seashore concealed by hills and an occasional rough shelter. A path leads down through rows of soft, white trees. At the base of the path stands a dirt pool layered in acorns and leaves. The leaves present a formal notion of green, thick in the manner of a disked fruit, with a flesh that lifts from the surface if the surface is agitated. I can laugh at this now.

One might cross this dirt pool to arrive near a tunnel that leads out over the sea. Or, if you will, the ocean. He is placed here at a time near to noon. For there was a bundle, most likely in his possession. You see, one simply allowed for the tunnel to deliver passage to the water. Is this clear? Cargo, in this manner, might render an obstruction. Haste, too, did literally disturb or constrict the channel.

But it is decided that he was smallish. Or anyway capable of being so. The bundle, too. But the footprints, well. And indeed there was a rag found somewhat abused in the opposite direction. In any case. Forgive me. There had been a pull-train from Corliss the Tuesday previous. Thus, the rare debris, or indeed, a second man.

An example of watching did persist, certainly. The town possessed a tower, anyway, a hollowed pylon—as indicate its fragments—whereof the lookout was practiced. The platform beneath the turret was rent to surcease and yielded down into a smaller clearing below, a toppling that must have occurred quite quickly. Perhaps the great rattling had commenced this activity. It is evidenced that the platform had accommodated a large chair. The oak was stressed to paleness in minute areas. The finish was scribbled free of the wood. Thus, the man. And, indeed, a console, a ledger, the articles of a small lunch.

In effect, someone had seen. There would have been flames erupting in small volume at the flower patches on the perimeter. Burning Lilac, for example, gives rise to a lush, golden steam. It is not clear whether sea water, in this instance, is subject to staining from smoke. His bundle, however. And the fact that he labored under a recent meal. It would be helpful to know. Perhaps the channel to the sea, the glinted soil.

For instance the town, in its entirety, was in the habit of presenting a church; it was held in different structures, for different periods, under the authority of a single man: Kearns. Please follow closely. It is a system, at least, that was chosen by the townspeople. A whitened room was used, fortunately. When possible, children were organized to the rear of the assembly, wherefrom they effused the town song. Likewise the adults practiced an activity known as the talking chant. So it is claimed. There were requirements to the assembly that are as-yet unknown. Evidence of rules exists, as does some trace of dance or exaggerated movement. In any case, although we can no longer speak of precise hours, the entire town was housed thus for the period of what might now be called late morning. Nor even, goes the assertion, did they emerge until the sermon—if it was a sermon—was finished.

Permit me this: The gentleman retained a handful of leaves, explaining the vegetable flesh on his wrists. A garment was loaded with fluid from the sea. The acorns, in as much as they can be distinguished from the debris, were distributed freely, some would say carefully, around the site. The airplane was lodged on its back. The gentleman's shoes, however, if they in fact belonged to him, portrayed the marks of one who has scraped, or indeed been made to do so, through tight stone quarters, as in a tunnel opening out over the sea. Exactly. No, nothing like violence occurred. I will allow for what is unknown, rather, although I do not like to leave it at that. The airplane, as it happens, was encumbered with animal life.

From the sea, then, there is no access to the town other than the single-runged ladder bolted into the cliff-face. The tunnel is situated roughly twenty steps above the water, although at low tide the ladder cannot be reached at all. He arrived at the tunnel just before the hour of one, at least, despite the official claim of noon. His bundle, it is certain, was arranged to effect floatation. Consider, though, the body in the hole. Sea water stains the hair, and yet a travel billet is fixed in a pocket of the trousers. It is allowed that the man went back to the field. Certainly the sermon had finished by then, if indeed there ever was a sermon.

It is upon me to confess my bias. For instance, I have certain feelings for the sea. But the shoes, well, no, it is not possible that someone would go to such trouble. His craft must have been anchored some swimmer's distance from the cliff, yes. And if indeed there is no position in the town which posits a view of the sea—other than the precise outer orifice of the tunnel—well, it is obvious. But permit this aside: The ladder simply could not support two bodies, as is proposed. The gentleman died before two in the afternoon, in fact. I'm sorry. To be fair, there exists an argument that the gentleman was involved. With the man. As with an accomplice. Thus the travel billet is inserted afterwards, when so viewed. And thus the gentleman is killed or dies in an area other than the field, slightly astride the path. But I am a believer, yes, of certain terms. So behold Kearns. The cermon was annulled by a loud report in the field. The tower, in the manner of the airplane, although certainly somewhat afterwards, was coerced to the surface. As such, a gentleman could indeed have been dragged down the path and jettisoned into the sea.

There is a road that used to terminate in a schoolhouse, goes the claim. Wire lightposts lean into the woods on each side, and birds, for that matter, are often undone in the glare. It is here that he is placed as stopping to rest. The man. Consider, then, that the water could be heard from the field, but could be seen only from the orifice to the tunnel. So, it follows. The talking chant, you see. The mid-day church. Well, it is particularly sad. Let us not dwell. But indeed so many animals perished.

As it happens, to interrogate a child would be beneficial. The schoolhouse, for one, had been destroyed. Otherwise, there was a stone hut affixed to the northern cusp of the field, although, again, I have incorrectly spoken of direction. Forgive me. Nevertheless the hut, the charred hay, a young girl's pallet. Considering the height of the tower, as it is projected, there would be an easy relationship between the two. If, for instance, the church occurred outdoors, as I propose. That one time alone, for example. And the song, so to speak, being released so near the field. Well. There was a great deal of singing in any case. Or so goes the claim. And the church, perhaps. But, you have no doubt heard enough. I only mean to be thorough. Please pardon me.

To conclude, then. It is determined there would have been wildlife other than that enclosed in the airplane. The chain, inasmuch as we can trust the report, divides the hut from the field, in order to—it is said—prevent the animals from entering—I do not exaggerate the words that were used—the living areas. Yes. But he started there just after the explosion; and again, the meal must be mentioned, if only to recall his possible composure, described as somewhat atilt, as if injured. Thus, a swell of debris at the foot of the path, ruling out something other than a man. And the bundle, flung without care while the fire erupted. It is not important, then, to explain. It is better to say: The acorns, so small. The shards, littered on the wing. As if. Indeed. Brought there afterward.

Carole Maso

Sanctuary

from <u>Defiance</u>

She'll have to go to work with the mother, that's all there is to it. She'll have to go to the phone company—there's no other way. She's going to have to stay silent and she can't—she's got to be invisible. She can't be seen, in other words, she's got to stay hidden all day under her mother's desk because no children are allowed there—it's not a kindergarten for God's sake, it's not a nursery or a petting zoo or a playground—it's a job, and the daily wage must be earned honestly.

So the child will have to be smuggled in before everyone else arrives. She's about five, I'd say, and she's already quite adept at practicing silence. Bright light filters through the dusty venetian blinds, striping the room. She gets under the desk and it seems her mother is always wearing the same striped dress and she is dizzied by it. Sometimes she can make the stripes move and swirl like a zebra walking, or a barbershop pole—but lots of times she can't, they just sit there on her mother's dress. Imprisoned by the design, nowhere to go; at least she'll be safe here, the mother reasons, in the incredibly cramped area near her feet. During the day she'll pass her bits to eat and drink. And the child armed with a flashlight will read and sometimes sleep, lulled by the drone of numbers her mother repeats all afternoon long—and by the heat. She falls into her mother's exhausted voice as it repeats Trafalger 2-5863. She will forever after associate tenderness with numbers, love with numbers—the song which first came from her mother's mouth. They were the code she spoke with the child, under the desk. A way to be safe.

She falls into the abyss of her mother's long sorrow. She feels dizzy, and it's so hot. Under the desk close up she sees the runs, more stripes, in her mother's hosiery, stopped right before the hem by small dabs of pink nail polish. See how it glitters like stars. She rests her hands on the mother's worn shoes—over the shoes that have been repaired one too many times now.

Zebras...Swirls...Stars...She's sleepy. Hour after hour the child drifts in a blur of numbers. Finding patterns for awhile, which dissolve then regroup forming new configurations. She dreams she's in a treehouse far up in the trees. Let t equal all the trees in the world she thinks. Let x, let x...

And Prescott 3-5836, and, and—aren't there an awful lot of numbers to keep track of here?

Until day is done and her mother puts down the black microphone finally and the numbers stop and she slouches toward zero. And the mother makes the sign of the cross and she pats the child's head, and motions for her to come out now and slowly they make their way toward home through a haze of numbers. The mind's dark emblems. Sanctuary. But on some days, and she can make out no discernible design of days—but on some days at the end of her shift, her mother would pull away after her endless litany, away from the desk—summoned by the shiny, new shoes of the boss and walk down the hall to his office. The child can see his feet sparkling, as he comes to take away her mother—and his feet seem to be making strange little dance steps, which she tries to connect on the floor after they've left, in an attempt to understand. It seems like an awfully long time that her mother is sequestered there down the hall, the better part of an hour as best as the child can calculate. She waits, as always patiently. Always such a good little girl. So quiet, so smart. So obedient.

But one day the shoes dance into the room and they do not dance away; they stay. And the child, of course, is still hiding—so she can see, but only a little. And the mother begs no, *anywhere but here*, and the mother pleads, *no, not in here* and the man laughs and says, *why not?* And he instructs the woman, the mother, her mother, to sit back down in her chair. She swivels away from the child and toward the black shoes of the man. *Yes like that,* he says, her legs still covered by the striped dress, poor creature, zebra caged, prisoner.

And the man begins, of all things, to sing. And the little girl lowers her head to the floor so that she can see him. He has taken his penis from his pants and he is twisting it in his hands, the big, bald man—and this part seems so unlikely—and yet, it is what she hears, he sings. Quietly at first: *Baa Baa Black Sheep have you any wool?* And her mother, in the most petrified, and the most tiny child-like voice sings back while patting her lap, *Yes sir, yes sir, three bags full.*

And he sings, *One for my—*

And she sings, *my master. And one for my—*

And he fills in the blank. And they sing together,

And one for the little boy who lives down the lane.

And then again: *Baa Baa Black Sheep have you any wool?*

Yes sir, yes sir, three bags full.

And three times she pats her private part.

And his penis is getting bigger and redder and she whispers, isn't that enough for now? and he laughs and reaches for her hand.

Oh no, Mrs. O'Brien; now you know what comes next. And in her weekly humiliation she takes off her shoes and stands up. And now the child will witness, and this in a way is the worst part of all: she sees her mother in darned stocking feet, move to the middle of the room. His penis is still out as far as the girl can tell, and her mother in stocking feet, places her hand on her hip and with the other arm makes a sort of S shape. It's funny, it looks funny for a minute, amusing, like maybe she'll laugh or something but then it becomes all too clear: her cracked, exhausted voice— her sad, necessary task

She begins to sing, in a meek and mortified voice, and he yells, *I can't hear you honey, a little louder,* until the mother and the daughter are just children together, cowering. I can't hear you. And she starts again, this time like a child in a pageant, she sings:

> *I'm a little teapot, short and stout*
> *Here is my handle, here is my spout.*

The man in the shoes has taken a seat on the mother's desk; the man in the shoes is moaning.

> *When I get all steamed up, then I shout*
> *Just tip me over, pour me out.*

And he is humming along as she repeats, just tip me over, pour me out, Again he moans. And the woman is on one foot, tipped over, off balance, emptied of everything, poured out, shaky on this one leg, and the man takes himself out into a handkerchief, only feet away from the girl under the desk. He motions the woman over to sit on his lap.

And the little girl under the desk prays hard—if only the numbers could start again. Surely everything would be back to normal then.

And he motions for the woman who is trembling now to come and sit in his lap, *here Baa Baa Sheep, he mutters, just one bag, Just one bag full.* And he lifts her dress slightly and fingers her garter belt and reaches up for her wooly stash. Ghastly, that the child should have to witness this and the woman is weeping.

And see now, how mysteriously the little child has turned into a girl all of a sudden, and then, she's even older and bigger, and she can scarcely fit under that desk anymore, and then she's even a little bit older—until they are just—mother and daughter, two women weeping together.

And the man goes faceless and empties himself this time into her scallop-edged handkerchief.

But it's not over yet.

Her eyes brim again and he is saying *shh, shh, Baa Baa Sheep* and she is already gagging as he puts the soiled handkerchief into her mouth and sings sweetly to her, *Baa Baa Black Sheep have you any wool?* And she, it is the routine, that much is plain to see, sings in a muffled voice, choking back, *yes sir, yes sir, three bags full.*

That a girl, that a girl, he says, and he reaches his hand deep into her mouth, saying suck on it a little. And then he takes the gag out and he pays her finally, and she is on her knees thanking him. *Thank-you sir.* Kissing his ring. To make ends meet—in those days, just to make ends meet. The woman genuflected in front of this bloated, preposterous God, all power-ful, and they the powerless—oh it certainly seems that way—errant slaves.

Someone, something deliver them, we pray, from this eternal sing song, from this absurd, this ludicrous scenario, this demented tea party, this sadness, this night without day. Grant them peace.

In the night which never ends the mother feverishly recites numbers in the sanctuary of her sleep.

And in the night, the child, small again, keeps her cold vigil over the mother's bed and takes careful, bloodless notes, reminders, love letters in a sense, to the woman she vows, she swears, someday to become.

Laura Mullen

The Dead

"Did you have a good time with her?"

He's been waiting for this and he doesn't ask who.

They're sitting in his car, his new old car, the car he got practically for free for just being a nice guy, like always, spontaneously helping the former owner, an old lady, to parallel park in Manhattan, which is where he's from. One minute he's standing there at the curb, his hands—because he can see she's having difficulties, going in wrong, turning too far, too late or early—held out in front of him, palms up, fingers wriggling, he shows you, he acts it out, *come, come, come,* with a grin, and then *stop, good,* waving, turning with a shrug and starting to walk away, and the next minute he's the owner of the thing. That is, after her *I'd give it away* had turned into, *for a hundred dollars*—which he paid. But of course it had cost him a lot more than that, in the end (this comes out gradually, once you're in it) what with insurance, and all the various things which had, almost immediately, started to go wrong.

They're waiting for it to warm up now, which, in this fierce cold, takes a long time.

"Did you tell her about us?"

They are far away from each other on the long bench-like front seat. An expanse of shining plastic-covered gold-toned vinyl between then. They hug themselves, hands tucked into armpits as though they were wearing invisible straitjackets, for warmth.

"Me," she amends, after a silence. The cloud the word makes hanging for an instant on the air.

His quick glance not too quick to read his expression: guilt making him frightened, and angry.

Her long, considering, skeptical, furious and frightened stare.

The parking lot covered in snow, dirty snow the plow has pushed up packed around it in a low, pale wall, out of which the evergreen trees thrust, dark. Behind them the lights of the dining hall have come on. Yellow windows gleaming, reflected on the grimy, ice-slicked snow.

How could he, after all, he practically lives with this woman—with the soft, forgettable name and with whom he has now, or so he said, nothing in common, but who he *trusts*—who's just come to visit him here for a few days. And gone.

He rubs at the windshield where it's fogged slightly with the side of his hand; clenched and gloved.

For awhile the car engine is the only sound, a faint rumble heard and felt. It's an old car, an old American car, huge, 'Indestructable,' 'a clunker,' painted a gold which has faded so as to be only the mutest recollection of a color, and the engine sounds at once extremely powerful—as though it could go on forever—and as though it were giving out, breaking down, on the verge of stopping cold.

He clears his throat.

She spent the weekend asking people there—who saw the other woman (or rather *the* woman, since it is she who is "the other..."), who met her—if she was smart, if she was beautiful, meaning *more*.

In front of them the black bakelite knobs of the silent radio; the muddy khaki vinyl of the dashboard covered in a thin film of greasy dust; the pack of expensive cigarettes they smoke, when they smoke, awkwardly, hold too carefully, inhale either too much or too little of, obviously amateurs; the tint across the top of the windshield, a narrow band of transparent blue or "aqua." Beyond which snow: the tree-lined road banked with snow, the golf course covered in snow, the small private cemetery you have to get someone who's been here before to show you, a small town, a mall.... Maps on the floor by her feet folded up again hastily, partly open still: the names and numbers of the highways and roads they're not familliar with, they never heard of, which lead back to the roads and the highways and the cities they know.

Years from now they could meet at a party—they'd have, from that interval, friends in common—and try to forgive each other, or come to something like an understanding. She might congratulate him on his forth-coming marriage, perhaps too emphatically. He might walk her home. It could be early spring: the trees with the barest feathery beginnings of leaves, yellow in the glare of the streetlights, the lights from shop windows, all that neon, and still cold. *And the car? Oh, it finally....* They will admit that they both were *desperately* lonely, well, *a little,* shrugging, *back then,* with a smile. And say good-night outside her door.

Now the extraordinarily clear, gelid air perceptibly darkening above the almost phosphorescent snow, the almost black evergreens. The white of the bare birches seeming starker, they are cracks running up into the dim-ming bowl of saturated blue and blue-green and blue-purple; fissures, bea-cons of a kind, something to steer by, where there are three of them grouped together, down at the far end of the long white field. That absence of color continued up into the sky, jaggedly.

In the headlights.

Taking the handbrake off, putting it into reverse and backing up slowly while turning (the lights rake the white side of a building, turn the boughs of pine and spruce and fir green again briefly, and lose themselves in the depth of the shadowed road) he says "I missed you." And reaches to turn on the radio.

Lance Olsen

Historical Uterine Dreams

DICK TRACY: FROM RUSSIA WITH LOVE

Kyla Lahudky, who sat with an increasingly bad back before an opalescent computer screen in a cubicle in a grimy redbrick building two blocks away from the Seattle Space Needle eight hours a day trying over her phonoid headset to convince people she had never met (and who were usually pretty rude to her) to purchase products she, Kyla, had never in fact purchased in her life, had a dream one night three years after the Iron Curtain turned to gossamer and then evaporated altogether.

It was an amber autumn afternoon in the dream, and Kyla's subconscious had chosen an omniscient point of view, despite Kyla's best efforts to the contrary. (She was a first-person kind of dreamer, all things being equal.) She felt like a camera man shooting a video for MTV might if the crane on which his camera was mounted had all at once been visited by a poltergeist. Suddenly she was looking at a park from a vantage point several hundred feet off the earth. Under a large oak was a redwood picnic table. The patchy dead grass around it was carpeted with tangerine and umber leaves. Kyla had the distinct impression Halloween was somewhere behind her, but not very far. At the picnic table sat a family eating—from what Kyla could see at this distance, squinting—tuna-fish sandwiches. Everyone looked gloomy. They ate gazing straight ahead, dull-eyed and slack-jawed.

Then this obese black car with tinted windows (Kyla didn't have a good grasp of car models, but this one had a Dick Tracyish atmosphere about it) crunched up a gravel road that hadn't existed three heartbeats ago. It stopped maybe ten feet from the family. One of the back tinted windows rolled down. A large white veiny hand cupping a plump rooster extended into the amber light and dropped the fowl on the planet, at which point it began flouncing and strutting, doing that jerky thing with its head and neck that roosters did when they wanted to scope out their entire environment really quickly...and there the car went, crunching away.

The kids—there were three of them, two boys and a little girl, none more than eight, all with genetically familiar big sponge-noses—snapped alert. A flash, and they were up across the dead leaves chasing the rooster. Another, and the rooster was up across the dead leaves chasing them. Another, and their parents were laughing and clicking their cheap sealed-in-plastic Kodaks and chasing the kids chasing the rooster and the afternoon's personality had altered for the definitely sunnier. At which point the gravel road coalesced, redux, the obese black car returned, the door opened a foot away from the rooster, which had paused to catch its little rooster-ial breath, and that same white veiny hand reached down and scooped the fowl up, the door closed, and the obese black car began crunching down the gravel road in the dream's afternoon light, which took on a palpably oyster-gray hue.

At which moment the little girl, whose name for some reason Kyla knew was Avis Bromnickel, looked at her brothers through half-lidded eyes and spoke a single word aloud: "Europe."

And then Kyla awoke.

Or maybe, come to think of it, the word wasn't a word at all but a tiny phrase, like "You're up," or even possibly something like "Stirrup" or "Syrup," the later being one of Kyla's favorite semi-foods.

The thing being the whole dream had been audio-challenged from the start, so the sudden advent of sound by way of the girl's clear voice surprised Kyla, who'd been paying attention to other matters, like for instance that exceedingly spooky large white veiny hand and who it might belong to, but that wasn't the point, as she explained the following Thursday (late summer: lemon light) during her lunchbreak to her dream therapist, Pat Schmier, this weird little vegan New Age aromatic-pouch-sporting meerkat in a crimson Vietnamese pants suit who curled her legs up under her and believed in astrology and seeing tomorrow and spoke with what sounded to Kyla like a Transylvanian accent and had like zero control over her lingual muscle, every once in a while which would just seem to sort of fall asleep and flop out of her mouth a little, then wake up and get all self-conscious and sneak back in again.

But that wasn't the point at all.

The point was this: Kyla Lahudky had just made a really big decision about her future.

UTERINE HISTORY

Kyla's parents, both deceased (Snoqualmie Pass: Pinto: evening: black ice: full gas tank), had fled a minuscule town called Smegtrava in north-western Bohemia in what was then Czechoslovakia just before the 1946 elections when the communists won 114 of the 300 seats in the national assembly, which amount didn't seem like a lot to anyone at the time, except it was in fact gobs more than most of the other parties had won...meaning, in February 1948, the arrival of absolutely no good at all for something like forty years.

And now Kyla herself was staring down the parentless barrel of her thirtieth birthday, a numerical concept that bore positively no relationship to the person who gave her—that thin-faced, perpetually puzzled-looking, kind of frazzled-haired brunette-dyed-strawberry-red-and-bobbed gal always appearing as if she'd just been asked a question by a person talking a language she'd never heard before—the once-over every morning in the mirror. She felt her history was becoming, well, all history...in this negative sense that she didn't honestly know who she was, historically speaking, had never asked her parents those really important biographical questions every son or daughter should ask his or her parents before they become too advanced in years and hence let's face it dispirited to care much (plus, if the truth be known, they'd never cared that especially much in the first place, being as they were part of that seminal Old World generation who shed their past like so much sunburned skin the nanosecond they stepped off the proverbial boat into the New World)...had only the mistiest outlines of very misty outlines of a narrative about where she'd in a socio-cultural hereditary sort of way come from.

So when little sponge-nosed Avis Bromnickel uttered that magic word to her brothers, if in fact little sponge-nosed Avis Bromnickel *had* uttered that magic word to her brothers, Kyla's dream's exegesis resolved into crystalline lucidity.

The autumnal park was her life, she told Pat Schmier, who curled in the cushiony chair opposite hers, bony fingers playing with this pouch of like oregano or something, just way too sincere and interested in Kyla for her own good, and the family at the picnic table was her spirit's current existential state, and the rooster that brought animation to both was...well, that rooster was none other than the Old World itself, in the form of one minuscule town called Smegtrava in northwestern Bohemia in what was then Czechoslovakia, currently the Czech Republic, which would chase her the rest of her days if she didn't decide to chase it.

And so she did.

Decide to chase it, that is.

She called her boss from a payphone the instant she left Pat Schmier's office and requested the two weeks of vacation coming to her and stopped off at her bank to fish out her passport (she'd gone to Cancun for Christmas, once, five years ago, with an acquaintance from work, such as he was) from her safe deposit box and headed straight for a travel agency she'd noticed a month or two ago down by the wharf and booked the next available flight (four days hence) out of SEA-TAC for London, and one from London to Prague, and then this train from Prague to Smegtrava, with pretty much all the money she'd carefully collected over the last half decade or so in her savings account.

She knew as she went about these chores she should be disconcerted, apprehensive, anxious even, by what she was doing, it being a pretty massive step and all on the broken ladder called existence, only she wasn't.

Deep down in her uterus in that corporeal suburb where she had tucked the idea of hope, Kyla Lahudky knew that her really big decision was the only really right one.

And, so...

SOUTHWEST CANADIAN MECHANICAL BLUES

She had momentary second thoughts, of course, at the airport, as she exited the gift shop, having bought a blue box of ear plugs, a robin's-egg bottle of Quiet World, a polychromatic bag of gourmet jelly beans, and a black horror novel with this semi-nude wholly-terrified teen cringing on the cover, which felt like it weighed something like five pounds, and almost walked into these two men in medias altercation.

At the elevator up to the observation deck and corridor of administrative offices this pale wasted-away guy in a motorized wheelchair was arguing with this red-faced three-hundred-pound guy in a business suit over who would get to ride the elevator first, it being, Kyla noticed as she strolled nearer, a one-person elevator. The door was open and the wheelchaired guy had got maybe two inches of hard-rubber wheel through it, but the three-hundred-pound guy had grabbed the grips on the back of the wheelchair to stop it from rolling any farther.

The thing's little electric engine wheezed as if it was about to suffer an apoplectic chernobylization.

"You hog," the pale wasted-away guy was saying in a southern accent over his shoulder, eyes on the floor, in that way wheelchaired people talk to erect people behind or beside them, "if you fuckin' could like control your weight or something, maybe you could take like the fuckin' stairs."

"Look who's talking, you little piece of fried shit," responded the red-faced three-hundred-pound guy to the top of the wasted-away guy's head, in that way erect people talk to wheelchaired people when the erect people stand behind or beside them, "if you had an ounce of goddamn *brains* you'd maybe like have goddamn looked where you were goddamn *driving.*"

"You're not fuckin' handicapped, man. You're just a fuckin' pig."

"Yeah, well fuck you. Hear me? Fuck. You. I got two words, okay? Two words. *Stop. Sign.* Ring any goddamn bells?"

The wheelchaired guy hit reverse.

His unit's gears whizzed and he rammed into the three-hundred-pound guy's kneecaps. Then he hit forward again, but not fast enough, because the three-hundred-pound guy, who started spontaneously sweating in this extraordinarily wet and icky way, caught the wheelchaired guy in the back of the head with his right hand, which was neither white nor veiny, while jamming the elevator door open with his left.

Only Kyla didn't stay around to see what would happen next, much as that gossipy side of her mind might have wanted to, this stuff carrying some pretty evil karmic charges as far as she was concerned.

She just lowered her head and trundled past expeditiously as possible to her gate, where the 747 was already loading, and, three-quarters of an hour later, was airborne thirty-five thousand feet over southwest Canada, dazed by the sleeping pills she'd just swallowed back in the restroom with this paper cup that commenced dissolving the moment she filled it with water, ear plugs doing a fairly lame job of stilling the continuous engine thunder around her, sense of time already one-hundred percent amok, mind sparking with bright white glossy ovoid objects that weren't exactly dream phantoms, and weren't exactly memories, and weren't exactly the faces of the British flight attendants leaning over her and asking her what she'd like to drink, but were, somehow, some creepy mosaic of all three at once.

BRAIN RAID: DREAM TIME

Kyla's consciousness unblocked again on a beaten-up train scudding through the green hilly Czech countryside one cloudy afternoon, that horror novel open to page 52 on her lap (though she couldn't remember what she'd read so far, yet had this feeling she was going to be quizzed on it any second), semi-hallucinogenic recollections of walking jet-lagged among the trees in Hyde Park during her layover in London and next wandering lost and disoriented through the narrow labyrinthian alleys of the old Jewish ghetto in Prague breathing like a sleeping dog's ribcage in the folds of her cortex.

This part of the journey took nearly three-and-a-half hours. Kyla got up every once in a while and navigated down the pitching aisle to the restroom or beyond to the buffet car past the loose faces the color of cigarette remains of people who looked shell-shocked by the twentieth century. She stood in the chilly space between cars, stretching her legs and cracking her tweaked back, watching a dense rush of forest give way to the broken bones of an abandoned factory, a crumpled town with many roofless buildings, glimpses of a café-au-lait river, more woods, great gray boulders bulging from steep rises. One time the train stopped in the middle of a wide flat field and three humorless teenage soldiers in olive-gray uniforms, pistols unholstered, appeared, knocked on the restroom door, checked inside when no one answered, released a panel in the ceiling, shinnied up to investigate, and, satisfied (though never meeting Kyla's eyes, never acknowledging her facticity), disembarked.

As the door slid shut behind them, Kyla realized for the first time she didn't really know a thing about her relatives.

She'd used a search engine on the Web, which she'd had access to from her cubicle in that grimy redbrick building two blocks away from the Space Needle, to attempt to track down the electronic version of the Bohemian phone book, but of course had had no luck. The last thing former Eastern Bloc countries had time or money for was to play around on the Internet. The public library wasn't much help, either, there being little more than a few maps of old Czechoslovakia there (budget cuts; bibliographic triage), and she'd had only a few days to prepare for her flight anyway, packing and all, so she gave up and decided to wait till she arrived in Smegtrava to deal with it.

In Seattle, her plan had seemed to make perfect sense. Here, though, watching those soldiers shrink into olive-gray beetles as they moved across the field, she wasn't so sure. What, for instance, if she reached Smegtrava only to discover that no more Lahudkys lived there? Or what if Smegtrava was way bigger than she'd imagined (the library maps were ambiguous on this matter, or at least she couldn't break their complicated codes) and they *did* live there, only she couldn't find them? Or what if she'd misread her dream altogether? Maybe that rooster didn't represent the Old World, but the New. Or maybe it signified something else entirely, like the cute guy Kyla was going to meet the very next day two cubicles over and fall in love with and kiss a week later in a café in Pioneer Square and live happily ever after with if only she didn't board that 747 and fly across Canada, the North Pole, Greenland, Scotland, England, the Channel, France, and Germany to this weird place? What if the autumnal park and dreary family didn't represent her current life at all, but her future one, the one she'd begin living the eyeblink she launched on her vacation in the Czech Republic and spent all her savings and went off on some wild goose chase after…after who knew what?

And what if little sponge-nosed Avis Bromnickel hadn't said what Kyla thought she'd said? What if she'd said something else?

What if she'd said, not "Europe," but, say, "You suck"?

Kyla shuddered and returned to her seat. She picked up her novel and began reading again, trying to lose herself in it, forget all that yucky stuff, only found she hadn't been concentrating really well to begin with and after another twenty minutes decided to go back to the beginning and start all over once more. This time the story resolved into a tale about a young New York postal worker who hated his body, really hated it, which he viewed as nothing more than some godawful prosthesis for his much-more-interesting mind, because it was so gooey and smelly and dirty and everything, his body was, and always yelled for his attention with its colds and micturitional needs, infections and hunger pangs, zits and kind of unnerving dark sexual urges. It made him want to throw up, in an Existential Crisis sort of way. The guy thus turned more and more into himself. He avoided mirrors. He didn't go outside unless he really had to. He started having flashbacks of an unhappy childhood where his schoolmates beat him up every afternoon after classes and made him eat worms and stuff. And, one day, he decided to punish his flesh for all the aggravations it had caused him. So he stopped cutting his hair. Which, he discovered, felt pretty good. So he stopped shaving. Which felt downright great. So he stopped bathing. And so on. And, needless to say, before too long he decided to cease going to work altogether, which as a matter of course made it fairly easy to stop eating and drinking.

Just about the point where he crawled into his not-very-festive-smelling bed with a meat cleaver and jerry-rigged tourniquet and pulled the sheet up over his musty tangled-hairy head in his cramped apartment on 4th Street between C and D, and Kyla got the first disagreeable hint of where this story was ultimately going (wondering meanwhile just why she'd picked it up in the first place, given that unsettling picture of the wholly-terrified cringing guy on the cover, but she didn't want to think about it too much and so didn't), she felt a kerchunk and looked up.

Through her window she saw Smegtrava Station: a single gray caved-in-roof stone hut with an emaciated cocker spaniel slumped out front like it'd just been whacked by a car next to a rusting open-doored refrigerator stuffed with apricoting old newspapers.

"Uh-oh," she said to no one in particular.

ARRIVAL: MY NAME

The station was empty.

There wasn't even anyone inside the ticket booth that leaned almost imperceptibly starboard in one corner next to a pile of roof rubble.

So Kyla, feeling not just a little uncomfortable, hoisted her olive-green knapsack with all her clothes in it over her right shoulder, took a deep breath, and, just as it started to drizzle, strolled onto the narrow, cobble-stoned, serpentine street lined with two-story stone and whitewashed houses that reminded her of the alleys in the old Jewish ghetto.

She slogged maybe thirty feet before she decided this wasn't working. To get out of the increasing precipitational mess, she stepped through a doorway into what looked to her like a bar from the exterior. Only she did-n't find herself inside a bar, but some sort of open space between two build-ings. She pushed on till she came to another doorway and tried it. Again, instead of entering an interior area she entered some strange architectural in-between zone. Which creeped her out, since she had never seen anything like it back in Seattle, or Cancun for that matter, meaning she decided to retrace her steps, except as soon as she did it dawned on her she'd covered way more distance than she'd remembered covering.

Each time she turned around everything behind her looked utterly dif-ferent than it did when it had been in front of her.

Plus she was getting wetter and the afternoon was getting tired and the light was turning the color of a pigeon's neck. So she picked another door-way at random, thinking surely this one would lead her back onto main street, and she found herself inside a claustrophobic smoky café.

Everyone stopped talking and turned around to stare at her when she entered.

Mostly they were elderly men, eight or nine of them, with frumpy tweed jackets and crushed berets. The aproned woman behind the shiny wooden bar with the espresso machine weighed almost as much as that ornery guy back at the airport elevator, except her face wasn't red. It was the color of skin worn by people who thought from birth sunlight was an overrated event.

Kyla smiled sheepishly.

She became extremely conscious of the rainwater trickling over her scalp and down her forehead, nose, cheeks and neck.

She reorganized a comma of brunette-dyed-strawberry-red-and-bobbed hair poking her in the eye.

"Lahudky," she said. "I'm looking for the Lahudkys. And, um, well, I thought maybe you could help and all. I'm from Seattle. America." She spoke like she was speaking to a roomful of deaf retarded people. "The United. States. Of. *America.*"

They stared blankly at her.

"My name is Kyla Lahudky," she tried again. "I'm. Looking. For. My. *Relatives.*" Then she remembered. She slipped her knapsack off her shoul-der, felt around inside it, and came up with her Central European phrasebook. She thumbed through it to the dog-eared page, really really self-conscious now, and put together the two sentences she'd been practicing for just over a week. "Dobry den. Kde je Lahudky?" She glanced up hopefully. The two men closest to her examined each other and shrugged. Kyla repeated the words, overemphasizing the break between each syllable. "Gdeh. Yeh. Lah. Hoot. Ki."

The guy on the right with tiny sunken eyes and a lots of epidermal issues to deal with squinted as if he were attempting to see some small animal way down the road through his windshield in a blizzard.

"Lahudky?" he said, tentatively.

"Yes! Yes!" said Kyla, nodding. "Lahudky! Lahudky!"

"Ah, ano, lahudky!"

He turned and said something to the others and everyone laughed. Then he stepped forward and gave Kyla what felt like a little welcome hug and ushered her through the doorway, out into that in-between zone, and onto the deserted drizzly main street beyond, unfolding his black umbrella and holding it over her head for her as they ambled down a block, him talking and talking, then turned left, then ambled down another block, then turned right, and finally walked through the entrance of what looked like a delicatessen, feathered limp-necked grouse hanging upside down by their scrawny legs, skinned hares, slick tubby purple-brown sausages stacked one atop the other like miniature greasy firewood behind the glassed-in counter.

A big bald man in a bloody apron with tufts of hair growing on his ear-tips clattered through the beads hanging in the doorway that separated the back of the shop from the front.

The guy with the tiny eyes and epidermal issues rapid-fired a round of language at him, and the guy with the tufted ears rapid-fired some language back at him, and then they both laughed and commenced coughing in unison like their lungs had simultaneously filled with jelly and the tufted-eared guy stepped from behind the counter, arms outstretched, still laughing and coughing, and embraced Kyla in a knock-down drag-out bear hug, linguistically rapid-firing and laughing and coughing the whole while…so much so that all Kyla could do, really, was smile, which is what she did, long and hard, till her maxillofacial muscles really hurt, because she knew she'd gotten to where she'd been heading for a long, long, long time.

FEAST: YOUR NAME

As she did, another voice exploded from the back of the shop, sharp and electrocutionally high, and, before Kyla had a chance to think about extricating herself from the big bald man's burly envelopment, the woman who must have been the big bald man's wife waddled into view.

She made her husband look sort of thin and emotionally understated. Her hands fluttered over her head like two white bats trapped in an attic, creating the impression she was being attacked by chiropteral mammals as she approached, and she wasn't talking so much as oratorically erupting, so, when her substantial weight slammed into Kyla, Kyla thought for sure she heard several vertebrae in her bad back crackle, only then she didn't hear much of anything for a while, not even the guy with the tiny eyes and epidermal issues bidding them what must have been a good evening and slipping out, because her ears were tintinnabulating like they did that time when she was a kid kneeling by her bike in the gas station in Tacoma, pumping air, and hadn't been paying attention to the pressure gauge, and her front tire blew up maybe eighteen inches from her head.

Only Kyla became aware of all that tugging and pinching going on around by her thighs, and, when she finally contorted her body enough in the double embrace of ample wife and husband to take a peek, she discovered three large-eared pink-cheeked children (who, interestingly enough, reminded her a little of Avis Bromnickel and her siblings from the dream) had conjoined with the noisy teratoid they'd all become and were trying to scrabble up her lower torso as if it were a tree trunk in a potato field, which just made her smile more.

Soon Kyla was being bustled through the shop amid jabbers just like an old friend, around the counter, into the rearmost area occupied by the family's modest flat. On the other side of the beads existed a small poorly lit room wealthy with the smell of fresh bread and cooked cabbage. In one corner hulked the large lumpy family bed over which was spread a tattered homemade quilt. In another stood a fake-woodgrain-veneer fridgelette, old white stove, sink, cupboard, and cedar chest. Against one wall sagged a maroon couch, on either side of which propped a fragile end table covered with a delicate lace doily on which perched a brass lamp. In the middle of the room, on a once-beautiful Persian rug, rose the family dining table, already set for dinner with unassuming ceramic ware and two partially burned candles. It was toward this that the family steered Kyla.

At first she made polite protests, raising her hands before her chest and turning her head slightly to the right, but the truth was she was touched…flattered, even…*good*…and the bald man's wife hurriedly added another place setting while the bald man himself disappeared through the beads to close up for the day.

When he returned, this time apronless, he was holding a bottle of wine. Chivalrously, he extracted a chair from the table and offered it to Kyla, who said thank you and primly took a seat.

What followed was the most wonderful evening she'd ever experienced. It was an evening crowded with red wine, white cheese, warm bread, tangy sauerkraut, spicy sausages, chewy potato dumplings and full-bellied laughter. The bald man, whose first name sounded like Otakar or maybe Oskatar took out a photo album filled with ancient black and white pictures of people Kyla imagined must have been her relatives, and told story after story that Kyla couldn't understand, but he told them with such relish and good-spiritedness, standing to act this part, running in place till he chuffed to act that, that Kyla couldn't help laughing along with everyone else at the table. And the bald man's wife, who's first name sounded like Maria or maybe

Matriva, tilted back her head from time to time and opened her very full mouth and cackled till her small brown eyes glassed with tears.

Everyone had seconds, and the children and Kyla had thirds.

Afterward, when Kyla made gestures indicating she needed to be off in search of a hotel, Otakar or Oskatar looked over at his wife and laughed some more. They'd have none of it. They wouldn't even entertain the notion. Instead, Maria or Matriva made up the couch for her guest, carefully and tidily folding under each corner of the sheet she produced from the chest, and then the extra quilt, and stuffing a pillowcase with towels for Kyla's head.

They gave her a moment to herself to wash up at the sink, then led her out back to the outhouse and waited demurely while she made use of it, then led her inside again where Maria or Matriva tucked her into bed just like her mother did before Kyla had turned thirteen and the children gave her a kiss each on the forehead and Otakar or Oskatar squeezed her hand like a loving father.

When the lights clicked off, and Maria or Matriva began to make schluffing sounds at the back of her throat from the family bed, and Otakar or Oskatar embarked on some deep-breathed journey, Kyla lay awake for a long while, gazing into blackness above her head, more content than she could remember ever having been. She realized for the first time in her life she understood what history was, and understood what it meant to be connected with someone else at a profoundly cellular level. She sat with an increasingly bad back before an opalescent computer screen in a cubicle in a grimy redbrick building two blocks away from the Seattle Space Needle eight hours a day trying over her phonoid headset to convince people she had never met (and who were usually pretty rude to her) to purchase products she, Kyla, had never in fact purchased in her life, and it was okay. She was staring down the parentless barrel of her thirtieth birthday, a numerical concept that bore positively no relationship to the person who gave her the once-over every morning in the mirror, and that was okay too.

Some things made sense, she decided, and others didn't.

And, understanding this, she felt her consciousness melting around her, and observed a dream approach tonight like a heavy rain across a lake.

DREAM HISTORY

In it, she didn't feel she was dreaming, but lying in this very bed in this very flat somewhere in a minuscule town called Smegtrava in northwestern Bohemia in what was now the Czech Republic. The only difference was her bad back didn't ache.

She stared up into the blackness over her head and somehow knew things she hadn't known before.

She knew, somehow, for instance, that that couple she'd seen fighting in front of the elevator in the airport was gay, and really loved each other a lot, even though they sometimes had a hard time showing it, and even though the red-faced three-hundred-pound guy who'd hit the pale wasted-away wheelchaired guy in the back of the head was going to die this Friday, alone, of a megalithic heart attack, while straining on the toilet in a stall in the men's room at SEA-TAC on his lunch break, his last thought being, not of his lover, but of whether or not he'd ever heard of anyone dying in this stupid a way before.

Which would send his pale wasted-away wheelchaired partner straight to Pat Schmier, Kyla's weird little vegan New Age dream therapist, who wasn't in fact a weird little vegan New Age dream therapist at all, but a huckster, or what in the profession they call a *sharecropper,* someone whose doom-filled readings just keep the lucrative clients coming back for more...so much so, in Pat Schmier's case, that Pat had last Monday purchased with her proceeds a nice little cattle ranch in Montana, which she planned to move to the following summer, take insurance out on, burn down, and then buy a mink ranch down in southern Idaho.

In the comfortable bed of which, one starry night two years hence, Pat would have her first honest-to-god life-changing dream, though not about her life, but about Kyla Lahudky's, her former client's, whose name Pat would no longer in fact be able summon with any articulate precision.

In Pat's dream, Kyla travels to a tiny town in the Czech Republic to discover her roots. After a long and arduous trek, she finds herself in the ramshackle house of what she assumes to be her relatives...except she's wrong because, back in the café at which she had asked directions earlier that afternoon, her request had been misinterpreted by the locals, who thought, since *lahudky* in Czech means *delicatessen,* that this stranger was in search of somewhere to eat, and so took her to the only place in town where you could get a full decent meal, the house of Oskar and Mariva Jeritza, who imagined they could make some pretty good money off this American woman if they treated her right, in addition to the undeniable fact she seemed really nice and all, and so they fed her, and entertained her, and showed her photos of various strangers they used to take snapshots of as a hobby many years ago, and put her up for the night, planning in the morning to present her with a reasonable but not unsizable bill for the last evening's proceedings, and then buy the television they'd always wanted so they could watch American shows dubbed into Czech of which, now, they only knew the names: *Baywatch, Melrose Place, Oprah Winfrey.*

Which bill Kyla would, it turned out, have been happy to pay since, no matter what, she'd come to understand some important things she wouldn't have come to understand had she not stayed with the Jeritzas, except that then Oskar and Mariva figured out the mistake when they saw the puzzled look on Kyla's face when they presented her with said bill, plus they'd had this really wonderful time themselves, and so, on the spot, they changed their minds.

They tore up the bill right there, and thought that would be that...but it wasn't, because then Kyla, having learned more than she up to this point had quite realized, asked if she could stay on with them for just a little while longer, a day or two, maybe a bit more, if she helped out around the deli, and cleaned the flat, and looked after the little ones (whose names were, it turned out, Avis, Brom, and Nicole), and so on, because she just needed some time away from the world Out There to think about a few pretty weighty things, and, after an uncomfortable moment, and much breath-holding on the kids' part, who also had come to delight in this really sweet stranger's presence, Oskar and Mariva said well, heck, sure, why not, at which point Kyla executed a little spring of joy and hugged them, and then started right in settling down, during the process of which, over what turned out to be just a whole bunch longer than a couple of days, she found she read less and less, unable to concentrate on the words upon the page of that stupid horror novel she'd bought back at SEA-TAC for more than maybe three minutes at a stretch...and then unable to even understand them at all.

And so it happened one snowy November afternoon, white-gray as cigarette ash, Kyla Lahudky put that novel down for the last time, and looked up from where she was trying to read behind the glassed-in counter at the deli, and realized the world outside the shop window had turned into hieroglyphics, pure indecipherable hieroglyphics, at which point she grinned, having found very real happiness.

Leslie Pietrzyk

Where Your Life Begins

"Who'll be there?" I ask my girlfriend Katy. "Will Dean be there?" It's a big party I'm getting dressed for, the people who went to college are home for Christmas. No one ever expected someone like me to go to college, so I didn't, whereas everyone expected them to go, so they did. Things are that simple.

"Why *wouldn't* Dean be there?" she says. She's always got an edge, an attitude; most people wouldn't like it much, but who says I'm most people? Dean's her ex-boyfriend, ex since last summer when she dumped him. Katy's been on my list since maybe sixth grade, and Dean's been off-and-on my best friend since about the same time. Not that we're anything alike. He's one of those guys whose parents buy him a car the day he gets his license, and when he totals it a month later, they buy him another one. I'm not at all one of those guys, but about everyone I went to high school with is. The only reason they let me in the school is because I'm one hell of a cross-country runner, and the school is big into winning state championships.

Katy says, "Dean, Brock, Phil. Jenn, Clara, Patrice. All those guys. Everyone."

That's another thing. Dean's one of those guys who's always got people around him, impressing him with stories, telling every secret they can come up with. When I got in with Dean, those people were around me, too. But no one every told me a single damn secret. I heard them all from Dean anyway, for what that's worth.

Outside the window snow coasts down, catching in a wind and twirling under the streetlight. The cracked-up cement parking lot across the street is one of the places the city dumps the snow they haul off the highway; already there're huge gritty black mounds that I guess will get even bigger before winter's over. Kids slide down them on cardboard when it's sunny. "For sure Dean?" I ask. That snow keeps coming.

Katy rolls over on the bed and looks at me. "What're you looking at?" she asks. Because I say I'm going to be a famous artist she's always wanting to know what I'm looking at, what I see. I've stood outside gallery windows with her. The favorite she picks is always the biggest, the most expensive. I didn't know that about her until we started going out.

"For sure Dean?" I ask again.

She sighs sharp like it's a blade coming down. "Yes, Dean. Yes, yes, yes. What's with you?"

I turn from the window and open the closet door and grab off the top shelf a dark blue T-shirt that says, IF I'M NOT WHO YOU THINK I AM, THEN WHO THE HELL ARE YOU? though the letters are starting to flake off. Dean's shirt. I pull it over my head. I snagged it at that party his parents had before Dean left for college; they hired some redneck to dig a pit and barbecue a pig in their yard. Dean and I hung out with him all afternoon and he told us stories about screwing his cousins in a barn back when he lived in South Carolina. All he'd talk about was barbecue or screwing his cousins. Dean's father kept coming over, wanting to see how the barbecue was going, saying useless crap to Dean like, "Mr. and Mrs. McBoring are asking what you're up to; go say hi to them," so Dean would go off and Dean's father would go off, and it would be me and the redneck and the half-cooked pig, none of us with nothing to say all of a sudden.

After we'd all eaten and the pig was only bones the dogs were begging for, I went upstairs to Dean's bathroom to take a whiz, and I grabbed the T-shirt out of the hamper, nudging around to make sure I got the best one there was. When I got downstairs, they were putting out dessert, bowls of already-cut watermelon with the seeds picked out, like no one had ever thought to spit a watermelon seed or eat right off the rind. "Black Diamond watermelon," Dean's father said, "the absolute best there is, can't get it in stores." The redneck had hauled it up from his brother's farm in South Carolina for Dean's father for an envelope of cash.

Tonight would be my first time wearing Dean's T-shirt because I liked to wait about six months. That way they thought they remembered the shirt, but they weren't sure. They watched me all night when they thought I wasn't looking, knowing there was something they weren't getting the way a cat can't figure out a goldfish bowl. I'd been snagging clothes off and on for the last two years, and not one of them ever got it. Like, at graduation I wore Brock's navy blazer with Phil's dad's tie, a white button-down I'd lifted from some dork's house at a party, and Dean's father's khakis, and what I heard from every parent was how handsome I looked, like out of the pages of a magazine, and the mothers and step-mothers kissed the air near my face and the fathers and step-fathers shook my hand too hard and slapped my back, and someone said, "This is where your life begins, guys," and I laughed, but they were serious.

I look in the mirror. The shirt's small, and I've been doing barbells since September, and I know I look good. It's like that; whoever's clothing it is, it looks better on me, like it should be mine. That sale crap my mom gets me on her employee discount at the mall never looks like their stuff does, not close.

Katy says, "When you're a famous artist and we're living in a penthouse in New York, let's promise never to come back to Detroit. No matter how hard anyone begs."

I can see her on the bed in the mirror. I haven't told her that lately I'm thinking L.A. I say what she wants to hear: "Promise."

"Is it important to keep promises?" she asks.

I'd never tell her that's not something I think about, so I say, "I guess so."

"Because I don't think I've kept one," she says. "Not one."

"Nobody keeps promises anymore." I'm still looking at her in the mirror, thinking "Dean's girlfriend," and something about that feels right, as if I should be with Dean's gorgeous girlfriend.

"I promised Dean I'd love him forever and look at that."

"No one knows what forever means," I say.

"Dean just can't care about anything," she says. "I think that's why he liked me, because I cared too much. I did all the work. You know?"

Sometimes she sounds too much like a high school senior. I know you're not supposed to think that, but I do. Maybe that's why leaving her behind wasn't as hard as it should've been for Dean; that summer all he said about it was, "Katy gave me the boot," and at every party after that, a line of girls huddled around him, laughing when he laughed so it was like he had his own private echo.

Katy says, "You're not like that. You want to be, but you can't."

"Is this psych class?" I ask, too loud for this small room.

She doesn't say anything, then she stands up and walks to the window where I was before, looks out like there's something more than snow to see. "Maybe you'll be the one I love forever," she says.

She's thinking about seeing Dean. Behind their backs everyone said it wouldn't last. Dean's father told him not to waste time getting serious about any girl until the last year of law school. She says, "If you love me, then you'll go warm up the car for me."

Do I love her? If you have to ask, you don't, right? I reach for the flannel shirt I nabbed from the lost and found at the movie theatre where I'm assistant manager. Lost and found doesn't count like the other stuff, but it's one hell of a shirt, the flannel naps just right; the squares in the plaid aren't too big, aren't too small; there's a frayed hole above the elbow.

Katy frowns, says, "Isn't that shirt kind of...?"

"Kind of what?"

"Kind of cleaning out the basement on Sunday-ish?"

I'm not even sure I hear right because she never says anything bad about what I wear. Why she loves me is that what I do is different than what everybody else does—what I wear, eat, say, the artist thing. So I ask again: "Kind of what?"

"Kind of cleaning out the basement on Sunday-ish? I mean, Dean's at Harvard now."

"Thanks to his dad buying his way in," I say, not anything everyone doesn't know, including Dean. I grab the car keys off the top of the refrigerator, start wrapping my scarf around my neck. "I'm warming up the car for exactly five minutes," I say. "If you're not down there, you walk."

"Oh, brother," she says.

I slam the door and clatter down the two flights of stairs, slam the front door even harder. A thin layer of snow coats my car, and getting in,

I slam the door so snow slides down the windows; the wipers get the windshield. Only AM comes in, so I'm stuck listening to a bunch of guys blow off at each other about the president not keeping promises he made to the voters. "Everyone knows those were election year promises," one guy says, "and it's understood that they won't be kept. Every candidate makes them." The way he talks, I feel people in the studio nodding.

Ten minutes later, just as the car warms up enough that I can unclench my arms, Katy gets in. She reaches over and pulls the seatbelt around me, buckles it, snaps off the radio in the middle of a weather advisory. She pats my knee. "It's okay," she says, "because you're the one who's going to be the famous artist." It's still cold enough that her breath comes out in quick, frozen puffs that melt into nothing.

I rev the engine hard, until it feels like the car should rip apart the road.

"Calm down, baby," she says, patting my knee again, "hey." But she loves it, loves this part of me; this is what they all like—even Dean's father, who invited me for drinks at his club last month because his vintage Corvette needed a new transmission and he wanted to know what to ask the mechanic so he wouldn't get ripped off—they all like every part of me that isn't them, even Dean.

Snow spews out from under the tires, and we're skidding damn fast down the slick road and the snow dances crazy in front of us. She laughs and claps her hands like, faster, go faster. It's what they all want from me, to do the things they won't do, and she puts her tongue in my ear and one hand down my pants, and I know we're going to pull over, the only question is where, and it's in the parking lot of an abandoned machine shop, and it's good like it always is.

Afterwards, she whispers, "Do you love me? Do you care?" and I nod, and she says it again, "Maybe you'll be the one I'll love forever," but it's no promise, it's nothing, and I shiver in the cold air for a moment. I can't get warm.

*

"Hey, Picasso," is what Dean shouts across the room. "How's the artist biz?" It's what his father is always saying to me, coughing up a big dumb horse laugh along with it, so I know Dean's dicking me over. Someone walking by hands me a half-empty beer bottle with a cigarette butt floating inside.

"Very nice!" I call, and then Dean's next to me so I hand over the bottle to him, and he guzzles what's left then heaves the bottle over some heads into a recycling bin by the door. Maybe it was stupid to wear the T-shirt; there was that one phone call from Harvard, but besides that Dean hasn't changed any. I can leave on the flannel shirt and he won't know.

"He shoots, he scores!" Dean screams in his radio guy voice. For a while he was fighting his father on the Harvard thing, and he talked about going to the radio d.j. school down on Ten Mile Road. "I'm gonna do it," he'd tell me, "I'll clean out that bank account they've got going for me and enroll my ass in d.j. school; I'll get a chateau in the slums like you. And in sixteen weeks I'll be on the air just like they say," and I heard that enough times so finally I pulled over into the parking lot, but he wouldn't even go in for a brochure and that's when he knew it was Harvard even though I'd known all along.

They say with real friends it's like you've never been away. But seeing Dean, all I could think was I hadn't gone anywhere, so why doesn't it feel right? So real fast I say, "The 'artist biz' is fine. Got some of my paintings up in a coffeehouse."

Katy drifts past, not looking at Dean. "My nude was up there," she says, on her way to another conversation. "Five hundred bucks a collector paid for it." We both watch her walk by, watching where she was for a moment. Dean's face twists, like he's in the middle of some kind of decision.

Then he high-fives me: "You sold one! Congratulations. Who bought it?"

"Didn't leave a name. Probably some pervert hot for Katy's body," I say.

Katy screams over, "He's an important collector!"

I raise my eyebrows at Dean.

"Five hundred bucks is five hundred bucks," Dean says. "Right?"

It's rent, it's gas, it's groceries, it's more paints, it's whatever, but it's never five hundred bucks, not the way he means, not how his father's always saying crap like, "The best thing your money can do for you is make more money." The best thing my money does is pay a bill or two.

"Pervert money is as good as any," Dean says. "Seriously. Congratulations."

"They told me to bring in more." Actually, when the lady gave me the money, she said I had "loads of raw talent, lots of energy," and she touched my arm a lot, like she wanted something to rub off on her. Hearing someone say all that was better than going to Harvard. But I couldn't say so to Dean.

"They condemn that rathole you're living in?" he asks.

"Hey—I pay top dollar for that rathole."

There's a moment of silence and I know he's going to say something about Katy, and I don't want to hear it but I can't think of what else to say.

"You know I don't care about you and Katy," he says. "I mean, maybe I did a little, but now I don't."

I look over to where she's standing, beautiful the way she's leaning, one foot propped up against the wall so her knee's sticking out, talking and waving her arms; I almost know what she's saying just by the way her arms move. I can't decide if it would matter to me if he cared. Like Katy said, Dean never cares much about anything. It's all a long joke to him, that kind of joke that's a story that goes on and on and on and ends with a lame punchline that makes everyone groan. That's what everything is to Dean, a shaggy dog story.

"Anyway, high school's over," he says. "And none of it mattered anyway. Like, who remembers what grade they got in chemistry?"

"I flunked," I say. "Big old F."

"Well, I don't remember what I got," he says.

"C," I say. "You were sure it was going to be an F, and then somehow it was a C."

"Lucky, I guess." He looks away. I know we're both remembering how we saw his father that afternoon in the chemistry lab, his back seeming to fill up the door's glass window. We watched as his father moved from the door to the lab table; his arms windmilling inches from a rack of test tubes, our teacher standing, putting up both hands as if a gun were pointed at him. That's when Dean turned away and slammed into the bathroom down the hall; I heard him banging a stall door like he wanted to rip it off the hinges. I watched long enough to see our teacher pull a red pen out of his labcoat pocket, reach for his gradebook. Dean and I had been lab partners, cheating off each other to get the same test scores. But his father didn't know that. When I went in the bathroom to find Dean, he was sitting on the radiator looking at the dull grey sky out the window. "Do you think I'll end up being like that?" he asked me. I told him no, but I was lying.

"So, how's school?" I ask. I don't like anything we've talked about so far, and I don't much like this either, but I can't forget that he went away and I didn't.

"School sucks," he says. "I'm not going back. I'm an artist like you, living the good life. Wine, women, and song."

"That's my life," I say. "That's it, exactly."

"Actually," and he lowers his voice so I have to bend close to hear: "I never went."

"Went where?"

"To Harvard. I mean, I went, but I didn't go." He looks around, thinking someone might be listening. "Existential, huh?"

"What are you talking about?"

"I got there and un-enrolled. Got a tuition refund. Hung out at Cape Cod."

"Cape Cod!"

"It's only a few hours from Boston. No big deal." Dean stretches long and hard and cracks his back. I think about his father and all that money, calling in favors from assholes who needed their butts kissed sweet and good, as he put it. This is way more than totaling your new car and getting another one, and Dean doesn't look like he gives a whatever. I don't know if he's lying because it's the way Dean always looks, like maybe it's the truth and maybe it isn't, but he can't be bothered.

"What'd you do at Cape Cod?"

"Made pizzas. You know they put clams on pizza out there? Disgusting."

"I don't get it," I say.

"What's not to get?" he asks. "It's simple. I didn't feel like it."

Without thinking, I say, "But it was Harvard."

"Fuck Harvard," he says. "What's Harvard?"

He seems to think I'm going to answer, but how do you answer that question? So he answers it himself: "Nothing but a bunch of buildings," and there's another empty silence and I'm thinking how I saw the score on T.V. for the Harvard-Yale football game, and how I've never been out of Detroit except for track meets and one week snowmobiling with Dean up north, how Boston and Cape Cod and even New York are just stupid places on a map to me.

"What about your father?" I ask.

He stretches, lifts his arms high above his head, and for a moment I think he has no shadow, but then I see it against the wall—it was just a trick of light that made me think it was gone. "Fuck the old guy," he says. His voice shakes, but it firms up as he keeps going: "Look, there's nothing more to say," and he smiles that quick brilliant smile that everyone loves, that I knew how to imitate to make everyone laugh. "I thought you'd get it, I mean everybody knew you weren't going to college, and the world didn't come to an end. What's college? What's the point?" Same stupid too-fast smile, then he slams his fist into the wall. "What's the point of any-thing? Christ. You *are* going to be a famous artist, aren't you?" he says. "I can't believe someone paid real money for one of your crap-ass paintings. Jesus H. Christ."

It's all-of-a-sudden between CDs, so everybody hears. I don't know what I'm thinking will happen, but nothing happens. The music starts up again just as suddenly, some song I don't know, don't like, will always remember.

"Hey, I'm kidding," Dean says quickly. "You know that."

I look over at Katy. I'm thinking she'll have that look on her face like if there was a knife around she'd be sliding it slow and straight across Dean's neck right now, but that's not at all how she looks. Her head's tilted, she's frowny, and it's like she's staring into a microscope, trying to see all the way down through the cells and into the atoms. That's exactly when I know it's the famous artist she wants to love forever, not me.

Dean says it again: "I swear I was kidding. You know I'm your biggest fan."

I should talk to Katy, I should say, "Remember? Someone bought my painting," I should tell her how L.A. is the place now and we could live on the beach and watch the sun fall into the ocean every night, that really why she loves me is because I'm not them.

I should tell Katy it's because of that phone call, the only one after Dean went away. It started with the phone ringing when Katy and I were getting hot in bed—I'd just come from hanging my paintings at the coffee-house—and I let the phone ring like ten times, and it kept going and Katy said, "Just answer it," and it was Dean launching into how great Boston was, how the people he was meeting all got like 1600 on their SATs or whatever, and how there was a room in the library named after his grandfather. He went fast like he was reading off a list. Katy twisted out of my arms and headed into the bathroom and the shower came on. On and on Dean went, barely a breath until suddenly he stopped. What did he think I would say to all that? Then he said, "There's some guy who wants me to backpack through Europe with him this summer." There was a pause and I could hear something like the sound of him breathing. "I don't know," he said, "this guy's way into art. All those museums." Another pause. "I don't know," he said again, "what do you think? Should I?"

I was going to answer—I really was—but then Katy poked her head through the bathroom door while the shower hissed behind her and steam rolled across the room. She called, "Do you have a clean towel?"

"What?" I said, tilting the phone towards her.

She called louder, "Do you have a clean towel?"

Dean said, "Asshole," and hung up. But then so was he only I never got the chance to say so because he never called me again.

Dean grabs my sleeve, holds on for a moment then lets go. He says, "Eighth grade—who helped you throw the stinkbomb in the principal's office when they wouldn't let you enter that picture of the naked chick in the school art show? That was me, thank you very much."

We were suspended for two days. It was supposed to be five, but his father raised hell. We waited in hard chairs across from the secretaries breathing smelly air through wet handkerchiefs while his father screamed at the principal behind closed doors. Dean had never been suspended before, but of course I already had a folder an inch thick because there was no one raising hell for me. It took a long time, and I remember watching the late afternoon shadows shimmy up the walls, and finally his father strode out of the office, buttoning his overcoat, pulling on his tight-fitting leather gloves, and he took us to his men's club for steaks and poured each of us a glass of red wine, my first time to drink with an adult. We clinked glasses: "To art and artists," he said, and men kept coming up to our table all night, shaking his hand, slapping his back, talking about things and people and places Dean and I didn't know, and we had to sit quiet and straight until he'd point to Dean and say, "This is my boy," and Dean would smile, shake someone's hand, say, "Nice to meet you, sir." I ate my steak so fast that Dean's father ordered me another because I was that hungry and it was that good. And I bet mostly because it was his club and he could do whatever the hell he wanted.

"C'mon," Dean says. "It was a joke. Promise."

He puts out his hand for me to shake, which I do. He's got kind of a fish handshake that makes it feel like nothing's really been settled, like we haven't agreed on anything. "No hard feelings?" he asks.

Everything is so damn easy for him. I shake my head, echo, "No hard feelings," and then I start unbuttoning my flannel shirt while he tells me about some waitress at Cape Cod who'd only do it with guys who were six feet or taller—but not with Dean because he's five-eleven, and he begged, but she kept saying, "Six feet tall's the rule," and I've got my flannel shirt off and tied around my waist when he catches onto the T-shirt, and he shuts up.

"Then what?" I ask.

"Isn't that—?" but he doesn't finish. His eyebrows tilt in and his eyes narrow. I pretend I'm thinking the tag's showing, so I reach back to tuck it in. Then I bend my neck slow like there's a deep kink I'm working out. It's this one moment when I know what's going on and they don't that I think is how it will be every day when I'm a famous artist.

Dean's about to go back to the waitress in Cape Cod, about to tell me if he finally got it from her or what, and that would put everything back where it was—but with a twist because I'm wearing the shirt. But Dean doesn't say anything, which isn't what he's supposed to do, so I say, "So what happened?" and I push my hand through my hair, like I'm thinking that's why he's staring at me.

"That's my shirt."

I get that look on my face, the look I give people when I say I'm going to be a famous artist and I see their smirky smiles because they're thinking, Assistant manager at Jiffy Lube, assistant manager at the Twin Oaks Cineplex, assistant manager for life, not even frigging all-the-way manager. It's a fuck-you look, but more than that; it's, Fuck you because we both know you're planning to remember me so you can tell everyone you knew me when and make it sound like we were best buddies. "This?" I say. "This is my shirt." It's like my words are slow bubbles coming up from under-water. I try to remember how I looked in the mirror, how putting on the shirt made it mine. In the car Katy raked her fingernails across it thinking it was me, my shirt, and it was until now.

Dean didn't care about anything, anyway; all the crap he had—cars, clothes, girlfriend, father—was nothing but water whirling down a toilet to him.

He plucks at the sleeve. "You think you're so great, being this starving artist living in the slums, getting your pictures up at coffeehouses. No one makes you go to college, no one cares if you pass chemistry. You think you're so great." He yanks at the neckline, and I twist backwards, slapping his arms away, but then he grabs me again, clutching handfuls of the shirt. He's breathing real fast: "You don't know what it's like for the rest of us, for me. It's not fair."

"Let go."

He tightens his grip. "You idiot. It's not the shirt, keep the fucking shirt. I don't care about the shirt."

"You don't care about jack-shit," I say, "that's your problem," and I grab his arms, try prying them away, but he's really got a hold. "You never went near Cape Cod, did you?"

Katy's not that far across the room, and there's no way she hasn't heard it all, and I have to go explain to her, but Dean keeps going: "What are you trying to prove with my girlfriend, my shirt? So you want to be me? Fine, be me," and he pushes me back so I knock up against the wall, and he's pulling his sweater over his head, popping the buttons of his jeans, poking one foot against the heel of the other foot to tug off his shoes, throwing his clothes at me, sweater, shoes, jeans, socks, underwear; he's standing naked, his shadow behind him bigger than he is, and there're clothes in a pile all around me, and everyone's stopped talking to turn and stare—they're so startled they won't even whisper—and Dean leans in close and says, "You want to be me? Well, do you?"

Of course I shake my head; everyone's watching, no one's breathing. It feels like the very end of my life.

Dean shivers, tucks his arms around his chest. He talks slow: "Okay, be me. It was my father who bought your crap-ass painting. It's in the back of our coat closet. That's what it's like being me," and he sets the words out there like they're on a table.

"Liar," I say, which makes him laugh.

"Red background," he says. "Crossed legs. Arm behind the head. Open mouth," and that's it, everything I am reduced to paint on a canvas. He goes on: "Now you know it's nothing, just my father taking over."

"Five hundred bucks is five hundred bucks," I say.

He laughs again. "Are you that stupid?" and he walks away, people stepping aside to let him pass, staring after him, staring at me, taking nervous sips of their beer.

What is there to do? I pick up the pieces of his clothes, one by one, folding them, until they're a neat little pile in my arms. Katy's watching where Dean went, and she should've come over by now; everyone's buzzing, but no one's saying anything directly to me. It's like when they all were getting their college letters or college test scores or college roommate names, how they'd stop talking when I came up. Did I think anything could ever change that?

I'm holding the clothes, looking at Katy looking at where Dean was. Her eyes are shiny-wet, deer-like, and one tear breaks loose and rolls down her cheek and then another. People group around her now, touching her shoulder, whispering in her ear; she's swallowed up by them so I can't see her.

She's sure it's about her, everyone thinks so. Maybe Dean does too.

But it's Dean's father going into that coffeehouse, leaving his car double-parked on the street, the engine running; once inside, the quick smile as he points to the first one he sees, not noticing it's the best, then pulling out his money clip from his pants pocket; tossing the painting into the back seat, maybe forgetting about it for a couple days, then taking it inside to shove in a closet, forgetting about it all over again.

That five hundred bucks bought me a bunch of paints, paid my rent. People see you sold one, then they think they better buy one too, and then the manager tells you to bring in more, that people are asking, people are talking, you've got a buzz. Then there's an article in the arts weekly, then the Sunday Arts section, *Detroit* magazine, and then you're in New York.

That's when Dean's father digs out that painting, shows off the signature to friends at a party. Dean says, "That guy used to steal clothes from us," and everyone laughs, exclaims, "How delightful, how eccentric, how charming, how quirky," and I'm the famous artist.

Does it matter how it begins?

No one's watching, so I head to the door, Dean's clothes still bundled tight in my arms. What the hell. It feels like something's over now anyway, like being released from a promise that everyone thought you'd made.

Outside, the snow's coming faster, looking like it's on its way to being the second big snowstorm of the season, like spring is forever-away. But I like snow and how it covers everything up, like those ugly gray sludge piles across the street from my apartment. They look just fine under a layer of fresh snow. Really, there's nothing like a big snow to turn everything glittery white again, and that's what I'm thinking, but just as I get to my car, a snowplow rumbles by, pushing all the snow to one side and clearing the road to bare pavement. My car's blocked in, and there's nothing I can do now but get the shovel from the trunk and dig like hell.

Kate Pullinger
The Visits Room

Every time I visit James in prison he tries to have sex with me. The visits room is crowded, overheated in winter, airless in summer. We are allowed to sit on the same side of the table. We start by holding hands, we progress to kissing, he places one hand on my breast. It makes him die, I can feel it, he would give everything away if he could just have me. Before I come to visit I get a letter from him; he tells me not to wear any knickers, to wear a big, long skirt. To sit on his lap, my skirt covering us, and then to move in a slow way that will let him get inside me.

We never quite make it. An officer always walks by just when I think it's about to happen, and they always make a joke about us trying to have sex and James always denies it and gets angry and I slide off his lap and back onto the chair next to his. Once the officer goes past James always, always, looks as though he is going to cry. But he never does. And neither do I.

✳

James killed his brother-in-law. It is an unalterable fact. Bobby was a violent man. We knew he used to hurt James' sister Maria. It wasn't straightforward slapping around, we knew he tortured her, the marks on her body showed us. Finally, after years of it, Maria threw Bobby out. James was relieved, we all were. We thought a happy ending had arrived.

But then Maria came round one Sunday. She looked terrible, her hair a wild mess, her face bruised and scratched. Weeping, she told us that Bobby had broken into the house and raped her, and gone off with their two kids. As she spoke I felt James' body grow tense. He had an idea of where Bobby had gone, I don't know how. So James went round to try and get the kids back, and they got into a fight, and James killed Bobby. He crushed his skull with a heavy old mirror that Bobby's new girlfriend had hanging on the wall. He drove Maria's kids to our place. Maria was happy to see her children, but I could tell something had gone wrong. James turned toward the front door again. I asked him where he was going. "To the police," he said, and I knew what had happened.

James was in prison on remand for a long time. When his trial finally took place we realised he would lose. We hoped for a verdict of manslaughter. He had no previous convictions, he had never been in trouble before. But they said he had gone round intending to kill Bobby, and I guess he had. He was convicted of murder and got life. He was given a life sentence.

The visits room is very bare. The tables and chairs are battered and old, the walls are grey, the barred perspex windows are filthy. An officer sits at a table on a raised platform. We are watched. Other prisoners have noisy, sociable visits but James and I often sit in silence. It is difficult to talk; I feel that James has himself only barely held in. When I'm there he will sit and clutch my hand and stare into my eyes for the whole two hours we are allowed together. He would never have done that outside.

I brought my sister Maureen to see James one day. At the next table another lifer, a young, good-looking lad, was being visited by his family. I saw him looking at Maureen, and she noticed too. They got to talking, we pushed our tables closer. James and I held hands while Maureen had a laugh with Ian. Now Maureen goes to visit Ian on her own. She says thirteen to sixteen years seems like a long time to wait for a man. She laughs and says how can you know you love someone without being able to fuck them? And then she blushes and looks at me and says she is sorry. I don't care. It's good to have someone to make the journey to visits with.

James tells me that Ian is a nice lad. He killed a woman during the course of a burglary. He was sixteen and he was not expecting anyone to be home. He graduated from young offenders prison to adult prison a few years back. James says Ian was just a burglar and never meant anyone any harm. James is changing; before, he would have rattled his newspaper and said he thought boys like Ian should be strung up.

✳

The visits room is not a good place to conduct a marriage. It is not a good place for anything except smoking and drinking cups of tea. James and I got married when we were both twenty-four, old enough and not that young anymore. We were happy to be married, we felt we belonged together. We used to have a good time with flying diaphragms, mucking up with spermicide, condoms that refused to unroll. Then we decided to have a child and we binned all the birth control. But no luck. I thought we should go to the doctor and get some help, see where the problem lay, but James didn't want to. He said we should just keep on having sex, and if I got pregnant that was good, but otherwise it was not meant to be. He said he didn't want to find out if it was his fault, or mine, something gone wrong inside one of us, something sour, barren, unfit. This way we are in it together, it is no one else's business, and I suppose, in a way, he is right.

Now that James is in prison I'm glad we don't have children. It would have made it all much worse. In the visits room the children often cry, and their upsets make it harder for the adults, I can see that. There is a little roped off area where volunteers play with the kids while their mothers spend some time with the dads. Someone has tried to make it cheery, but they haven't succeeded. The wall murals look gruesome, the plastic toys dirty.

I brought James' sister Maria to the prison once. It wasn't a good visit. Maria cried the whole time, she went on and on about her fatherless children, about being on her own, about how much she misses Bobby. I was stunned. James is her brother. I would not have brought her if I knew she would say that. James sat pushed back in his chair with a completely blank expression on his face while Maria's despair rolled over him in waves. You killed my husband, she said, plain as day, everyone sipping their tea and laughing together in the crowded, smoky, hot, visits room. James said nothing, but I could see him harden, I could see him drying out and stiffening in his chair. Maria's voice got louder and louder. You murdered my husband, she said again and again. I couldn't listen to any more: I hit her, I slapped her across the face. She stopped talking, stopped sobbing, and just sat there on the filthy, lop-sided metal chair. I looked up and saw the officer watching us, a look of contempt and disgust on his face. Two bitches and a murderer and their sordid argument. At that moment I wished we all three were dead.

✳

Last month I was invited to go to the prison for a Lifer Family Day. I received a leaflet in the post, inviting me. There would be speakers talking about life sentences and the system for lifers, there would be time for both inmates and their families to ask questions. There would be an opportunity to have lunch with James. A whole day together, an entire day spent sitting in the visits room. The leaflet said it was a hard-won opportunity and not to be missed.

We are allowed two visits per month if I go on the weekend, four if I can get there on weekdays although that's difficult. The Lifer Family Day would not be counted against our visits. I saw James a few weeks before and I asked him if he thought I should bring his parents, perhaps his brother William who still talks about trying to mount an appeal. James said no, he was looking upon it as a chance to spend time with me. I could not help it, but part of me was filled with dread. A whole day in that room, a whole day of being next to James but no chance to be with him. Of course I agreed to go, I sent in my name, and I travelled up to the prison first thing that day.

When I arrived the visits room was already crowded. The tables we usually sat at had been pushed to one side and rows of seats were arranged in a large semi-circle. There was an overhead projector and a lectern and a number of men in suits. I found a chair in the back row. We heard the keys and key-chains rattling and the prisoners' door opened and James and the other men came through. When he saw me he smiled and I felt the same searing pain that I always do. Sometimes I dream that when I leave the visits room James comes with me. We are outside in the fresh air, and the flowers, and the breeze.

James sat down beside me. The speakers started speaking, putting diagrams up on the overhead projector, explaining how a life sentence is served. The basic principle is that everything takes a very long time. The average length currently served is 15.4 years, but some men are in for much longer. Years in one institution are followed by years in another institution.

In between there are one or two meetings. The speakers used words like sentence planning, sentence review, even probation once or twice. It was very absorbing for the first hour. James kept one hand on my knee and the other around my waist and when I looked at him his face seemed younger, more serene. We had a tea break. Maureen was there along with Ian's family, so we got together and had a chat. James was talkative, relaxed, nearly effusive. He told one or two stories. The speakers started up again, and then it was time for lunch.

It was wonderful to eat with James again. I had not seen him eat for such a long time; we had not eaten a meal together since he had left for the police station that day. Someone had gone to a lot of trouble over the food, there were sandwiches, bits of pie, pastries and cake. The mood in the visits room was slightly euphoric, everyone piled their plates high. Ian's brother fetched us pitchers of water, pots of tea. It was like being at a banquet, it was like our wedding all over again. James smiled and ate, and then smiled with food in his teeth. He kept one arm around me. I fed him triangles of sandwiches. We toasted the table with our mugs.

In the afternoon, the speakers started up again. The overhead projector went on, and one of the deputy governors began to talk. The room had become warmer still. People had urgent questions, lots of hands were waving, prisoners argued their side passionately. But in the back row where James and I were sitting it was a different story. In the back row couples were kissing. We had eaten together and now we wanted more.

I got onto James lap, like I had done countless other times. He buried his face in my shirt, opening one or two buttons with his teeth. I could smell him and beneath his prison smell of tobacco and staleness, there was the smell of James. I couldn't believe what was happening. There were no officers strolling up and down the aisles, we were as far away from an officer as we had ever been. I smoothed my skirt and kept my face turned forward so I at least looked as though I was listening. James fumbled, and it was awkward, I had to lift my weight from one leg to another. But then—I had to turn, I had to bend slightly, it was a bit painful—it happened. I could hear James trying to control his breathing. A few heads turned, and quickly faced away again. I felt him, I felt it all, it was piercing and complete. James buried his face in my back and bit me hard instead of crying out.

I slid off his lap. Our smell was drowned by cigarettes, food and sweat. There were disapproving glances, but I didn't care. This was all we had to hope for, this was all we would get. The afternoon ended, James held me tight in his arms, and I left.

✳

I know that it is wrong to kill. I know that Bobby should not have died. James is in prison now, we are paying for Bobby's death. It is a huge debt, and his sentence is very long. But James is just James and I am his wife and the visits room is our asylum.

Jessie Seigel

The Eunuch God

What time is it? Marty opened his eyes. He checked the clock. It read twelve. *Midnight or noon?* He stretched an arm out from the bed, cracked the blinds and squinted at daylight. *Noon. Head like a balloon. Mouth dry. No energy. Not to turn over, even. Not to get out of the bed.*

The phone rang. Marty reached over and knocked the receiver out of its cradle. The receiver fell, dangling by its cord a few inches from the floor. Marty could hear a small, distant voice coming from the other end. "Hello? Hello? Martin! Are you there?"

Why did the mountain climber answer the phone? Because it was there. Why do I have to talk to people just because they want to talk to me?

"Martin! I *know* you're there."

Why did I get involved with Marlene? Because she was there. And now she's there again. With a sigh, Marty hoisted the phone cord and put the receiver to his ear. He didn't say anything. Just lay there, listening.

"Martin? I can hear you breathing you little shit. If you don't say something in 10 seconds the police will be there in 60."

Marty hesitated. Then, very slowly, very cautiously, he whispered into the phone. "What?"

"Have you got it?"

Marty lay on his side and thought about the situation. Marlene had given him some rocks to fence. And he'd fenced them. But then he'd lost the money. *On what? A horse race?* It was hard to remember in the mornings. *In a crap game? No. On a horse race. Harness. Advice: never bet the harness. Stick to the real thing.*

"Have you got it?"

"I don't think so clearly in the mornings," Marty mumbled into the phone.

"Listen, you louse. Don't think you can stall me. Don't think you can cheat me. 'Cause I know some guys. You know what I mean? I *know* some guys."

"Don't get hysterical," Marty said. He propped himself up on one elbow. "Don't get hysterical. I just need a little something to clear my head. Hang on a sec."

Marty hauled himself out of bed and went to the door of his apartment. It was one in a set of ramshackle garden apartments without gardens, and when he opened the door he peered first to the right and then to the left along the walkway which fronted the various abodes. His neighbor's milk had been delivered, was sitting in front of her door. She hadn't collected it yet. No one in sight. He furtively ran a hand through his hair and, stepping barefoot out onto the pavement, slipped over and swiped the bottle. He looked up as he headed back to his own place and saw her mail had been delivered too. *Why not?* He shrugged and pulled the mail out of the box, carrying it with the milk bottle.

As he went into his apartment, his neighbor's door opened and Marty looked back. The woman's kid—what was her name?—Lurleen?—was looking over at him. Staring at him with her huge solemn eyes. He hid the milk and the mail behind his back, grinned at her, and winked. Then he went in and shut his door.

He could hear Marlene swearing on the phone. He picked it up. "I'm still here. Just give me a sec to get it together." He put the phone down again, popped open the milk bottle and spread his newly acquired mail out on the table.

What's here? Marty turned the first envelope over in his hand. Opened it. *A check. That looks promising. The neighbor's alimony? Child support? The check would keep him in cigarettes. But it wouldn't satisfy Marlene. What else?* He took a swig from the milk bottle and rubbed his stomach. There were some bills—phone, electric, milk company, loan company— nothing helpful there. Some advertisements and solicitations—one for orphans in Mexico, one for some born-again Christian outfit raising money to send missionaries off to the heathens in the orient.

There was a magazine. Marty flipped through it. He stopped for a moment at an ad for Virginia Slims with a sophisticated career dame angle—for independent career women—that sort of thing. He moved on and stopped again, this time at an article about a traveling exhibit of Olmec artifacts found in Guatemala. There was a big photograph of one statue which was missing from the exhibit. It had been stolen some months before. Marty stared at the photo of the stone god, a rounded figure with an elongated forehead. The god was peculiar though. It had a hole where the bellybutton would be—so there was some effort to be anatomically cor- rect—but it had neither breasts nor a penis.

So what is it? A man, a woman, a Eunuch? Marty scratched his head. The Eunuch God. He took another swig of the milk, gave a satisfied sigh, and picked up the phone.

"So, Marlene. What's up?"

"Don't you give me 'What's up' you son-of-a-bitch. Don't you spin me some story when you've been avoiding my calls for days. You just tell me you've got it."

"Got what?" Marty said.

"My MONEY!" she screamed.

Marty pulled the phone away from his ear. "Shh," he soothed. "I got it. I invested it."

There was sudden silence on the other end of the phone. "You invested it? Like what? In stocks?"

"No. Not stocks."

"So what do you mean 'invested'?"

Marty picked up the solicitation from the born-again Christians. "I met a guy," he said.

Marlene snorted. "Met a horse, more likely."

"No. No, seriously," Marty said. "I met a guy. He's a preacher. You know, one of those born-again, fire and brimstone types. Anyway, he's got this obsession with the Olmec civilization."

"The what?"

"The Olmec civilization."

"What the hell is that?"

Marty smiled, beginning to enjoy himself. "Jeez, Marlene," he said scornfully, "Don't you ever read a book or a magazine? The Olmecs were an ancient civilization that spanned Mexico, Guatemala, and Honduras. They predated the Mayans and the Incas."

"Then they're dead," said Marlene. "Like you're gonna be if you don't stop stalling."

"I'm not stalling. I'm trying to tell you, aren't I? This guy has an obsession. He's dying to obtain an artifact that he thinks will help him to convert some Indian tribe in Central America. He thinks he can use it to get them to stop fornicating."

"To stop what?" Fornication was not a word Marty had ever used. 'Fuck,' 'ball,' 'having sex,'—very occasionally, 'making love,'—but never 'fornicate.'

"Fornicating," Marty said. "You see, this particular artifact is a statue. It's the Eunuch God."

"What are you pulling?"

"No, really. If you pick up a copy of *Life,* you'll see it yourself. It's a small stone statue missing a major part. It was supposed to be part of a traveling exhibit from the National Mexican Museum, but it was stolen." Marlene's silence sounded promising, and Marty continued. "This guy really wants the statue and I've convinced him that I can get it for him on the Q.T. But, you've got to spend money to make money, right? I had to lay out enough to put on the right kind of show for him. You know that."

"So what's the game?" Marlene said cautiously. "And what's it worth?"

"I figure it's worth at least five hundred thousand." Marty could hear the dollar signs clicking in her greedy little brain. "The game is simple. He and I each put up half, to show our good faith, to be held by a third, neutral party."

"That old gem? What is he, straight off the farm?"

"There's one born every minute." Marty looked at the Virginia Slims ad in the magazine. "I figure that you will come in as an art dealer from New York," he said. "You know, someone sophisticated, classy, someone with the connections to get the item. By the time he figures out he's been had, he'll be so far in it, he won't be able to tell anybody without incriminating himself."

"So what did you spend the money on?" Marlene said.

"Well, you know. I had to set myself up too, didn't I? As a dealer posh enough to have connections with a posh dealer like you...the works. Then there's the downpayment on the five hundred thousand. We've already put that aside."

"O.K.," Marlene said. "O.K. I'm in. When do we meet to plot it out?"

"Give me a few days to finish priming him."

"O.K." Her tone was grudging, but she accepted it.

Marty hung up the phone. *Right. That should hold her for the moment.* He felt exhausted. He lay back down on the bed and closed his eyes. Through the walls he heard his neighbor yelling at her kid and the muffled voice of the kid answering.

"I ask you to do a simple thing," said the mother. "What are you, a moron? You can't even do a simple thing like get the milk? Where's the God-damn milk?" Marty strained to make out the little girl's answer.

"But, mama, I did. I went for the milk. It wasn't there. Please, mama." Marty put the pillow over his head to shut them out and get some more sleep.

✳

"Please mama." The little girl pled. "The milkman hasn't come yet."

"What do you mean the milkman hasn't come yet? It's 12:00 in the God-damn afternoon. What are we gonna do without milk?" The mother, looking haggard, stared blankly out the window. She was still in her nightgown, her hair tangled, sticking up oddly on one side and pressed down against her head on the other, as if she'd slept hard on that side the whole night.

"It's o.k., Mama," said the little girl, taking her mother's hand. "We don't need the milk anyway."

The mother turned to look at her. The child was stick thin. And pale. It made her gray eyes look large in her head. And solemn. It's not natural, the mother thought. A child's face should have laughter in it. The mother cupped a hand to the little girl's cheek for a moment.

"Of course we need milk, Lurleen. You're growing. Your bones need milk. I need milk," she muttered. "I need milk. I need milk for my...for my God-damn coffee." She poured herself a drink from a half-empty bottle on the table.

"I"m making coffee, mama." Lurleen tried to take the glass away.

"Go away Lurleen." The mother waved a hand at the girl. "I'm getting ready to call those bastards." She took a couple of shots of clear liquid courage, picked up the telephone, and dialed a number. It rang. A man answered.

"Borden Company."

"Where the hell's my damn milk?" she shouted into the telephone.

"Excuse me? Who is this calling, please?"

"You know who's calling. The same one's been calling for the last three weeks. I pay for milk. Where's my damn milk?"

"Madame, there is no need for profanity."

"Profanity?" The mother was working herself into a rage. "Profanity? You haven't heard profanity. You don't know what profanity is. I've been calling for weeks and you bastards keep telling me that you've been delivering the milk but I haven't got any milk. I don't have money to waste on this crap. I don't have time for this crap. I—"

"One moment, Madame. I'll get the manager."

"You do that," the mother said. "You just do that. Yeah. Let *him* tell me why I don't get my God-damn milk." The man was gone from the other end of the phone. "Let him tell me why I'm not getting any checks. Why my ex doesn't answer my calls." The mother poured herself another shot and nodded to herself. "Tell me why I got laid off. Why I'm living in this rat-trap. Why life is just one big sewer-hole. Just tell me why. God-damn why." She stared out the window again.

"Hello? This is Mr. Williamson, the manager. Can I help you?"

"Never mind," said the mother, and she hung up the phone.

She finished the drink and, leaning her head against the back of the couch, closed her eyes. The little girl brought a pillow and pushed it behind the mother's head. The woman opened her eyes for a moment. "Tell me one of your stories Lurleen. You're so good with stories." She closed her eyes again. Lurleen sat at her feet and held her hand.

"Once upon a time," said the little girl, stroking her mother's hand, "There was a ram that lived on a green mountain. It ate grass and basked in the sun, and wandered up and down the mountain hillside, and was generally happy—except when men came around because that usually meant that they wanted to kill the ram and feed it to their god. So when men came, it would run and hide in the forest until they left.

"But one day, the ram saw a man and his son climbing up the mountain and he saw men at the bottom of the mountain shaking their heads sadly and saying how the father was going to sacrifice the son to his god, and how sad it was, especially since it was the man's only son.

"The ram thought, better you than me for a change. But somehow he felt sad too, and curious to see what would happen, and so he followed them up the mountain.

"When they got to the top, the father and the son built an altar and the son lay down on it, and the father raised his knife. At that moment, the ram felt a wave of relief that it wasn't him up there on the altar. And for that moment, he felt safe and comfortable, and he sighed and thought, 'God's in his Heaven. All's right with the world.'

"Then, all of a sudden, an angel called out the name of the father, telling him not to kill his son, and pointing out the ram. The ram, startled, caught his horns in the thicket he was hiding in. The ram started struggling wildly, trying to get free of the thicket. And while he was struggling, he asked himself, was this the bad luck of horns and thickets? Or his own stupidity for following the men up the mountain? Or the anger of the man's god? And when they caught him and bound him and carried him up to the altar, he just looked up at the sky and thought: why?"

Lurleen's mother patted her on the head. "You don't tell very comforting stories Lurleen," she said. And then she fell asleep.

✳

There was a low knock at the door. Lurleen got up and answered it. It was the milkman.

"Can I speak to your mother, little girl," he said.

Lurleen looked at him with her big gray eyes. The child could hear the desperation in his voice. "My mother's asleep," she said.

"Can you get her?" said the man.

"She isn't well," said Lurleen. "I don't want to wake her."

"I don't care, wake her!" the man said vehemently, and there was something scary in his eyes. But then, he saw the sudden alarm in the little girl and he said, more softly, pleading, "I didn't mean to scare you. I don't mean anything. I just want to talk to her. I just want to ask her something. Please. I need to talk to your mother." He took off his hat and held it in his hand. "Please." The little girl continued to stand in the doorway and stare quietly up at him. When she did not move or respond, the man turned, sat down on the stoop, and put his head in his hands.

Then Lurleen came out of the house and shut the door. She came and sat down on the stoop next to the man, and looked quietly up at him until he took his hands away from his face.

"Why is your mother out to get me?" he said. When she didn't answer, he stared into the distance. "I was doing o.k. You know? I mean, I had a little trouble a lot of years ago, and for a long time after that it was really hard to get a job. Then I got this job. And it was good. I liked it. Clean white uniform. Drive around in a truck all day. Fresh air. A little exercise. I met my wife delivering the milk." He smiled a little. "I took her to the hospital in the milk truck when she had the baby. And Borden's is the milk in the baby bottle."

"I never cheated the company. Not by even one bottle of milk." The milkman recounted his actions on his fingers, trying to sort it out. "I come to a house," he said. "I put the bottle of milk on the porch by the door. I leave. At the end of the month I come to settle up. All of sudden the company starts getting calls from this line of apartments. Just one here and there at first, but then more. And then all the time—from your mother. They brought up my old record. They said I was too much trouble. And they 'had to let me go.' Said if I went quietly they wouldn't bring any charges. They wouldn't make any trouble for me elsewhere." The man shook his head. "I should have fought it, I guess. But I've got a wife and kid now, you know?" He turned and looked into Lurleen's eyes. "I swear. I never stole your mama's milk. I've put it on this stoop every single day I was supposed to. So why? Why is your mama making trouble for me?"

Lurleen took the man's hand between her hands and warmed it. Then, to sooth him, she began. "Once upon a time…"

314

Lewis Shiner

Castles Made of Sand

Jim worked for a rental company—jackhammers, barricades, portable signs. He met Karla when he hired some temporaries from the agency she managed. There was just something about her. A sense that if anybody ever sprung her loose she might be capable of almost anything.

They got off to a slow start. She phoned just as he was leaving to pick her up for their first date. She was still at the office and would be there at least another hour. Could she come by and get him instead, late, maybe around nine?

Jim said okay. They had a slightly out-of-kilter dinner during which Karla drank too much wine and Jim too much coffee. When they got back to Jim's apartment, Jim asked her in, little more than a formality. She begged off because of an early meeting the next day.

This is going nowhere, Jim thought. But when he leaned over to kiss her goodnight she met him with her mouth already open.

She was a little overweight, with permed hair somewhere between blonde and brown, almost no color at all. Jim's hair was black and thinning, and some mornings he felt like a toy whose stuffing was migrating out of the arms and legs and into the middle. He was in the final stages of his second divorce. Karla had been married once, briefly, right out of high school. That was now a while ago.

It wasn't like they were laughing all the time. Mostly they talked about things that happened at their jobs. None of that seemed important to Jim. What counted was that, from the first, he could see they needed something in each other.

Karla was in no particular rush to have sex. Still, after a few weeks, it was clearly only a matter of time. Jim carefully raised the subject one night as they lay on his couch, watching old sitcoms on Nickelodeon. Karla thought they should make a big deal out of it, go away for the weekend. Maybe down to Galveston.

The next day she called him at work. She'd just seen a thing in the paper about a sand castle contest at Surfside Beach that coming Saturday. "Sure," Jim said. "Why not?"

✳

It was a two hour drive to Surfside. Jim had been in a fender-bender midweek so they were in a rented Escort, courtesy of his insurance company. They got there around noon. They had to buy a beach parking permit, a little red sticker that cost six dollars and was good through the end of the year.

Jim was uncomfortable in baggy swim shorts and a T-shirt with a hole under one arm. He didn't want to put the sticker on a rent car and not get the rest of the use out of it.

"Maybe you can peel it off when you get home," Karla said.

"Maybe I can't."

"I'll pay for the sticker, how's that?"

"It's not the money, it's the principle."

Karla sighed and folded her arms and leaned back into the farthest corner of the front seat.

"Okay," Jim said. "Okay, for Christ's sake, I'm putting it on."

They turned left and drove down the beach. It was the first of June, indisputable summer. The sun blazed down on big cylinders of brown water that crashed and foamed right up to the edge of the road. The sand was a damp tan color and Jim worried about the car getting stuck, even though there was no sign of anyone else having trouble.

They drove for ten minutes with no sign of a sand castle. The beach was packed with red cars and little kids, college boys with coozie cups and white gimme caps, divorced mothers on green and yellow lawn chairs. Portable stereos played dance music cranked so high it sounded like no more than bursts of static. They drove under a pier with a sign that said, "Order Food Here," only there was no sign of food or anybody to give the order to. The air smelled of creosote and decay and hot sunlight.

Finally Jim saw a two-story blue frame building. A van from a soft-rock radio station was playing oldies at deafening volume and there were colored pennants on strings. It was not the mob scene Jim expected. He parked the Escort on a hard-packed stretch of sand and they got out. The sea air felt like a hot cotton compress. A drop of sweat broke loose and rolled down Jim's left side. He didn't know if he should reach for Karla's hand or not.

There were half a dozen sand sculptures inside the staked-out area. Jim looked up the beach and didn't see anything but more cars and coolers and lawn chairs. "I guess this is it?" he said. Karla shrugged.

At the far end was a life-size shark with a diver's head in its mouth. It had been spraypainted in black and gray and flesh tones, with a splatter of red around the shark's mouth. Next to it a guy and three women were digging a moat. They all had long hair and skimpy bathing suits.

Jim stepped over the rope that separated them. "Is this it?" he said to the guy, half-shouting over the noise from the van.

"There's the big contest over on Galveston. They got architects, you know. Kind of like the professionals, and we're just the amateurs."

"I thought there would be, I don't know. More."

"The Galveston contest is big. They got, like this giant ice cream cone with the earth spilling out of it, they got animals, they got a giant dollar bill made of sand. I mean, perfect."

Jim looked back at Karla, still on the other side of the rope, and then said, "You do this every year?"

"Nah, this is my first time. I thought, what the hey. It's free, anybody can do it. You should enter, you and the lady. They got buckets and shovels and stuff over to the van. Hell, they got twelve trophies and not near that many people. You're sure to win something. There's a good spot right here next to us." He pointed to a stake with an entry number on it, stuck in a flat piece of ground.

"I don't know."

"You should at least go look at the trophies."

Jim nodded and the guy went back to work. It was too early to tell what his was going to look like. Jim stepped back over the rope and he and Karla looked at the other entries. There was only one real castle, pretty nice, looking like it had grown out of the top of a low hill. There was a sea serpent with a long tail. The other two both seemed to be some kind of humanoid figures, slowly emerging from the sand.

"This is kind of a let down," Jim said.

"I wonder what they do with them after," Karla said. Jim could barely hear her over the music.

"What do you mean?"

"They're too high up for the tide to wash them out. That's what's supposed to happen, right? Digging moats and everybody running around, trying to delay the inevitable?"

Jim shook his head. "Want a Coke or something?"

"I don't know. Do you want to enter? Get a trophy?"

"I don't think so."

"Come on. It might be fun."

Jim looked at the flat patch of sand, the stake. He couldn't see it. "I'm going back to the car for a Coke. You want one or not?"

"I guess."

✳

He took his time, trying to shake his mood. Nothing was ever easy. Everything was a struggle, and usually an argument besides. He unlocked the trunk and got two Cokes out of the ice, which was mostly melted already. He popped one and took a long drink, then started back.

He couldn't find Karla at first. He wandered around for a minute or so, then found her down near the water line. She'd taken a bucket and a garden trowel from the contest and built herself an elevated square of sand. On top of that she was dribbling watery mud from the bucket, making little twisty upside-down icicles. He watched her make five or six before she looked up.

She seemed to be blushing. "I used to do this when I was a kid," she said. "I called it the Enchanted Forest."

He squatted on his heels beside her.

She said, "You think this is really stupid, don't you." She took another handful of mud, made another tree.

"No," he said. He looked from the Enchanted Forest to the Gulf and back again. Close to shore the water was brown and foaming, farther out it was a deep shade of blue. He felt something inside him melting and collapsing and washing away.

"No," he said. "It's beautiful."

Phil Shöenfelt

from Junkie Love

This morning, I got a real shock when I went downstairs to use the bathroom. All through the night, Cissy had been having some kind of wild party in her room, the first time in weeks that I've heard any signs of life coming from inside there at all, and I'd passed a couple of her guests on the stairway as I was going out and they were coming in. The girl, Carol, I vaguely knew as some friend or acquaintance of Cissy's from King's Cross, a dire and fucked-up street prostitute who wouldn't hesitate to rip you off or stick a knife in your back if she believed there was anything in the deal for her. I thought of her as a repository for every germ and infestation that the human body was capable of carrying, a walking virus in fact, and that she was hanging out with Cissy right now could mean only one thing: she had come across a large sum of money, probably stolen from some trick, had used it to buy gear, and now needed somewhere quick and convenient where she could shoot-up and where no questions would be asked. The guy she was with was a tall, muscular, black man who I had never seen before, but who I assumed was her boyfriend, or her pimp.

Some more people arrived later, but I didn't see who they were—just heard a lot of laughter and shouting, and I jealously imagined all the heroin and cocaine that was being consumed, while I was again down to my last fifty mls. of methadone. When I went to bed at around three a.m. the party was still in full swing, and occasionally I'd hear loud music and gales of rabid laughter, whenever someone opened the door of Cissy's room to go to the toilet next door. It was as if she'd been resurrected from the dead after weeks of cold abstinence in her bolted and shuttered burrow, and I imagined her regal now, sat up in her bed directing the proceedings, dressed all in white and with her rudely severed hair starting to grow back, at last, in tufts and spikes that stuck out at crazy angles from her head. Above all the noise and mayhem, I'd occasionally hear her raucous cackle, or her voice declaiming excitedly, "Listen, listen to me, will you?!" as she attempted to elucidate a point, or tell some amusing story to her assembled company of cohorts.

This morning, at around ten o'clock, I awoke with the sickness already upon me. Cold and shivering, yet covered in pungent sweat, I finished off the methadone, then shakily made my way downstairs to the bathroom to take a piss. At first, I thought I had walked in on the big black guy taking a bath, and I stepped backwards quickly, my hasty apologies hanging in the silent air like a swarm of hovering flies. But then the split-second glimpse I had caught of him registered itself in my brain: something wasn't quite right, the bathwater was a murky brown colour and the man was motionless, apparently floating, just beneath the surface of the water.

I opened the door again and peeked inside, and this time I was sure. If a black man can be blue, then he was blue, almost dead in the water, with only a faint bubbling around the nose and lips where they broke the surface to indicate that he was still alive. He had shit himself while he was unconscious, and the yellow-brown water had left a tide mark of scum around the sides of the tub, as the level rose and fell slightly with the O.D. victim's unanchored body. I stood there in shock looking down at him, unable to move or act, a prisoner in a frozen, but fleeting, moment of time. The house was silent, no-one was awake yet, and as I stared I found myself focusing on the froth around his nose and mouth, and the sunlight shining on the bubbles that occasionally burst there. Despite his build, and the massive bone plates of his shaven skull, he reminded me of a child who has been crying and whose nose has run, blubbering through the snot and tears, waiting to be coddled and comforted for some unjustified wrong that he feels has been inflicted upon him. Big as he was, he looked oddly vulnerable, naked and afloat in his own diluted shit, also younger now that the hard facial lines had relaxed and softened with his unconscious state—almost as if he were the innocent kid brother of his own streetwise and brutal self. And I experienced some kind of vision, a synaptic flash that exploded in a rapid succession of images, and that revealed to me, in tortuous and precise detail, all the stages of his life so far: the pain and everyday humiliations of childhood; his first sexual encounters; the confusion and anxiety of teenage love; later, the women he had fucked, beaten and exploited; his time in prison; the thefts, robberies and murders he had committed. It was as though our wires had somehow become crossed, and as his physical life trickled slowly away, one part of his soul, or spirit, had jumped across the intervening space and invaded me, like a parasite or virus abandoning the host body it has corrupted and consumed, honing in unswervingly on some new and relatively untapped source of nourishment. Suddenly, I seemed to possess, or was possessed by, an entire catalogue of images that were not mine: a host of memories and sensations that came from the inside of someone else's skull, and that raged within me like a swarm of angry wasps, or some random electrical charge that I had unconsciously attracted. Just for one moment I understood everything perfectly and, as I turned to go, I looked down for one last time on this poor, abandoned carcass, floating in its sea of execrescence. And I realised with a sudden, total and illuminative clarity that this other was also me, and that just as surely as I was playing host to his past lives, he too had welcomed me into the flickering and dying light of his own unconscious brain. And in that same instant, I forgave myself for all my sins and transgressions, as I forgave those who had sinned and transgressed against me, and for one fractured, blinded moment I knew what love was, both for myself and for the other; and reaching down into the stinking brown mess, in which traces of shit and vomit now floated to the surface, I pulled the plug from its hole and allowed the foul water to drain away with a horribly evocative gurgling sound.

I lifted the man up as best I could, sliding his body along the residue of slime that coated the bottom of the porcelain tub. At least now he was in a sitting position, with his arms draped over each side of the bath to prevent him from sliding back down again, and I tried to bring him round by slapping his face, but he was too far gone for this to work. As it was impossible for me to lift him alone, I decided to go for help, and, crossing the first floor landing, I banged loudly on Cissy's door. This was her work, after all, and the least she could do was to clean up her own mess.

After several loud knocks, I heard signs of life coming from within the room and eventually the door was opened, just enough to reveal Cissy's fogged and befuddled eyes, her crazy fright-wig of hair, and the shoulders of the long white nightdress she seemed always to be wearing these days.

"What the fuck do you want? It's not even ten-thirty yet, an' anyway I haven't got any gear to sell, we did it all last night, so piss off and let me get some kip."

Her cold and fucked-up manner sucked the light right out of me, and all the old hatred and poisons came flooding right back in, as I struggled to control the rising tide of rage and violence that threatened to overwhelm me at any moment.

"There's a friend of yours has been blowing bubbles in the bathtub all night. He's just about snuffed it, but if you call an ambulance quick you might still save him. That's if you're in the least bit interested..."

Cissy looked totally confused for a moment, then she opened the door wider, stepped across the landing, and went into the bathroom. Behind her, in the room, I could see four or five tangled bodies, laid out at various angles across the floor and bed, and an assortment of spoons, syringes, soot-blackened silver foil and overflowing ashtrays lying on every available surface. I heard Cissy's sharp intake of breath from the bathroom and a whispered, "Oh Jesus, Brian...," and then she was running back across the landing, screaming at the top of her voice, "Carol, Carol, wake up for fuck's sake, it's Brian, he's O.D.'d, we've got to get help, quick." She pushed past me into the room and shook Carol roughly to wake her.

"Come on, come on, wake up you dozy cow, Brian's O.D.'d, we've got to call an ambulance!"

Carol groggily raised her head. She didn't seem to know where she was or what was happening at all, but Cissy slapped her around the face a few times and pulled her protesting and uncomprehending out of the door and into the bathroom, where the sight of her half-dead boyfriend had the desired effect of bringing her to her senses.

"Oh my Gawd, Brian, Brian," she wailed in a piercing Cockney lament, her voice cracked and shrill, her hands clutching at the air as if there were some invisible enemy, or demon, she was battling with.

"Brian, Brian, oh Brian, wake up please, oh fuck, what am I gonna do, oh Jesus, Jesus, Jesus..."

"Shut up, you stupid bitch, you'll wake the whole street! Listen, we've got to call an ambulance, but I've got to ditch my things first, otherwise we'll all get busted. No, you go and call the ambulance, I'll tidy up and try to keep Brian alive—no, I'll go, fuck all the stuff, he's gonna die if we're not quick." And with that Cissy dashed back into her room, pulled on a coat and, was out of the door in seconds. Carol was holding onto Brian's wrist, still keening and wailing hopelessly, while gradually the other people in Cissy's room were beginning to come round and starting to realise that something was seriously amiss. Quickly, two of them were down the stairs and out the front door, but a third did stay with Carol and began to massage Brian's heart, while all the time she continued to moan and cry. Obviously, after he had O.D.'d, someone had put Brian into a bath full of cold water to try and revive him, before either leaving the premises or going back into Cissy's room and passing out. They must have all been so loaded when it happened that things had got confused—possibly, Cissy and Carol were already unconscious, and if they had woken at any point they proba-bly thought that Brian had just gone to the toilet, or maybe to the all-night garage for cigarettes, and had simply forgotten about him. Now, Carol was wailing and weeping for her lost love, a blood-chilling and desolate sound, and as I made my way slowly back up the stairs, I wasn't sure if what I'd just witnessed was low tragedy, or high farce.

Don Skiles

Chet Baker Dies in Amsterdam

1

Born Chesney Baker, Yale, Oklahoma, December 1929. Yale, Oklahoma, after the Great Crash; Panhandle Land, Dustbowl, Oakie-Arkie Heartland. Bleak December in a place no one forgot.

But Chet went back, even from London.

Bix Beiderbecke, born Davenport, Iowa. "Davenport Blues." Chet Baker cuts an album *Let's Get Lost*. Cowboy.

Front teeth knocked out in alley in San Francisco, 1968, by five tough guys. Two years to return to playing.

2

Begins to play in school, largely self-taught. Small Oklahoma school, wind whistling through interminable winters. Blue wind of highway sound. Tentative notes in small schoolroom, smelling like all schoolrooms smell—chalk, floor wax, books, sweat, kid smell. Band practice.

Army in Oklahoma plays "Taps." Bugle boy. Stillwell. Ft. Sill. Freshly starched, pressed khakis, with knife crease. Oklahoma moon. Oklahoma trumpet. Oklahoma.

Four notes.

3

When he is ten, the Baker family moves to Los Angeles. 1939. It is still a small city, the air clean, the sky bright blue, Mediterranean, palms sharp, black silhouettes, cut-outs. Edge of the continent, the edge of the country, the edge of California.

He goes down to the Pacific, and takes out his horn, and plays while the surf comes in, white like a big head on a beer, warm wind throwing spray in the sun-dry air. Southern California is one word. Sweet. It is very, very sweet.

At night, he comes back down to the beach, and plays and people up on the pier ask about it.

"Who's that playing? Out there..."

"Yeah. It's just some kid. He hangs around. You know how these kids are these days. What can you do?"

"Sounds pretty good to me. How old a kid is he?"

"Like I say, mister, he's a kid."

Chet "Kid" Baker. Give me some sound, over on the pier, down by the lighthouse, down on the beach, down where the surf pounds so loud it's quiet when you're actually down there. Down there. Very blue.

4

At 16, he joins the Army. They hear him play and put him in the band, and he gets some formal musical training. Better yet, they send him to San Francisco, to the Presidio, where the big Sixth Army Band is, one of the best.

There are some very good, cool musicians in this Army band, and they like what Chet sounds like.

"It's different, the kid...you can't pin it down. The tone, eh? It's the tone, the goddamn sweet tone he's got..."

"The wimmen'll fuck him to death."

"Greek god—what's his name? Sang..."

"The Sirens. The fucking Sirens, man. They tied the dudes to the mast so's they couldn't put in, land."

"Nawh. It ain't no siren shit...

He goes down to China Beach, plays in the wet fog early in the morning, with the sun coming up. Crazy.

Oh crazy man. Dig it. "You gotta dig this cat. He's something special."

At San Francisco State, Paul Desmond is playing his sax. Dave Brubeck is listening, nodding, smiling.

In Barksdale, Gerry Mulligan is honking, honking, honking. Cheeks puff way out!

Way out.

5

But they discharge him from the Army. The War is over. America is at peace. The world is free. He is let out.

He smokes grass in San Francisco, and smiles. He has a soft, high-pitched voice, a boy's voice, uncertain, but quick.

He is intelligent.

In 1948, he re-enlists. He's assigned to duty in Los Angeles. He keeps his buddies in the Sixth Army Band, and plays with them in clubs in San Francisco on weekends. He plays small club dates in Los Angeles, even out at the beach–Hermosa, Redondo, Pismo, Venice, Huntingdon. You can smell the salt and sand and sun in his horn. And something else.

Nobody can say what it is, but they want to hear. Need to hear it. Get lost in it, like you can with a girl, down by the beach, in a parked car on a warm night. Get lost in it.

Time stops for a while.

6

Chet gets out in 1952, and plays with Mulligan in Los Angeles, in the first Mulligan "street band," which has no piano. They cut their first records together. In 1974, they will have a Re-union. But now they are young, and riding high.

They play at Howard Rumsey's Lighthouse. The Lighthouse All-Stars. Jazz on a Sunday afternoon, a long, sweet jam session, with the big sun setting into the Pacific.

Shelley Manne hears them play. Dave Brubeck hears them. Paul Desmond hears them. Jimmy Lyons, a San Francisco disc jockey, hears them.

Stan Getz plays with Chet Baker, and teaches him "Stella by Starlight."

In 1953, he is voted Trumpeter of the Year in *Metronome*. The West Coast "cool" jazz sound is established. Predecessor of "laid back" of years to come. It is not Eastern, it is not hard-driving, urban, cocaine speed fucking be-bop. No sir. No way.

7

Baker goes to Europe in 1955, with a new quartet including Dick Zwardik. The group is very successful. But Zwardik dies under mysterious circumstances in Paris.

Baker's drug problem sets in. He later says "Most of the musicians I admired took heroin. I wanted to try it."

He goes to see Balzac's coffee pot in Paris. It is snowing in Paris. There is snow on the towers of Notre-Dame, in the Place de la Concorde, Place Vendome, Place Pigalle. The Boul Mich is a swirl of snow. It is snowing in Clichy, and out beyond the old walls of Paris. Snow.

Stan Getz will go to Denmark in the late Fifties for a similar reason. He will return in 1961 and make a landmark album, *Focus*, with Eddie Sauter's orchestra and arrangements.

Baker's recordings of the middle 1950s, especially those with the Mulligan street band, are already prized collector's items.

He is still in Europe. An album photograph, one of many of the same style, shows a sexy, beautiful young woman, the mist of adulation in her dark eyes, gazing up at him as he plays. In another, Baker has his shirt off, and the young woman touches his horn tentatively as he holds it casually by his side.

He is the Elvis Presley of jazz.

8

Chet Baker spends a year in jail in Lucca, Italy, in 1966 on drug charges. Lucca, Italy. The olive oil capital of the world.

He plays his horn in the jail, and the jailers let people in to hear him. Then, he is let out of the jail to play in clubs in Lucca, returning after the gig to the cell.

His playing sounds, one Italian says, like a fine woman's legs in nylons.

Baker returns from Europe, after a hiatus of nearly ten years. He gigs around the country, a ravaged face, eroded like Oklahoma soil. Not yet forty.

But jazz is nearly defunct for the public, especially for youth. Jazz is passé. It is old. The kids, who buy the records, don't listen to it anymore. Nobody will come to a club to hear it. They go to other types of clubs— The Matrix, where The Jefferson Airplane starts up, on Fillmore Street, is a hot club.

A young entrepreneur, Bill Graham, starts a dance venue in the old Fillmore Ballroom, also on Fillmore. An organization with the name of The Family Dog showcases new groups in the Avalon Ballroom on Sutter Street in San Francisco.

Long-haired, bearded, angelic youths walk barefoot now in the foggy streets by the bay, passing Chet Baker. They do not know who he is.

In 1968, that watershed year, Baker is set upon in an alley in North Beach in San Francisco by five hoodlums, who beat him badly. They beat out his front teeth, a catastrophe for a trumpet player.

The world is changing very rapidly. Acceleration.

10

Women burn their bras. Pantyhose is triumphant. A man lands on the moon. Everybody sees it live on tv.

Baker begins to try to play again. Asked how it feels playing regularly again, he says, smiling, "Show, don't tell."

11

Early morning hours in San Francisco. "Jazz at Ann Arbor" plays on KJAZZ, from Alameda, and a couple fuck, slow and hot, in a car out on the Great Highway.

Chet Baker, trumpet. Ron Neely, drums. Carson Smith, bass. Russ Freeman, piano.

Recorded live May 9, 1954, Mothering Sunday, at Ann Arbor.

"That was nice stuff," the woman says, combing her hair, gesturing at the radio.

12

Chet Baker makes a re-union with Gerry Mulligan at Carnegie Hall in New York. 1974.

They sound very good.

He will have, in the strange way of these things, a "hit" record, in the Top Ten of the pop charts.

Baker has made a come-back. He is voted Come Back Artist of the Year.

They say he came back "from drugs."

13

Baker settles in London. There are not enough serious jazz venues in the United States, he says, and it is a culturally distressing observation.

"There are none in Los Angeles, San Francisco..." he says in a television interview, smoking a cigarette thoughtfully.

He is articulate, obviously sensitive. If anything, more sensitive.

He is quick. Elusive.

14

Bruce Weber begins to make a film about him. The crew follows him for two years. Weber comments that he looks like a boxer.

Baker says he thought about writing his autobiography, started to, and then stopped.

He shakes his head.

15

He plays in a club in London, and Van Morrison sings with him. Elvis Costello sings with him. The club is full, quiet.

He sits to play, does not stand. He is slumped almost in an S. He cancels dates Stateside; too ill to travel.

He closes his eyes when he plays, and he nods when the others play.

The sidemen are British, intent.

It is London, wet rain on dark very late evening streets, this.

Big taxi hiss, after door chunks shut.

16

Maybe someone was passing by, looked over, looked up.

May 13, 1988. 3:10 am. A Friday. Amsterdam. Second story window of hotel.

Let's Get Lost.

A long way from Yale, Oklahoma, Chet Baker. Somebody was listening.

"Maybe it's sad..." he said once. "But not while you're playing."

Julia Slavin
Beauty and Rudy

"Rudy flew a Piper Arrow with a ton of the finest Mexican money can buy and crashed and burned in the Everglades," Gil said, driving out of the woods and back onto 95 in a maraschino Impala. "They say the heat from the fire melted a medallion with the sun, the moon and the planets on it and he's got the solar system branded on his chest." Gil looked at Stan in the rearview. "They say there're some pretty free women up there, Stanley. And some folks into astroprojection, you know, out-of-body type stuff. Something I mean to try."

"*Astral*projection isn't real," Beauty said, trying to rub the pounding of a nitrous hangover out of her temples.

"People think it's a crock because nothing ever materializes," Gil said. "But things have materialized."

"Like what?" Beauty asked, wishing she could get in the back seat with Stan, and that Stan weren't her boyfriend's best friend.

"Oh, semiprecious stones, keepsakes. They say out at Rudy's farm a strand of pearls materialized on a chair."

"Are there going to be any drugs there?" Beauty asked, cradling the bright blue nitrous tank in her lap. "'Cause I got to get off the N, Gil. The N's making me dotty. My brain's ba-booming around in my bean like a cat in the dryer."

"Have I ever seared you wrong, Beauty?"

"Steered, idiot. S-T-E-E-R-E-D."

✳

What a tiny delicate jewel she was: five feet tall and everybody wanted to touch her. Her mother thought she should be on TV and arranged a job doing the ads for Big Bob's Bad Boy Toyota and Used. Beauty the Big Bob Girl was how she was known around Hollywood, Florida. Big Bob said he'd do anything to sell you a car. But it was Beauty who was shot out of the cannon, kissed the monkey, and flew on top of the airplane. Beauty told Big Bob that if he ever exposed himself to her again she'd go to the Consumer Protection Agency about the rolled back mileage on some of those used cars. But Big Bob couldn't resist apple cheeks, apple breasts, an apple bottom. And so, after ransacking the back office, Beauty accepted Gil's invitation North, where he promised to siphon the blues off her.

"This is it?" Beauty asked, rifling through the box of groceries Stan and Gil brought out from The Buck 'n' Dough. "This is all you got?"

"That and this," Gil said, showing her the contents of the Buck 'n' Dough cash register.

"I can't eat any of this," Beauty said.

"There's lots of good stuff. Snowballs, Ho Ho's, Vienna Sausage, soup," Gil said, opening a can of Chicken 'n' Stars.

"How're we supposed to heat it up?"

Gil bent his neck back and poured the can of Chicken 'n' Stars in his mouth. First in was the broth flecked with solidified chicken fat, then came the stars which slipped out of the can in one gelatinous disk and blopped in his mouth, splattering soup all over the windshield.

"I hate you. I wish you were dead," Beauty screamed and kicked her foot through the glove compartment.

Gil unwound the hose of the nitrous tank, forced Beauty's head down, pried open her jaw, plunged the end of the hose in her mouth and made her suck tank until she slumped down in the seat, happy.

"There's no pleasing that woman, Stanley," Gil said, opening a can of Bacon 'n' Bean. "No matter how I try. I tell her of the pyramids, semiotics. All she wants to do is bang. Consider yourself lucky."

Stan lit a new Old Gold from an old one and finished picking out the coupons from the Old Gold cartons they took from the Buck 'n' Dough. He was only seven thousand coupons away from the Winnebago. Gil had no idea just how lucky Stan was.

*

Proceeding without knowing the direction, the travelers chanced upon the ferry that took them across the choppy sound and around the curvey roads of Firefly Island. Arriving at Rudy's farm, Beauty saw rows and rows of fruit trees and life-size statues the color of human flesh with green-painted genitals. On closer examination, Beauty saw that they weren't statues at all, but the guests of the farm involved in various forms of free love and Tai Chi. One couple was in a position that Beauty used to laugh at before she met Gil.

Some mischievous goats tried to butt Beauty, Gil, Stan and the nitrous tank back in the Impala. Beauty screamed; the goats *bah-h-h-hed* with delight. But suddenly the sky darkened and the goats ran away. Across the farm a man came walking. A man so frightful to look at the travelers were ready to faint with fear. Was it a man? It had the shape of a man, but the skin of a beast. Tufts of hair grew here and there on its back, front and head through thick grafts of skin and scar tissue. Beauty could see that half its face was extraordinarily handsome. But the other half was buried in a zigzag of angry red scars. Its chest was as scarred as its face and its back was as scarred as its front. Beauty knew if she blew chunks now, she'd blow and she'd blow and she'd blow herself inside out. Rudy walked right up to her. They always know, Beauty thought.

"Scared?" The beast said in its terrible voice.

"No," Beauty said. She started to feel her saliva thin, preparing her mouth for regurgitated Burger King.

"Touch it," Rudy said.

Beauty, trying to hide her fear, touched its chest with her finger.

"Youch!" Rudy said and recoiled like her finger was a red-hot shishk-abob skewer. Then it laughed and slapped five with the men and the goats came out from behind the trees to butt the guests and the sky brightened. Beauty kecked Whopper on Gil's shoes.

✳

"Don't let that scaly old beast bother you," Linda, a nice woman in lots of Hindu print clothing said. "He's got a good heart." Linda held Beauty's head in her lap and stroked her hair and gave her parsley tea for the nausea.

"Stan and I are gettin' off the N," Beauty said, happy to have some female companionship. "Really. I'm gonna suck this tank and then we're definitely gettin' off."

"Shhhhh," Linda said.

All around her, people spoke of nothing but Rudy. Beauty heard snippets as she fell in and out of consciousness.

"...a firebomb in Greenwich Village. Rudy was trapped in the basement for two days."

"...lit himself on fire to protest the war."

"...he used to wear an Indian peace symbol around his neck..."

"...Nepalese temple balls around his neck..."

"...the search party who found him said they..."

"...glowed red like liquid steel."

Beauty dreamed she was a player token in the game of Mystery Date, moving door to door looking for The Guy in the Dinner Jacket. But behind every door was The Dud. But then she realized that The Dud was the most handsome of all the dates. Surely The Dud was Stan, Beauty thought.

✳

Beauty skipped through the orchard because Stan loved her. She picked an apple but it was wormy so she dropped it.

"The Koran said it was a banana," Rudy said. Beauty was startled by his unexpected appearance in a tree.

"What?" She asked.

Rudy disappeared from the tree and appeared standing in front of her. "The forbidden fruit. The Koran said it was a banana." Beauty tried not to look at his scars but she couldn't help it. "I lit myself on fire," he said. Beauty thought she'd faint. Rudy laughed that she believed him. "I was a lucky Pinto owner," he explained. "I bought this farm with the settlement money. Are you all right?" He touched her arm. She slid away from his hand. "Why do you shudder when I come near you?" He asked.

"I don't," she said.

"I like physical closeness," Rudy said, moving closer. "It doesn't mean anything. I just like it." Now she could feel his horrible breath on her face.

330

"I like it too, I just…" Beauty felt her saliva thinning again. "How come you're not astralprojecting with the others?" She asked and stepped sideways.

"Because I think it's a crock," Rudy said.

"They say a strand of pearls materialized on a chair."

"I put them there," he said.

"I have to get back," Beauty said.

"To Gil?" Rudy asked. "Or is it Stan?" Beauty was speechless. "Don't be mislead by appearances, Beauty."

"You don't know them," Beauty said.

"I know you," Rudy whispered.

"They say you had sex with a dog," Beauty said.

"I loved her," Rudy said and disappeared before her eyes.

✳

"Hook 'em, cook 'em," Gil said. "The Cinder. I'm tired of moving around. I want the farm."

"I'm not hookin' the Cinder," Beauty said.

"Why not?" Gil said.

"Because it'll make me sick. And I'm not gonna cook."

"Fine," Gil said. "You hook, Stan'll cook."

"Why do I gotta hook at all? Why can't you just cook without the hook?"

"'Cause he's sneaky, The Cinder. Got eyes all over his body. And he likes you."

Beauty hoped Gil would die soon.

✳

Beauty was startled by the sudden appearance of Rudy by the pond. "What are you doing?" She asked.

"Going for a swim," he said, naked. Beauty looked around for Stan to see if he was waiting in the woods for the cook. "Coming?" Rudy asked. Beauty pretended to be shy about taking off her clothes. "Dang," Rudy said. "You debs from the South."

"I'm not from the South," Beauty said. "I'm from Florida." Peeking, Beauty noticed the part of Rudy which had been spared the Pinto explosion. "And besides, it's freezing. Aren't you freezing?"

"Scar tissue doesn't get cold," Rudy said. "Feel it." He took Beauty's hand. She pulled away. He laughed.

"You're always trying to scare me," Beauty said. "But I'm not afraid of you, Rudy. I walk under an umbrella of protection, the love of the man I love: Stan. You shouldn't laugh at people and you shouldn't try to scare people. It isn't nice." Beauty surprised herself as much as Rudy. And then Rudy didn't look scary anymore. He started to cry, big acid tears that burned through the Earth and dripped out over the Seychelle Islands and landed on the bald spot of the British explorer Sir Peregine Pomsomby-Smythe's head.

331

"Bleedin' birds," Peregine said.

"I know I do things that scare people," Rudy cried. "And I act superior, but I can't help it. The physical pain left over from the accident makes me irritable and people expect to be afraid of me so I give them what they want. If I don't they'll stop coming and then I'll have no one." Rudy cried and cried and more tears burned through the Earth. "You know," Rudy said, wiping his eyes with an asbestos mitt. "I used to be a pretty good-looking guy."

"You're still…"

"Don't give me false compliments, Beauty. I hate them. I'm deformed and hideous."

"You're not so bad," Beauty said. "Why, with the right hair style…" She wet her fingers and tried to smooth down his hair but no matter how much saliva she greased on his head, the hair popped back up like an inflatable clown toy.

"Could you ever love me?" Rudy asked.

"No," Beauty said.

"Is my company so contemptible?" He asked.

"Oh no," she said.

"Try?" He said, unzipping her cutt-offs.

"I-I-I," she said. "I'm not into this."

"Get into it," he said. "Get into me." And he pulled off her cut-offs and knelt at her feet.

It's a shame, she thought, that he is so ugly, for he is so good.

✳

"I don't see why you had to kill him," Beauty said. Stan ran a chef's knife through Gil's ear. The knife had done little and he'd had to run another knife through Gil's other ear. Gil was in the process of an out-of-body experience when he saw two chef's knives sticking out of his head.

"Guess I ain't coming back," Gil said.

Everything was better with Stan. Gil stuck it in, shot off and didn't go down. Stan could dry hump for hours and ate Beauty like filet. Gil yacked and yacked, "I invented the bacon cheeseburger, you know. At Smiley's on Rt. 4. I said Smiley, throw some bacon on that burger and so it was." Gil thought he was funny, "I believe in parallel universes and in one of them are your missing car keys." Stan was a mute. But now that Gil was gone everything seemed different. Too tired to raise her pelvis to meet Stan's anymore after a three hour dry hump, Beauty went to sleep and had a nitrous dream that she was a Chinese man rowing a boat through the blood stream of a Chinese man rowing a boat through the blood stream of a Chinese man rowing a boat through the blood stream of a Chinese man rowing a boat.

✳

"Here's what you're looking at, Toots," Detective Mallory said. "You got your two consec. l.s.'s for the murders of Robert Buck Brown A.K.A. Big Bob, and the unidentifiable owner of a '64 model marachino Impala, and you got your big three-0 for conspiracy. *Capisce?*"

"I'm telling you I don't know where Stan is," Beauty cried.

"Look, Honey Pot," Mallory's voice became gentle. "I got a gift set of six ginsu knives with two unaccounted for. If you're trying to harbor this Stan character, keep it in your toboggan (he meant noggin) he doesn't give a rat's hooey for you."

Beauty's mouth formed an upside down crescent moon and she cried so hard no sound came out.

Mallory rubbed his face. Time was when he knew every license plate on the rock. Trouble? He could seal the whole rock—stop the ferries, the barges, nobody comes or goes—with a phone call. But since these Rudy People came onto the rock, the rock was an open sore. Wide open for any two-bit pathogenic opportunistic infection to pus up *his* rock. It was the Rudy People who burned his house down while he was off playing the clown for the brats at the policemen's benevolence picnic. All he owned now was what he had on his back. The big ruffled collar made his neck itch.

"Somebody's got to answer for Gil," he whispered and lit an exploding cigar.

✳

Beauty looked up at the ceiling of the barn. There must have been a hundred-thousand fireflies up there, oxidizing and glowing, oxidizing and glowing. Luciferin. Heatless light. They use it to attract one another. Rudy taught her that. She remembered how she used to collect them in a jar when she was little and let them go in her room. They'd be dead in the morning.

"No," Rudy said, entering her. "Just sleeping, they're nocturnal." Beauty hated it when he read her mind without asking. She hated the sweat between his scales, the way he'd be nice to animals and then eat them, that he had to have sex every seven minutes. She was starting to miss Stan again. Even Gil, a little bit.

"Hold your horses, I'll get them," Rudy said, climbing the ladder to the loft of the barn.

"Get what?" Beauty said.

"You were about to say, you stupid idiot get me my seconals."

"I was not."

"You were too."

Beauty wished he'd shut up and die.

"You shut up," Rudy said.

"You shut up, you stupid idiot and get me my seconals."

Rudy stood at the top of the loft with a fresh erection and threw down the bottle of seconals. Beauty held up her hand and squeezed it shut hoping the bottle would end up there but it landed in the hay and opened and the little pills rolled into the abyss. Beauty started to cry.

"I wish you were dead," she cried over and over, pounding the hay with her fists.

Rudy took her in his arms and kissed her face.

"There, don't cry, Beauty. Isn't this better than jail? You saw that Linda Blair movie. Say, how 'bout I go to the dentist for fresh tank? Would that make it better?" Beauty nodded, put her arms around him and kissed the Jupiter brand on his chest for luck. She felt better. "Now," Rudy said. "How 'bout that blowjob?"

"Get out! Get out! Get out!" Beauty screamed.

Dang, that woman gets mad faster than any woman I've ever seen, Rudy thought as he walked into the warm sunshine looking for his favorite goat. Must be that macrobiotic diet she put herself on. "Seen Timmy?" He asked a steer. The steer tilted his head in the direction of the sugar house. Come to think of it, Rudy thought, the whole last millennium together had been a bitch.

Maya Sonenberg

Baby 1995

ONE

I'm lying here tied to this bed, not really tied, not by irons or chains or rope or shackles. So not really tied and it's not a bed but a couch, not a bed of straw in a dungeon even if it feels that way sometimes. It's a couch in a nice living room with a fireplace and cool blue walls we painted together right after we moved in and a giant screen TV Marco just bought for me—an extra special Christmas present just for this occasion. Because I'm tied to this bed by our baby. I'm fertilized, impregnated, I'm in a delicate condition. I want to have this baby. Yes, I do. No, I don't. I don't want to have this baby. I don't. I want to.

I'm tied to this bed by pain, pain from this baby. It's pinching nerves, pressing on them, sitting on them so I can't move. No, I know it can't really sit yet, not at this stage. It just swims like a tadpole in a pond. Sciatica—nerve like a line of fire from the hip into the thigh, a string pulled tight, a needle, six hundred pins. From the French *sciatique*, I looked it up. From Old French and back and back, from Medieval Latin *sciaticus*, alteration of Latin *ischiadicus*, from Greek *iskhiadikos, iskhias, iskhiad-*, sciatica, from *iskhion*, the hip. I can't have an operation cause it's too risky. I can't go to a chiropractor cause God knows what he'd turn around. I could find an acupuncturist but the insurance won't pay. And I can't take drugs cause they'll hurt the baby—not aspirin or Advil or Tylenol even. "Well," the doctor said, "a Tylenol once in a while won't hurt." He smiled and patted my shoulder. I'd have laughed at him but I was in too much pain. The insurance will pay for drugs all right—Codeine, Demerol, Morphine—but I can't take those, my doctor says I can't take those cause they'll hurt the baby. I'll have a baby with two heads or no arms or a hole so we can see into the stomach like that cow they keep around here for the Ag students to study and the school kids to visit and then what'll I do? "How would you feel?" he asks. "Wouldn't you feel guilty," my husband asks, "for bringing a damaged thing into the world?" Damaged goods, damaged property. And that's one thing no one wants—a damaged baby. They won't even buy one cheap. He wouldn't want a damaged baby. "Baby, baby, baby," he says when he comes home from work and it's time for the backrub, the footrub, and the kisses. "Baby, baby, baby," he croons, feeding me whole grain muffins and bright green spinach and broiled chicken and anything else I can stand to swallow. When I beg for ice cream he pets my hair. "Now, you know that's bad for you," he says. "How about some nice strawberries all whipped up with yogurt. I got them special; they're not in season you know." But that frothy pink color makes me sick, that feeling I fight all day, like my stomach will bubble right out of my mouth, even if I nibble those crackers we leave on little plates by every chair for when I can stand to sit up and by the bed for when I wake up in the middle of the night. "Give me those berries and I'll puke," I say. But then I eat my bread and vegetables and chicken like a good girl. He cooks for me at the end of his own long day and how much more can I ask for? I smile and I mean it even though I dream ice cream, ice cream, ice cream. I hallucinate it: chocolate with a cherry, whipped cream too. But I can't have it cause gaining too much weight's bad for the baby— and me sitting here, lying here, tied to this bed, I'm not exactly getting any exercise. I can't feel it yet but I picture it rolling around in there, little sala-mander, getting enough exercise for both of us. I say to it, "I'm eating for two, you exercise for two, and we'll get a treat." We'll have that half glass of champagne on New Year's Eve the doctor promised us; it's just three days away. Come on, Baby, we'll listen to Christmas carols together—peace on earth, good will toward men—all that crap.

I'm so organized we were prepared for everything in the lab, every damn thing. We had a foot stool so I wouldn't strain my back. We had a chair on wheels so I could roll around with ease. We had a grounded filter on the computer screen to block out radiation. We'd isolated everything possibly dangerous. And of course there were dangerous things—those birds had been washing up on the shores for almost two years. And even the dead ones—who knew what might still be living in them, what had killed them? Mostly, I'd be working in my office anyway, supervising, writing, overseeing the work through that glass window reinforced with chicken wire. And for two months it was fine, but we weren't prepared for this. I try to work at home. Carol drops reports off for me to review but the numbers swim on the page like little minnows. She calls with questions only I can answer, but I just say, "Yes, sure, go ahead with that. Sounds good," and I know she has to go ask someone else. I can't work. I can't follow the line of an argument. I can't spot the flaw that's upsetting the test. Oh baby, you lit-tle worm, you pest, you damn barnacle, get me through this somehow.

I know babies really can't do anything for you; they're too little to do anything except scream and cry and shit and eat and that's why we're sup-posed to love them—because there they are, helpless, and we can help them grow up into something great or at least into "whoever they want to be"; we can give them love, we can give them freedom. Until one of them gets pregnant and the baby starts sitting on the nerve that runs down into her leg and the nerve turns into a prison—just like bars of fire, just like an elec-trical wire. If I lie just right, with a pillow under my knee, it doesn't hurt so much but then the calf cramps and the muscle there turns into a stick of dynamite. I have to sit up and squirm and scream and massage it and that sets the nerve on fire again. But I can't take drugs cause that might hurt the baby. And I wouldn't want to be responsible for that.

But I do want this baby. I do I do I do, I say when the nerve knits up again. I say it in time to the throbbing. I've waited a long time for this, watching those other mothers with their sweet-faced infants in the grocery store, watching the relatives coo over every tiny cousin. I've waited a long time to have a little girl and dress her in Baby Dior rompers, and later velvet dresses and matching ribbons for her hair. A little girl to buy Barbie dolls for and those baby dolls that drink from a bottle and piss so you have to change the diapers. A little girl to take to ballet lessons so she can wear a tutu that shows off her chubby thighs and take to flute lessons and later she can go to cooking class. No—a little girl to take to the library and stack up piles and piles of books for her to read: Nancy Drew, *The Railway Children, Alice in Wonderland*. A little girl to play chess with, to collect moths by their silky wings and tadpoles in a jar. I think about all these plans when the pain gets really bad—like razor blades and bowie knives, carving knives, machetes, switchblades and bayonets cutting me til the blood comes. That's what it feels like, hot blood running up and down my leg. I think how this little parasite embedded in me will finally disengage.

On the ultrasound I can see it and it just looks like shadows. Feeding on me. "I positively think that ladies who are always enceinte quite disgusting; it is more like a rabbit or guinea-pig than anything else and really it is not very nice," Queen Victoria said, despite her nine children. I could stop eating I guess; I could eat more, I guess, make it grow faster, get this over with. Ovum and sperm, zygote, blastula and embryo, fetus shaped like a chicken. That's where we are now. Some sort of Frankenstein monster, some sort of Caligula, some sort of Godzilla, some Thing I can't even imagine—the Creature from the Black Lagoon, Rosemary's baby. Look at a monkey, you'll have a monkey. Slap your stomach and your baby will have a birthmark shaped just like a hand. I keep dreaming about being trapped in a tunnel, sunk in a lake of slush with a baby the size of Mount Olympus. I keep telling myself ribosome, nucleus, cytoplasm, chromosome; little fetus, that's all you are.

I keep waiting to get misty-eyed like my friends. If you don't do it, you'll miss it. If you don't do it, you'll be sorry. It'll hold your marriage together; it'll split your marriage apart. Ah, Marco. "Where's my baby? When's my Baby going to give me a baby?" he said. He said, "If you don't do it, you'll miss out on the mystery of life." Women, we're supposed to be closer to it, to that mystery of life; we're in tune with the moon and the tides, cycles, out of historical time, magical and mysterious and paradoxical, closer to nature. Lying here, I've never been further from it. I can look out the window all right, stare at the dirty melting snow. I can listen to the rain ding on the metal awnings. I can count and count and count the Christmas lights on the house across the street. I can watch the fog clear in the morning so I can see the clouds build up, put my hand against the glass and feel the cold. At the lake it's never cold; it's hot and dry around that slick sheet of salty water, brush growing up its sides, and the sky is blue. You take the train down from Indio, down down below sea level and off in the distance you can see the Chocolate Mountains, the Superstition Mountains, Rabbit Peak. Even with a hundred and fifty thousand dead birds washed up on the shores, it was beautiful. I open my eyes and it's raining here again, one damn drop after another. They'd kill for this water down there, those fools. Maybe it's just that I'm in pain, maybe it's just that I'm in pain.

TWO

Nobody wants a damaged baby, except for those Mother Theresa types you see on TV—and I see a lot of TV—who adopt fifty AIDS babies and nurse them until they die. I know we're all supposed to be like that—give up for our babies because they "give us so much, so much love." But this baby isn't doing anything for me except giving me the time to watch a lot of TV, except giving me the excuse to build another room onto the house, except giving my mother an excuse to come out and visit me, except—because of the pain—giving me an excuse to scream a lot and moan a lot and cry whenever I want to and have her or Marco come and put cold rags on my forehead. All those things you can't do out in the street or the office. Try moaning out loud on the bus and see what happens.

My mother gave up everything for me. She wore my old underwear with the elastic stretched out so I could get silk ones. She wore my old socks, the ones with holes in the heels, so I could buy stockings. She cooked nineteen thousand meals for me before I left home for college and insisted I eat everything she put on my plate. She vacuumed my room nine hundred and thirty-six times, took me in for ten sets of shots, wiped innumerable bloody knees, shrieked countless times when she found my failed science experiments—bananas left under the bed to rot, field mice deprived of food to see how long they'd last, every household cleanser mixed together to force some sort of explosion. And now she's here taking care of me since I can't get out of this damn bed. "So, you finally got knocked up," my father said on the phone when I told him he was going to be a grandfather. "Well, we waited long enough. You've been married ten years. I was beginning to wonder, but hey, listen, take care of yourself you hear, and now here's your mother. I know she'll want to talk to you." "I'm pregnant," I said to her when she got on the phone. "The bloody thing keeps tweaking my sciatic nerve. It's killing me."

She's been here two months now, from the end of January, when it became clear Marco and I couldn't do this alone. When she came, she brought books for me. She brought *Helpful Hints for Your Pregnancy* and *The Well Baby Book, A Child Is Born, The Womanly Art of Breastfeeding*. She brought *Be Pregnant, Be Beautiful*. We've read them all but none of them give more than a sentence to sciatica. They pass if off as a possible inconvenience, the way the doctor says, "Now this may pinch a little," right before he drives a needle into your arm. And we've spent days coming up with lists and lists of unlikely baby names. It's taken months to get from the ordinary—Jennifer, Patrick—to the odd—Cimarron, Eugenides. Months and months, and now she's seen all the damn trees blossom, the crocuses and daffodils come up, and the tulips start to lose their petals. Next she'll see the rhodies bloom in front of every house, identical rhodies and azaleas in front of identical three bedroom split-level ranch styles, the same pinks and reds and oranges everywhere because the deer won't eat them. Every afternoon, she takes her umbrella and goes for a brisk walk up to campus. She walks around my lab building and reports back to me. When she's feeling particularly peppy, she insists I hobble out to the carport and smell the air, even though the rain drips off the overhang right onto my head. "Breathe, breathe, breathe," she says, and she stands up straight and takes the air in deep like she's setting an example for a two-year-old. Like I'm only bent over double with pain cause I want it that way. "Smell that springtime smell," she says. Then she starts humming. I know she doesn't mean it. I know she's being really nice to me but I don't want to be nice to her. I don't want to be nice to anyone. She even lets me scream when the pain gets really bad. Or I tell her that's why I'm screaming but really it could be anything— maybe it's the fact that my friend can call up and talk about *The Brady Bunch* for hours and I can talk about them with her—they're back in, they're back on Nickelodeon, they're back in a movie. Maybe it's the fact that my mother and I watch Donna Reed's perfectly run household on TV every day and then we watch 99 in *Get Smart* with her little suits and matching hats even when she's pregnant, neat little outfits in a houndstooth check. I have to watch her when I can barely get out of my nightgown and into a clean pair of sweatpants in the morning. Maybe it's the fact that it's been raining for months straight. I watch it out the window: gray milk, gray sludge, gray mud, gray ash, gray slush, gray slime. I start saying gray, gray, gray, gray, gray. It takes my mind off the pain. "That pain should be gone by now," the doctor said, "but I guess you're carrying low. Perfectly natural though. Don't you worry about a thing."

My mother says, "Let's watch that TV show set in Hawaii and we can imagine it's sunny here too. I'll move all the plants in here, that nice palm you have in the bedroom. We'll close all the curtains and turn up the sound extra loud so we can pretend we're in Hawaii too. You'll like that, won't you?" So we turn it on and watch Jacques Lord, El Más Macho, and Book-em-Danno run around being tough and then they bust some poor shmuck who's running drugs in order to support some leftist political cause. I keep trying to see around the people, just look at the scenery—looking for beaches and oceans with big waves, mountains covered with rain forest, waterfalls, and maybe a volcano about to blow—but even when I can see around the people, all I see are high rises and cars from the 70's (big Impalas, and Cadillacs), maybe a city bus. Local color means girls in hula skirts and flower bras who you look at but never talk to and they're always smiling. What drugs are they taking? I think. When it's over, my mother says, "Now isn't that better?" "Sure," I say. Yeah sure, I think. Let's watch it again tomorrow. It's on every afternoon at two, a TV trip to a tropical paradise where the hero wears a suit that looks too small. He has an implacable set of wrinkles and hair slicked in place with nitroglycerin and contraceptive jelly. "Hey, we can watch *Gilligan's Island,*" I say. "That's set in the tropics too," but my mother says, "No, I can't. Those people are too stupid even for me to watch," and we both laugh. She's OK sometimes, I think. I think I shouldn't be thinking this way anymore about my mother. I should have gotten over this. I should have gotten over how she wore the same winter coat for fifteen years while I was growing up so I could keep getting new ones.

She's flipping through the channels and she finds *Star Trek: The Next Generation* where there are women starship captains but they're always the captain of some other ship. "Now that Counselor Troy," my mother says, "she's got real woman's intuition. See, in the future they'll recognize how important that is." She reaches over and pats my hand and I think, Jesus Christ, I used to be a biologist but I can't remember anything, anything at all. I used to be able to think! What's happening to me? In the middle of the night, I wake up and I can't remember if we tested for avian cholera yet or avian botulism, how much selenium we found in their livers, how much mercury, how much chromium, how many birds have died. Jesus, I can barely remember that DNA is a double helix. All I can remember is: this is when the baby develops fingerprints, this is when the baby's eyes open; this is how much vitamin A to take, how much niacin, how much folic acid; this is how Samantha does her tricks—she wiggles her nose—and this is how Jeannie does hers—she crosses her arms and blinks her eyes. I keep dreaming about those damn birds, floating in some liquid suspiciously like amniotic fluid, and I break into a sweat. When I wake up I remember they're in the Salton Sea; it is like amniotic fluid. I call Carol and she says, "Don't worry. Just relax. We're doing fine here. And your name's still going on that article as lead author. Just stop worrying. It'll all be waiting for you when you come back. Those dead birds aren't going anywhere." I think of a hundred and fifty thousand grebes belly up in the Salton Sea, with their pointy bills and ruby eyes and vestigial tails and the fleshy membranes along their toes. Those clumsy bastards, they can't make it on land. They say a little confusion is normal—leaving the house without keys, misplacing your purse. They say to slow down, make lists, check the items off—pick up dry cleaning, get dog groomed. They say to post notes on the inside of the front door—is the stove off? Is the answering machine on? But what if you can't leave the house? What if you're tied to the house? What if the baby sits on your sciatic nerve and *just won't move?*

I put the phone down and my mother says, "What's the problem, honey?" I say, "We were talking about Connie Chung announcing to the world that she's taking time off from work so she can get pregnant. Isn't that ridiculous?" I ask. "What's it like, giving birth?" I ask.

"Oh wonderful dear," my mother says, "I got you in the end, the best thing I ever did." I think how my friend Marcia said, "Yup, great, just like getting run over by a Mack truck," but then a month later she said, "Oh, I never said anything like that, I'd never. You're making it up. It's not that bad."

"You're shitting me," I say to my mother. I turn on my side even though that makes it hurt more, even though that sends a spasm rocketing through my leg, ricocheting from hip to knee to toe. There's a coil wound tight and pulling tighter, and I feel the baby move. I've been feeling it for a while now, "quickening" they say, the fluttering and hopping and kicking. I try to decipher what it's saying, like Morse Code. Maybe it's telling me a secret; maybe it's teaching me a language only the two of us can understand; maybe it's telling me to get my act together. Then it kicks me in the ribs, sticks an elbow God knows where, wherever that damn nerve starts its flaming journey, and I'm off for an afternoon of bitching and groaning.

"I just don't know what to do with you when you get like this," she says, and when Marco comes home she meets him at the front door and tells him I had a pretty good day until "That woman Carol Something called from her work. You try and talk to her Marco. She should be so happy after all you two have been through trying to have this child and look at her—she's like this instead." I can just see her throwing her hands up in exasperation. Hell, I'd do it too if I could just sit up, if I could just stand and then walk out of the room, right out of the house in exasperation—you bet I would.

When Marco comes over, I say, "Go away, you fucker. You got me into this mess in the first place." I can hear my mother clucking in the background but Marco just says, "OK baby, OK baby. It's good practice for what I'll hear during labor. Might as well get used to it." He chuckles, but he won't take his fucking hand away from my hip even though I can swear the heat from his fingers is making the pain worse, razor sharp darts when he pats pats pats.

The other day I almost fainted, stood up to go to the bathroom and felt so dizzy I had to sit right back down. "Head between the legs," my mother shouted and pushed my head down with her hand. I called the doctor because I was scared. "A little dizziness is normal at about this time," he said. "Don't you worry about it. It just means there's a little less blood going to your brain, but the baby will be just fine." When he hung up, I really did put my head between my knees. When I was twenty-two I went to my mother's gynecologist with a vague pain somewhere near my left hipbone, cramping periods, sharp stabs when someone screwed me from behind (but I didn't tell him that last one). He stuck his gloved hand up inside me and felt around like he was testing tomatoes at the market, looking for perfectly ripe ones. The whole time I stared at the ceiling where they'd plastered a poster of two adorable kittens. The whole time the nurse made sure the modesty sheet covered my knees. Later, when I was dressed, the doctor looked at me like he didn't recognize me. Then he looked at some notes he'd made. He said, "Cysts on the ovaries. We'll have to do some tests, possibly operate." I swallowed hard and my hands began to shake. "But I'm going to Hudson Bay," I said. "We're leaving next week." I'd finished the first year of grad school and my professor was taking me to Canada for the summer to help her study geese. "You'll have to put it off.

341

If we operate it could be a long recovery," he said. "I know you're upset because your plans have been disrupted, but what could be more important than your reproductive health?" His hands were folded in that fatherly way on the table. His white coat was immaculate, fat as a gander's belly. He leaned forward and said conspiratorially, "Nothing's more important than that, is it now?" How could I say it wasn't the most important thing to *me*? Later, I realized I could have died. It could have been ovarian cancer and not benign cysts. But he didn't say that. He didn't say, "Listen, young lady, this is serious, really serious. You could die here." He didn't say, "There's nothing more important than *your* health."

Am I creating all this? I can't be making this up, can I? It really was Demi Moore naked on the cover of *Vanity Fair* looking like a goddamn Madonna with one hand over her breasts and the other holding up her huge belly, and everybody arguing: she shouldn't have done it; yes, she should have done cause it's beautiful. Then with the next baby, just as big, they did her up in black lingerie and high heels, but nobody argued about that because she wasn't naked, you see. And then Courtney Love—denizen of Hole, guitar smashing punk band—couldn't be outdone. She got herself into *Vanity Fair* too, a picture of her pregnant belly, her swollen breasts—said she's gonna stop doing heroin cause it's bad for the baby, said pregnancy's been so good for her acne she didn't even have to have her pictures air-brushed. And she's right, you know, despite everything, this pregnancy's been wonderful for my skin; I'm fucking glowing. Sophie Tolstoy wrote in her diary, "I am nothing but a miserable, crushed worm, whom no one wants, whom no one loves, a useless creature with morning sickness, and a big belly, two rotten teeth, and a bad temper, a battered sense of dignity, and a love which nobody wants and which nearly drives me insane," and she didn't even have to think about underwear with an elastic panel or an entire industry based on pre-natal vitamins. The linea nigra and red palms and the mask of pregnancy. We're talking indigestion and anemia, bleeding gums and varicose veins, leg cramps and hemorrhoids and edema. I'm retaining water, the doctor says, my feet plump as pigeons, fingers fat as Ballpark franks, Texas hots, pigs in blankets. 90% water—is that all we are? Water and a fetus with thin shiny skin? Oh baby, rosy piglet, little thing.

THREE

Oh, am I heavy, big with a bun in the oven, sick of my confinement—that's what it's called, you know. Lying here or hobbling around, the pain's not so bad now—just a steady sizzle—but every day that belly gets bigger. "You can come out now," I say to it. "It's OK. You can breathe out here now. Come on already, let's get this over with. I've had enough," I say. "It hasn't exactly been a picnic for me either, you know," my mother says every time I gripe. "You haven't been the nicest person to get along with these past five months." "Maybe I have something to bitch about," I call after her as she retreats to the kitchen.

Outside, I hear some college boys saying, "Don't dis me, babe," when a woman doesn't answer their catcalls. The rain's finally stopped—just like it does here every first of July—and the sun's come out hot and steamy. She's wearing shorts and sandals and a tank top. When she crosses the street, they hoot after her as if she's put on those clothes just for them. On TV I saw how some man in Boston killed his pregnant wife and blamed it on two black kids, and the world believed him for a long long time. On TV now, everyone in this little town is learning French by watching TV. They're all saying, "*Le mouton est blanc*," and outside there are real sheep looking in the barbershop windows but the people don't even see them. Don't tell me it's wrong for me to say these things because it's men who hate pregnancy, that I'm acting just like a man—disgusted, hateful, disregardful of life, glorious life. That isn't it at all. You can't even begin to compare.

I think how if this baby's a boy and we get into a war somewhere—some war in our national interest—he could get drafted and then get killed. Along the way, he throws out all that stuff you so busily taught him: don't tease girls, don't touch girls if they say not to, don't hit people, solve things by talking about them. He throws all that out and when he gets to this far away nation or this village where everyone has dark skin or slanty eyes, he rapes the first woman he sees, then he hits her, or maybe he has to hit her first if she's not good. He shoots the first man he sees; he doesn't ask questions first. Or if he gets sent to some far off country where the people are already killing each other, and he doesn't forget everything you taught him but instead he picks up a child and spends five hours finding her mother, he rebuilds a road, or he gets two fighting leaders to sit down at the same table and leave their guns outside, someone back home on the Senate floor stands up and says, "Bring the boys back home. It's not in our national interest."

My friend Marcia comes over and brings her little boy. He's six now and he takes one look at my giant belly and hides behind his mother. He's scared even though I've taped a dime over my belly button so it doesn't stick out. After we feed him ice cream though, he comes around. "When's your magic moment?" he says. When we laugh, he adds, "You know, when you get to hold it for the first time," as if he's speaking to a bunch of idiots.

Or if it's a girl, maybe if she's good, she'll get to be crossing guard at school. She'll play soccer and basketball and softball but she won't ever get to make money at it. Maybe if she's lucky she'll get a scholarship. Maybe she'll want to fly planes and even though you argue with her endlessly, she goes into the Navy and learns to sail jets off the decks of aircraft carriers. Despite everything, you're proud, but then her jet crashes and in the midst of all your grief—your baby girl is gone! her body never recovered from the sea—you have to listen to some old general on the news saying, "This just proves women can't fly planes." Maybe, instead, she'll be on the debate team in high school, and everyone will say she should be a lawyer. She can do that now pretty easily and maybe even get to make partner and make lots of money but then if she ever wants to have a baby of her own (and I WANT grandchildren) she'll have to quit or maybe if she's with a really enlightened firm, she won't have to quit and won't even have to come back to work full-time for a while, but at the least she'll hear whispering, "The men don't slack off like that when they have babies"—which is what happened to Marcia. She'll think that maybe they should, that maybe her husband should—if she has a husband to father this baby—but if she knows what's good for her she'll keep her mouth shut.

On TV, thirteen white men faced off against Anita Hill. "Erotomania," they said. "Perjury," they said. "Have you ever read *The Exorcist*?" they asked. "It gets all tangled up in this sexual harassment crap," Simpson said. And Howell Heflin huffed and puffed his way through the hearings, waving that cigar around. Three years later, he pulled a pair of panties from his pocket during a press conference and laughed like it was some kind of prize. On TV we could watch the Gulf War in Technicolor—tracer missiles and smart bombs, F-16's, and Stealth Bombers. We're talking that weird green glow in the sky and lights like falling stars surrounded by haze. We're talking bombs hitting targets all marked out with circles and X's and then a splatter of electrons and the TV screen set up like a computer game. We're talking about the fact I can turn on CNN and see a war any day of the week: Bosnia, Rwanda, Haiti, Somalia, LA, Detroit, New York and Chechnya. And that's just for starters. I can turn it on and see body bags, dead bodies, body counts, and I can scream and scream for hours, as if those 13 white men and all the others could hear me. As if Newt could hear me, as if he'd stop in the middle of a speech about putting poor kids in orphanages and look up and maybe just pause to take a breath but definitely do something to show he'd heard me. As if they'd all—Jesse and Ollie and Ronald and George and George W. Bush the Third and Bob Dole and Michael Huffington with his millions—stop, look out of the set right at me and, just like McNamara about Vietnam, say, "It's wrong. We were terribly wrong."

We're talking kids killing kids and fathers killing kids and mothers killing kids and fathers and mothers killing each other. "What's this world coming to!" my mother says. It drives her right out of the house and on to the porch where she's fanning herself with the newspaper. Maybe that's what I was aiming for, to get her out of the house—her with her good suggestions that I know are right, for writing calm and reasonable letters to my congressman, to my senators, her suggestions for doing volunteer work for Planned Parenthood or Habitat for Humanity ("I'm sure there's something you could do at home. Stuff envelopes or something," she says in exasperation), her suggestions for lifting my legs into a new position that won't hurt so much, her suggestions for staying calm ("It's better for the baby"). She snatches that newspaper right out of my hands in the morning now. "It doesn't need to upset you," she says. "Just stop worrying. It's none of your business anyway." How can she say that when I wake up in the morning to hear a whiny voice on the radio say, "It's like those people are double-dipping. You know, they get them foodstamps and then the kids get that free lunch at school. I don't want my tax dollars goin for that"? How can she say it's none of my business when I wake up in the morning to hear a North Carolina legislator tell me women don't get pregnant when they're "really" raped? "None of the juices flow. It just doesn't happen," he says. When I wake up and hear that Newt divorced his wife, Jackie, when he first won election to Congress and she was diagnosed with cancer? When I hear that David Duke, one-time Grand Wizard of the Louisiana KKK, is running for governor again on the ticket that all people with AIDS should be tattooed in the genital area with glow-in-the-dark ink? I hear it and I want to throw up even though morning sickness hasn't bothered me for months. You see, if they're saying these things it means there are lots of people out there who believe them. After I've screamed myself out, my mother suggests I take some deep breaths and concentrate on knitting baby booties so this baby's tootsies won't get cold. Even she agrees it's a cold cold cold world out there—even though this baby's due any day now, in the heat of July. "No, not the Fourth of July," I said to the doctor. "I don't think I could take it," and I kept thinking red-white-and-blue, flags and patriotism, Veterans of Foreign Wars and Daughters of the American Revolution. I keep thinking how just up the street we wouldn't buy a house because the teeny tiny print at the end of the contract still said if we sold it again, it couldn't be to black people. "Fraid so. Fourth of July's your due date," the doctor said. "Now, calm down, just calm down. Everything will be OK. You'll probably be late and get to go to the parade anyway, but I'd suggest skipping the fireworks." And I think, "Shit. The fireworks. The only part of the Fourth that I like!"

It's afternoon and I've been yelling at the TV off and on for hours. They're holding hearings to cut funding for school lunches. They're holding hearings to find funding for another bomber. They're holding hearings on the nomination of Henry Foster to be Surgeon General, and Bob Dole says he won't let the nomination come to a vote on the Senate floor because Foster performed a perfectly legal procedure which happened to be an abortion. "Stop yelling," my mother says. "You can't do anything about any of this anyway." And I say, "Maybe that's why I'm yelling. Because they can't hear me. Because they won't hear me." I think, Little Baby, how can I love you so fiercely when I don't even know you? You're crammed in there, waiting, with your thumb in your mouth, your glassy slate-blue eyes closed, hiccuping. I'm so scared for you.

When Marco comes home at dusk, I scream at him that they're cutting the clean water act and I just heard on the news that one fifth of the cities in America already have substandard water. He says, "I know. I know. Those shits," he says. "What are we going to do?" he asks and he hugs me. I'm already thinking about letters to the editor, ads in *The New York Times* signed by every scientist in the country, but I take a break to open the bag he's brought home. He's brought us those red-white-and-blue rocket popsicles. We sit on the porch slurping on them, unsure if the world's going to blow up. The temperature's dropping to something bearable, and the sky's a limpid purple. On Tuesday night the fireworks will send up shocks of white and green and blue against that backdrop. Carol called the other day—they've followed up an old lead and think it's probably algae that finally killed the birds. It's the same blue-green algae that blooms off-shore and makes shellfish inedible, perfectly natural, but how do you separate them? The bacteria and the chemicals that allow it to flourish, all the selenium from agricultural run-off that weakened the birds' immune systems? I think of the grebes doing their mating dance, the ones that are left, the way they seem to stand on the water and turn their heads from side to side, showing off their golden plumes. I think of their mellow voices, the koo-r-r-eep call across the lake, saying they're here, hoping for a reply.

Piece of Blue

Bambi washes dishes at the Diamond Star truck stop where Iowa fits into Illinois but what she really does is play guitar. Acoustic.

She wears long pale blue gloves while she washes dishes. She wrote a song about them, about how the gloves are like an infinite longing of blue, like little blue skies, the road to wide open spaces she wants to see.

"You're one weird kid," Terry, the day shift waitress, tells her. When Terry misses her shift—sometimes she goes driving off with a trucker, "forever," she always says—Bambi waits tables in her place.

"I know someday the right man's gonna drive through here, and he's gonna take me with him," Terry says. Terry gives Bambi tips on hair.

"Honey, if I was naturally blonde like you, I'd work it. Why just look at you, all that plain hangdog hair. Tease it up a little, and lighten it a shade or two. At the very least you could comb out some of those knots." Terry's cotton candy hair is streaked three shades of yellow—ash blonde, honey blonde and platinum. After the hair, she advises frosted lipstick, that's the finishing touch.

Bambi dreams of leaving the truck stop and the Midwest. She'd like to live by water. She lives with her grandmother, Maggie, in a small clapboard house unpainted for 10 winters with a narrow, weedy backyard and one fruitless apple tree, behind which runs a train track. The china rattles when a train passes, though most of Maggie's china is plastic. Maggie, who took Bambi in when she was eight, cannot for the life of her figure out why her daughter would name a child Bambi.

"I told her, 'Lucille, you're just setting up that child for a life of ridicule. And tragedy. That child will never have a chance. You just watch, her daddy will die in a fire or something.'"

The truth is, no one knows where Bambi's father is. He left when she was five. Bambi's mother said "Well, honey, we'll just have to find you another daddy," and the men lined up outside their trailer like a string of pearls, Maggie said, but all they wanted was to run their hands down her mom's long back and hitch up her short skirts.

The men had smells. Brut, that was one Bambi remembered. And beer. The beer smell was everywhere, and they wore a lot of plaid shirts although there was one nice man, the only really nice one, who wore cowboy boots and plain tee shirts. He'd been coming around for a couple of months, and he could cook, thank heavens because she was so tired of TV dinners and pot pies and macaroni and cheese from the box, and he said he'd rather die than eat Jell-O. He told Bambi that not only was she a cute little thing, but he could see talent bursting out of her eyes and fingertips, musical talent, and then he left his guitar to get some more beer and was in a head-on with a Sunoco truck. Bambi's mother, who had certainly seen men come and go, just plain lost it when this one went, and after getting out of the hospital, went to live with her sister Kate where she seems to get along fine but she doesn't talk anymore and brushes her hair all day. Kate hides the hairbrush when Lucille's hair gets a little too thin. Bambi moved in with her grandmother, 200 miles west of Kate's house, and takes the bus to see her mother at Christmas and Thanksgiving.

Bambi wrote a song about a woman who combed out all her blonde hair. She carries a little lock of her mother's hair in a silver heart Maggie gave her on her 16th birthday. It's the only jewelry she wears.

Bambi's 19th birthday falls on a Saturday and she has the day off. It's a hot August day, and she takes her guitar and walks through the tall scratchy weeds to the train tracks thinking she'll write something on the pleasant side, or least with a happy ending. But about a foot from the tracks, right where they start to curve, she sees a champagne-colored dog lying still on the champagne-colored stones. Its front legs are tucked under him, his head turned like he'd been hit there, not hard enough to bleed, but hard enough, and flies ornament his blond eyelashes, and she sits down by the dog's body and writes a song.

At work the next day, Terry tells Bambi to try dressing up. "Try a mini, it won't bite you know." Bambi only wears jeans. Even when she fills in for Terry she wears jeans but with a white apron.

"We got to get out of here someday," Terry tells Bambi. "Someday we'll find Mr. Right."

"Nobody's ever my type," Bambi says.

"Well, just what is your type? I ain't never seen your type."

"I don't want a guy in a plaid shirt and baseball cap and blue jeans slipping down off his paunch."

"Men is men, honey, you can at least try to have a good time."

"I don't want to have a good time. I'm waiting for a guy who's kinda tragic, who likes animals, who thinks even dead animals are beautiful and could imagine what they were like when they was alive, can fix a saggin porch, barbecue and write poems or songs or something, and mostly drive me away to a house by the edge, to a house with blue shutters by the sea. Otherwise, we can just keep on driving. We can pull into truck stops or Howard Johnson's and hold coffee cups, real cups, not paper, to warm our hands and I'd never have to wash the dishes, all those lipstick marks and greasy fingerprints, and we'd stop at scenic overlooks and see things that look like postcards and watch rivers and see tall white birds, and birds with shiny blue feathers and watch the colors in the sky change along the horizon, and maybe write songs on the way."

"On the way to where, Bambi? You ever think of settling down?"

"Terry, I'm already settled down." She holds up her hands in the rubber gloves and soapy water drips to her elbows. "Down as far as you get."

"Bambi, honey, you're depressing."

"Thanks," she says, and means it.

One day a convertible, not a truck, pulls in and a young man in black jeans, not blue, walks into the Diamond Star.

"I got a real live wire for you honey," Terry says running back into the kitchen to get Bambi.

She yanks off her apron and hands it to Bambi. "Go on, wait on him."

The young man's legs are long and stretch out under the seat of the booth across from him so his boots disappear. He's wearing a white tee shirt greyed by dust. Something about the way he's sitting makes his shoulders angle forward, the bones poke out like clipped bird wings. No cologne, she can tell when she stands over him and hands him a menu.

"Hello Blue," he smiles with the easy charm of someone who doesn't stay in one place too long. The handsome smile of a man she worries may have had far too happy a childhood.

"The name's Bambi." She smiles but not easily the way her mother always had.

"Bambi Blue," he says. The white teeth and wind chapped lips stretch into a convertible smile but this time something seems sad about him.

"What'll it be?" Bambi asks.

"I had a dog called Bambi," he says.

"What kind of a dog?" She thinks about the champagne colored dog with the pinioned arms on the tracks, how it blended with the landscape, complimented it even, its hardened stone body with crewcut smooth soft fur on the smooth stones.

"Looked like a deer. Dappled fur like moonlight hitting his back through leaves, and a long pretty nose. He, well," and the young man looks out the window. The convertible looks as blue as the early cloudless sky but with red paint glinting through a scrape now and then. "Um, I'll have a burger with Swiss."

Back in the kitchen, Terry falls all over Bambi.

"I have a feeling about this one. This could be the real thing. He's so cute. Something different about him, I swear I can feel it. What's his name?"

"I don't know. How am I supposed to know that?"

"Cause this is a truck stop and you have to work fast. So what did you find out?"

"He's got blue eyes, almost too blue, and wavy black hair. Looks like he uses pomade."

"He say anything to you?"

"He told me he had a dog."

"You're doing fine. Getting to the basics. Nothing's more basic than a dog."

The young man is staring out at his convertible like he's got something valuable in it. Or like maybe he's crazy about his car, driving his car and feeling the wind pressing his tee shirt against his chest and painting his teeth with coolness and rushing into his mouth while he sings.

"Pony," he says, and holds out his hand when she comes back with his order. He has long fingers like someone who plays piano or holds paint-brushes and his nails are clean, relatively, for out here.

Bambi puts the plate down in front of him, softly, not with the usual heavy institutional clatter. She shakes his hand, his left hand.

"That sure is a nice name. You traveling alone?"

"Not exactly. I got a coupla things in my Galaxie. My harmonicas. And my guitar," he smiles. "It's like an old friend."

"I know what you mean. I play too."

"You do? You learn out here?" The young man scans the parking lot scattered with wide-bodied trucks, and the grunts and rumbles of engines lose their background humdrum quality and suddenly seem loud and vulgar.

"I didn't take lessons, if that's what you mean. I taught myself, you know, listening to things, the radio and everything. And I had a book, for chords. Everything I play is my own stuff."

"Must be lonely out here," he says and runs his finger around the rim of his plate, slowly, like he has all the time in the world. "What do you write?"

"Not about any one thing. Things I see. Like down by the railroad tracks behind our house. On the roadside. And things I've never seen too, that could happen miles from here. And the wind. How the wind sounds behind the house, how it feels in your hair. And sometimes I write about hair. People who comb their hair too much."

"Sounds pretty sensual. Will you play me something? I'd really love it if you did."

The young man looks down. Through his black lashes she sees glimpses of blue, his eyes, cold as blue glass, not warm like the hot coffee sound of his morning voice.

"I got to work."

"Come on, just one song. We could go for a little drive while you play," and he winks. His lashes are long, longer than hers, and she takes a step away.

Bambi shakes her head but smiles.

"You could always play me something, you know. You could lean out on that car of yours and play me something. I'll leave the door open."

"Tell you what," he says looking out at the highway. "I'll play you one song. Then I have to go drop something off." He looks up at the car. "But I'll come back." He looks into her eyes, not up and down her legs like the men her mom brought home, and she knows she has never seen more dangerously beautiful eyes, his pupils wide and wild like he's looking at a good poker hand. "I'll come back for you. I'll come back for you, Bambi Blue."

"You don't eat Jell-O, do you?" she asks him when she sees him finishing up, and it occurs to her that his eyes have that same see-through effect.

"Hell no. I'd sure love a cup of coffee though. That okay?"

"That's just fine."

Back in the kitchen she combs her hair and sees that her face is flushed like pink makeup. He's so handsome and hasn't called her "Doll" or "Hon." When she carries over the coffee it swirls recklessly in the cup, sloshing into the saucer. She puts it down and her hands are trembling and he touches, just barely, her fingers. Her silver locket throbs against her chest and she feels a wave of dizziness, like floating.

"I must be dreaming, Bambi Blue," he says, and kisses her hand.

When he leaves, she hears small stones scatter under his boots and when she looks out, after hearing the trunk slam, he's holding a red guitar. It's glistening, polished, without a single smudge mark. He's holding it pridefully, stroking its curved flank like he has a lot of feeling for it, the way some people seem to feel about their cars, maybe more feeling for the guitar than people. Maybe he'd just never met the right girl before.

He sings. His voice is warm, crooning, sweet and hot in places, and she feels it burn in her chest and her heart beats too fast. She can't make out any of the words, just feels the sound of his voice, like a temperature, sticky like maple syrup spilled on the counter. She thinks about leaning against his shoulder in the car. The kitchen light is a golden firefly, a luminous moon, because it'll be the last day. Maybe she'll give notice, but that wasn't likely with the car waiting, top down, they could put it up when it got chilly, August nights were like that, and they would just drive. He would ask her to sing, ask her why all her songs were so sad. He would understand. "These songs are all sad because I wrote them before I met you, Pony."

He stops singing. Bambi hadn't planned to go outside. She thought it would be more romantic if he just drove away and came back later, like something in a movie. But she steps out of the door as Pony is staring at the strings sparkling in the late summer light. He doesn't see her coming up behind him as he opens the trunk and lays the guitar on a piece of plastic that covers a bulky tarp stained dark and wet. She stares at his hands and the polished guitar, and catches a glimpse of a delicate hand with pink polish, not even chipped. Jutting out from the tarp, stiffened into a fist and clutching a pale blue guitar pick.

He doesn't see Bambi until he's slammed the trunk. He seems taller now, thinner, his eyes even bluer outside.

"Hey, how long were you standing there?" he says. His pupils are constricted. Through his lips, his teeth sparkle.

"A long time," Bambi says. She smiles and looks down. Blonde tangles fall across her face.

He pulls a tendril of her hair and then walks slowly, too slowly, around to his door and hops over it and eases into the seat. The vinyl is red and warm—she is trembling, imagining her body jerking over speed bumps— and she runs her hand along the top of the passenger side.

"Get in." He starts the car. The motor idles.

"I'm not ready," she says.

"I think you are," he smiles.

She shakes her head, no.

"Last chance."

He drives off, turns back to blow Bambi a kiss and accelerates.

Bambi stands on the gravel where she imagines she feels the heat of his singing, where maybe a remnant of the shadow of his Galaxie still cools the stones.

She picks up the phone to call the sheriff. She'll have to call information for the number. That will give Pony some time. She jots down the number on a blank receipt. She starts to dial. Thank heavens it's not a push button phone, with a push button, you don't have time to think, it all happens so fast. She could visit Pony in jail, touch hands through Plexiglas and wait for him like the women in movies, he could even be innocent, he looked innocent enough, and his hands, ringless unmarried hands, were poetic, maybe even fragile. The sheriff she is dialing is a married man, married three times, the first two got boring, she figured, there was no real love in him, just plain coming home at night with his beer belly and big swollen hands the color of raw bacon, and his newest wife would have pork chops and gravy waiting for him to eat in front of the sports channel, there was no music in him, and he was there the time the young man who robbed the convenience store got his head kicked in and accidentally shot.

Pony is not like him, a bacon man. She puts the receiver down.

She wants to tell Terry. Someone should know. But that would change things. Bambi doesn't want to be tragic. She'd rather be left behind with the sound of his voice resonating like something already familiar, too familiar, like looking at old prom photos or wedding photos, or something else you do with a man. A man you could love until he drives away, or dies or kills you or whatever, because that's how love ends up when it's the real thing, at least that's what Terry would say.

That evening the late-shift waitress comes in and Terry squeezes into a lemon yellow dress with pink roses at the bosom and says, "Well Bambi, I guess this dream didn't come true, maybe you're better off, you never know." Then Terry slides into her good, uncomfortable shoes and stares across the parking lot and the muscles in her face slump like they do when she stares at herself in the grey windows at night after a handsome trucker has driven off and the line deepens between her eyebrows like a furrow, like a place to plant a small flower.

When Bambi drives home the land is flat and waterless and the sky is darkening. An overly exuberant pink at the edge of the sky will soon be crushed into evening. She makes up a song about how Pony's eyes could blend with that landscape on a day with cold, painfully clear, dreamless air. She'll play it for Terry tomorrow morning while she's making the coffee.

Debra Riggin Waugh

A Little Pagan Holiday

I'm dating this woman who calls herself a pagan, and at first I'm thinking *what the fuck?* because I really have no idea what a pagan is, but anything that smacks of religion makes me feel a little creepy when I'm in the same room with it. I'm afraid she might be one of those "spiritual" dykes, who performs rituals in circles with other women in the moonlight and wears lots of purple and jewelry with stars on it.

She says she wants to celebrate Beltane with me, and I say "you wanna what?" and she explains that it's a little pagan holiday. At first I think she says it's a little *pig* on holiday and I'm picturing the two of us maybe eating a bacon, lettuce, and tomato sandwich and sipping frozen drinks with little paper umbrellas in New Orleans or the Caribbean, but then I realize I must have heard wrong because, well, my hearing's not quite what it used to be. So now we've established we're talking about pagan holidays and not pigs on vacation, which makes sense because us eating BLTs in some fun place sure wouldn't be much of a celebration for a little pig named Beltane.

I want to be open-minded—culturally adaptable, if you will—but still I get a little nervous and politely but firmly explain that, although I like her very much, I will not dance naked in the moonlight with her and a bunch of other women and I don't do circles!

She explains that Beltane is a spring holiday about planting and ensuring fertility of the crops. It's an ancient Celtic feast, she says, with bonfires and various rites of purification. And, although once upon a time the holiday involved a young virgin and a man dressed up like a deer or a horned god or something, today basically the only observance required is that we, pardon the expression, "fuck our brains out." Now this is a holiday I can sink my teeth into, so to speak, and I agree to observe in this manner all pagan holidays (of which it appears there are many)—and Flag Day, Arbor Day, Cinco de Mayo, Groundhog Day, and Bastille Day. Isn't Norwegian Independence Day or the Feast of the Immaculate Conception coming up soon?

I suspect this woman may be pulling my leg about the sex requirement on holidays and during full moons in Scorpio, and she certainly doesn't need such elaborate schemes to get into my pants—it's just not that hard. But as long as she promises I won't have to run around some cornfield with a buck-naked man with antlers strapped on his head, she can sign me up as a member of the loyal order of pagans today.

Diane Williams

THE BRILLIANTS

The sky might not have been too bright for them. The clouds were innately ornate. There were too many clouds.

The man was elated by the abundance of decorative clouds, by their prominence.

The man picked up off of the ground scraps of anything from trees. On that particular day, the woman had forgotten her purpose.

Yet on another day, the woman had been the one to clean up. She vacuumed. She washed. She sponged the surface of a bottle of mineral water. She rinsed the nail parings down the drain. The sink was wetted with greasy water, leftover water, yellow water, white watery water, water which is not transparent water. This is water.

The water has only been appreciated since the beginning of last week, after the discovery of the patches of irridescence in it.

The water is somewhat rare, has a slight turbidity. The value of water is fairly low, has a very low value, the lowest.

The woman and the man are of modest value.

One method is used to determine their value, mine.

Pairs of people have a relatively unimportant vitreous luster. They command sympathy, have heart attacks, weeping spells. They grow suspicious.

A man alone in the natural world is tidy.

Contributors' Notes

memoirs

Nick Cave was born in Australia in 1957, and achieved early recognition as a founding member of the rock group The Birthday Party. His novel *And the Ass Saw the Angel* (Penguin, 1989) and his two volumes of lyrics and poems *King Ink* (Black Spring Press, 1989) and *King Ink II* (Black Spring Press, 1997) supplement a prolific stream of recordings and gigs with the Bad Seeds. His latest CD is *Murder Ballads* (Mute Records, 1996).

Joan Haverty Kerouac (1930-1990) married Jack Kerouac on November 17, 1950. The marriage fell apart in July 1951, after Joan discovered she was pregnant with Jack's daughter Jan. Her unpublished memoirs, *Nobody's Wife,* cover the years 1949 to 1951. After her death, her children went through the house and discovered pages of the manuscript hidden about the house, even behind the walls. *The Wedding Chapter* was published as a chapbook in an edition of 240 copies for the Beat Generation conference at NYU, in May of 1994.

Richard McCann's *Ghost Letters* won the 1993 Capricorn Poetry Award, and the 1994 Beatrice Hawley Award. He is also the author of *Dream of the Traveler* and *Nights of 1990,* and the co-editor (with Margaret Gibson) of *Landscape and Distance: Contemporary Poets from Virginia.* His work has appeared in *The Atlantic, The Nation,* and *Esquire,* as well as in numerous anthologies, including *The Penguin Book of Gay Short Stories.* Richard lives in DC where he co-directs the graduate program in creative writing at American University.

Gregg Shapiro's poetry and fiction have been published or are forthcoming in a wide variety of magazines and anthologies including: *Spoon River Poetry Review, membrane, Columbia Poetry Review, Modern Words, Christopher Street, WordWrights!, Illinois Review, The Evergreen Chronicles, Amethyst, Hammers, Private, The Quarterly, Blood To Remember* (Texas Tech University Press, 1991), *Mondo Barbie* (St. Martin's Press, 1993), *Unsettling America* (Viking/Penguin, 1994), *Mondo Marilyn* (St. Martin's Press, 1995), and *Reclaiming The Heartland* (University of Minnesota Press, 1996), to name a few. His music reviews, book reviews and feature stories also appear regularly in *Nightlines, New City, The Texas Triangle, Outlines, En La Vida, The Weekly News, Bay Windows,* and *Illinois Entertainer.* He lives with his life-partner, writer Rick Karlin, their dog Sasha and cat Goober in Chicago's Andersonville neighborhood. Gregg appeared in *Gargoyle 35.*

poetry

Patience Agbabi is Nigerian and British, and blends elements from rap, punk, ska, and blues in her performances. Her book of poems is *R.A.W.* (Gecko Press, 1995). She lives in London.

Elizabeth Alexander is the author of *The Venus Hottentot* (University Press of Virginia, 1990). Her latest collection of poems *Body of Life* has just been published by Tia Chucha Press. She teaches at the University of Chicago.

Bob Arnold is the author of the trilogy *This Romance (On Stone, By Heart, This Romance)* as well as *Where Rivers Meet* and other books of poetry. Coyote published his travel book *American Train Letters* in 1995. For many years he has worked as a stonemason making a home in Vermont with his family.

Jeanne Marie Beaumont's poems have appeared in *New American Writing, Antioch Review, Seneca Review,* the anthologies *Mondo Barbie* and *Mondo Marilyn,* and other friendly venues. Her book, *Placebo Effects,* a 1996 National Poetry Series selection, is forthcoming from Norton in fall of '97. She is editor of the journal *American Letters & Commentary* and lives in New York City.

Paul Bennett's writing appears constantly, almost always under other people's names. He has written two books (on a subject which no longer fascinates him) and has collaborated on several screenplays. Writing in his own voice, he has published fiction for young readers and a handful of poems. Paul lives in DC.

James Berry, now a septuagenerian, was raised in Jamaica. His latest volume of poems is *Hot Earth, Cold Earth* (Bloodaxe, 1995). He was also the editor of the seminal Anglo-Caribbean anthology *News for Babylon* (Chatto and Windus, 1984). He lives in Brighton, in the U.K.

James Bertolino has been writing poetry, fiction, essays and non-fiction since the early sixties. His seventh and eight volumes of poetry, *First Credo* (1986) and *Snail River* (1995), both won the international QRL poetry competition and were published by the *Quarterly Review of Literature Poetry Series* at Princeton University. James had poems in *Gargoyle* 27 and 37/38.

Kevin Bezner's collection *In the City of Troy* is just out from the Cincinnati Writer's Project. Kevin had a poem in *Gargoyle 37/38.*

Valerie Bloom is a Jamaican poet whose work is usually read in a pungent patwa. Her books include *Touch Mi! Tell Mi!* (Bogle l'Ouverture, 1982) and Duppy Jamboree (Cambridge, 1992).

Katherine Burger writes poetry and fiction, but is primarily a playwright. Her one-act play *Way Deep* was published by Samuel French and has been performed throughout the United States. Her current project is illustrating a novella she wrote about her cat.

Michael Collier teaches English at the University of Maryland, College Park. His three books of poems are *The Clasp and Other Poems, The Folded Heart,* and *The Neighbor.* Michael is also the editor of *The Wesleyan Tradition: Four Decades of American Poetry.*

Lynn Crosbie's poems in this issue are reprinted from *Pearl,* her new book of poems which is not being distributed in the US. Her other books include *Miss Pamela's Mercy* and *VillanElle* and she lives in Toronto, Canada.

Jim Daniels' next book, *Blessing the House,* is forthcoming from the University of Pittsburgh Press in Spring 1997. Other recent books of poetry include *M-80* (Pittsburgh, 1993), and *Niagara Falls,* a long poem (Adastra Press, 1994). He edited the anthology, *Letters to America: Contemporary Poetry on Race* (Wayne State, 1995), and wrote the screenplay for *No Pets,* a 1994 feature film directed by Tony Buba. Jim had poems in *Gargoyle 1* and *35.*

Donna Denizé is a teacher of English at St. Albans School for Boys in DC. She is a graduate of Howard University and Stonehill College. In 1986, she received grants to attend the Bread Loaf School of English, Lincoln College at Oxford University, and the Johns Hopkins Summer Writers' Conference.

Denise Duhamel is the author of five books of poetry: *Exquisite Politics* (with Maureen Seaton, Tia Chucha Press 1997), *Kinky* (Orchises Press 1997), *Girl Soldier* (Garden Street Press 1996), *The Woman with Two Vaginas* (Salmon Run Press 1995) and *Smile!* (Warm Spring Press 1993.) Denise had a poem in *Gargoyle 37/38.*

Russell Edson's latest book is entitled *The Tunnel: Selected Poems of Russell Edson* (Oberlin College Press, 1994).

Elaine Equi's books include *Surface Tension* and *Decoy,* both published by Coffee House Press. A new collection, *Voice-Over,* is forthcoming in 1998. She has recent work in *APR, Conjunctions, Grand Street,* and forthcoming in *New American Writing.* Elaine was interviewed in *Gargoyle 24,* and had poems in *32/33.*

Sunil Freeman has lived most of his life in the DC metro area. He works at the Writer's Center in Bethesda, MD, where, among other things, he is managing editor of *Poet Lore.* Sunil has poems recently published or forthcoming in *Bogg* and *WordWrights!* He performs with Michael Schaffner and Jim Henley in the group Men Without Drums. His book of poems is *That Would Explain the Violinist* (Gut Punch Press, 1993). Sunil had a poem in *Gargoyle 37/38.*

John Hegley has been captivating audiences for 25 years as a comedian/poet-singer-songwriter-guitarist. He began his career at London's notoriously tough Comedy Store. His work includes the 1988 ep *I Saw My Dinner On TV* which features Robyn Hitchcock, the CD *Saint and Blurry,* plus the books *Glad to Wear Glasses, Can I Come Down Now, Dad?,* and *Five Sugars Please.*

Michael Horovitz has spent most of his adult life as a poet, singer-songwriter, jazz and blues kazooist, clown, impresario, visual artist, translator, literary journalist and editor-publisher (mainly of New Departures publications). His poetry books in print are *Midsummer Morning Jog Log,* a 700-line rurual rhapsody illustrated by Peter Blake (Five Seasons Press, 1986), and *Wordsounds & Sightlines: New & Selected Poems* (Sinclair-Stevenson, 1994). Michael was interviewed in *Gargoyle 14,* and had poems or prose in 9 and 10.

Barbara Hurd is the recipient of two Maryland State Arts Council awards in poetry (1993 and 1995), winner of the 1994 Artscape competition, and the author of *Objects in this Mirror* (a chapbook). Her work has appeared in numerous literary journals. She teaches creative writing at Frostburg State University in Frostburg, MD, and is program director of The Western Maryland Writer's Workshop and the Mountain Lake Writers' festival.

Reuben Jackson loves New York City madly, but still lives in Washington, DC, where he works as an archivist with the Smithsonian's Duke Ellington Collection, and writes music reviews for the *Washington Post.* He still thinks O.J. did it, and that the 1996 Baltimore Orioles were robbed. His book of poems is *fingering the keys* (Gut Punch Press, 1990). Reuben had poems in *Gargoyle 34, 35,* and *37/38.*

Mahmook Jamal was born in Lucknow, India in 1948. His family migrated to Pakistan in the early 1950s and came to England in 1967. He edited and translated the *Penguin Book of Urdu Verse* (1986), and has also scripted, produced, and directed many music, drama, and documentary films, mainly for Channel 4. His poetry books are *Coins for Charon* (Courtfield Press, 1976), and *Silence Inside a Gun's Mouth* (Kala Press, 1984). He lives in London.

Ron Kolm is an editor of *Appearances* magazine and a member of the Unbearables (as well as an editor of their anthology from Autonomedia). His work has appeared in *Redtape, New Observations, Public Illumination Magazine, Semiotext(e),* and *Between C&D.* His books include *The Plastic Factory* (Red Dust) and *Rank Cologne* (P.O.N. Press).

Inge Elsa Laird, born in Germany of Hungarian and Jewish ancestry, has lived and worked mainly in England since 1962. Her minimalist poetry, prose, and translations have been published in the *Financial Times, Jewish Chronicle,* etc. She is co-editor of *New Departures,* and co-organizer of Poetry Olympics, in addition to working as an interpreter/translator.

Michael Lally was born in Orange, New Jersey in 1942. Since winning the New York Poetry Center's "Discovery Award" in 1972 and editing the seminal new poetry anthology *None Of The Above,* he has gone on to act in both television and movies. His books include *The South Orange Sonnets, Rocky Dies Yellow, Catch My Breath,* and *Cant Be Wrong.* He currently lives in Santa Monica, California.

Fran Landesman was born Frances Deitsch in Manhattan to a Seventh Avenue dress manufacturer and a former newspaperwoman. She attended Temple University and studied textile design at the Fashion Institute of Technology before running into Jay Landesman, editor of *Neurotica* in Greenwich Village. They gravitated to St. Louis where Fran wrote lyrics to Jay's musical productions: *The Nervous Set* (which played Broadway in 1959) and *Molly Darling*. The couple transplanted permanently to London in the spring of 1964. Fran's books include *The Ballad of the Sad Young Men* (Polytantric Press, 1975), *Invade My Privacy* (Cape, 1978), *More Truth Than Poetry* (The Permanent Press, 1979), *Is It Overcrowded in Heaven?* (Golden Handshake, 1981), *The Thorny Side of Love* (sun tavern fields, 1992), and *Rhymes at Midnight* (Golden Handshake, 1996). Fran is a frequent broadcaster on BBC radio and had a musical, *Did We Have Any Fun?*, with music by Simon Wallace, performed in London in the spring of 1996.

Priscilla Lee is a Chinese Buddhist witch in training. Her poetry has appeared in *Phoebe, ZYZZYVA,* and *Kenyon Review.* By day, she works as a technical writer at a company called Oracle.

Gwyneth Lewis, writes in her first language, Welsh, and also in English. Her prize-winning first volume of poems, *Parables and Faxes* (Bloodaxe, 1995), won accolades from the late Joseph Brodsky. She lives in Cardiff, Wales.

Paul Lyalls was born in 1965 in Goole, a shipbuilding town in Yorkshire. He's lived in London for a long time and is immensely proud of the fact that he was alive the last time England won the World Cup. He has published several short books of poetry and almost makes a living performing throughout the UK.

Joanna McClure was born Joanna Kinnison and grew up on her parents' U Circle desert ranch in the foothills of the Catalina Mountains near Oracle, Arizona. She met Michael McClure when they were both students at the University of Arizona. After she divorced her first husband, Albert Hall, she moved to San Francisco and married McClure. She wrote her first poem in 1958. Her books—*Wolf Eyes* (Bearthm Press, 1974), *Extended Love Poem* (Arif Press, 1978), *Hard Edge* (Coffee House, 1987)—contain only a portion of her written work from 1960-on.

Jeffrey McDaniel's book of poems is *Alibi School* (Manic D Press, 1995). His poems have appeared in *Ploughshares, Exquisite Corpse, Epoch, Willow Springs, Phoebe,* and *Best American Poetry 1994.* Jeff has performed his work at the 1994 Lollapalooza Festival, the Moscow Writers Union, the Globe in Prague, the National Poetry Slam, and at venues throughout the U.S.

Heather McHugh teaches two-thirds time at the University of Washington in Seattle and is a core faculty member of the MFA Program for Writers at Warren Wilson College in Asheville, N.C. Her most recent books are *Hinge & Sign: Poems 1968–1993* (a National Book Award finalist) and a collection of essays *Broken English: Poetry and Partiality.* Heather had a poem in *Gargoyle 37/38.*

E. Ethelbert Miller serves as an editor on various literary publications, including the *African-American Review.* Author of eight books of poetry, he is a board member of the PEN/Faulkner Foundation and the director of the African American Resource Center at Howard University. His most recent collection of poetry is *First Light: New and Selected Poems* (Black Classic Press, 1994). He is also the editor of *In Search of Color Everywhere: A Collection of African-American Poetry.* Ethelbert had poems in *Gargoyle 4, 5,* and *35.*

George Myers Jr. is the author of *Natural History, Worlds Without End* and *Alphabets Sublime.* He is books editor for *The Columbus Dispatch,* in Ohio; and a former director of the National Book Critics Circle.

Peggy Pfeiffer coedited *Gargoyle* from 1988–1990. She lives these days in Santa Fe, New Mexico, where she runs her own graphics company, GraphX.

Margaret Randall was born in New York City. Her family moved to Albuquerque, New Mexico, when she was in 6th grade and she attended the University of New Mexico. She lived on the Lower East Side from 1958–61. A prolific writer, her books include *Giant of Tears* (1959), *Ecstasy is a Number* (1960), *Small Sounds From the Bass Fiddle* (1964), *Songs of the Grass, October, Water I Slip Into At Night, 25 stages of my spine* (Elizabeth Press, 1967), *So Many Rooms Has a House* (New Rivers, 1968), *Part of the Solution* (New Directions, 1973), *Cuban Women Now* (The Women's Press, 1974), *We* (Smyrna Press, 1978), *Albuquerque: Coming Back to the USA* (Left Bank, 1986), *This is About Incest* (Firebrand, 1987), *Coming Home: Peace Without Complacency* (West End, 1990), *Walking to the Edge: Essays of Resistance* (South End, 1991), *Sandino's Daughter Revisited: Feminism in Nicaragua* (Rutgers, 1994). Between 1951 and 1985 she lived in Mexico City, Cuba, and Nicaragua. In 1989 she won a lengthy battle with the U.S. Immigration and Naturalization Service after it tried to deport her because of opinions expressed in her work.

Simon Scardanelli, songwriter and composer, has released records under the names of *Big Bam Boo* (1988–90) and *The Eye Camera* (1993–4), as well as under his own name. Scardanelli is currently studying 20th Century Music at the University of Sussex (Brighton, England) and working on a collection of songs for CD release in late 1997. For further information, e-mail: fauzl@central.susx.ac.uk

Maggie Smith has a degree in Horiculture and has worked as a florist. She's an AiE Poet-In-the-Schools in Maryland. Maggie's poems have appeared in *Poem, Pudding, Bellowing Ark,* and *Slightly West.*

Rose Solari's first full-length collection of poems, *Difficult Weather* (Gut Punch Press), was selected for the 1995 Columbia Award by Carolyn Forche; in 1996 she received an Exceptional Merit Media Award (EMMA) from the National Women's Political Caucus for journalism. She is currently at work on another collection of poems, *Myths and Elegies,* and a novel. Rose teaches at the Writer's Center in Bethesda, MD. She also appeared in *Gargoyle 36.*

Sparrow lives in New York City and is the only member of The Unbearables to actually appear in the *New Yorker.* Sparrow had poems in *Mondo Barbie* and *Mondo James Dean.*

Darrell Stover is a native Washingtonian now residing in Cary, NC. He directed "The Spoken Word Performance Ensemble" through 8 years of presentations and workshops culminating in the publishing of their anthology, *Bad Beats Sacred Rhythms,* and a live audio recording of same. Darrell has appeared in a *Good Morning America* segment on poetry, in the anthology *Fast Talk Full Volume,* and has recorded on the Eightball Label with "Peace Bureau" the Acid Jazz release *Acoustic Soulful Bebop Booms.* Darrell recently acquired an M.A. in writing from Johns Hopkins University with an emphasis in Science writing.

Silvana Straw's most recent adventures include a retrospective of her work entitled *The Uncle Silvana Show* through the WPA/Corcoran; and a collaboration with Guillermo Gomez-Pena in *The Dangerous Boarder Game* through the Washington Performing Arts Society. As the DC Poetry Slam Champion in 1993 and 1994, she competed in the National Poetry Slam in Asheville and San Francisco. From 1993–96, she produced the Poetry Bonanza Series at the Black Cat. She is currently organizing a poetry slam to be held at the Smithsonian in Spring '97. Publications include, *The WPA Document, Gargoyle 35, 36, 37/38,* and *Hungry As We Are.*

Andrea Tetrick hails from the sleepy little burg of Bishop, California, on the eastern side of the Sierra Nevada range. Currently living in Arlington, Virginia, she was most recently published in *Rain City Review, Northwest Literary Forum,* and *Pucker Up.* Her first volume of poems is due soon from Soft Skull Press.

David Trinidad's most recent book of poems is *Answer Song* (High Risk Books, 1994). He lives in New York City.

Laura Ulewicz was born in Detroit into a Polish-American family. After experimenting with Chicago and New York, she settled in 1951 in San Francisco where she lived in the Haight and Golden Gate Park; worked as a camera girl in night clubs and strip joints a few blocks from the soon-to-exist City Lights; hung out in North Beach; thought she was in heaven till the scene was publicized as "the Beat Generation" and the streets became full of pushy men eager for Free Love. Studied with Stanley Kunitz in Seattle, then landed in London where she met with THE GROUP at Lucie-Smith's and won a Guinness Poetry Award (money and publication of *The Inheritance*). She returned to the Haight in 1964 and worked at, then managed, then owned the I-Thou Coffee House and later the Root of Scarcity Herb-Grain-Coffee Store. She organized readings, art shows, etc., and had a radio program on KQED-FM interviewing writers. Settled in 1973 in the Sacramento Delta where she lives "fairly successfully in the Bronze Age" raising various kinds of garlic and everlasting flowers for sale at Farmer's Markets.

Lee Upton is the author of three books of poems: *The Invention of Kindness, No Mercy,* and *Approximate Darling.* She's an Assistant Professor at Lafayette College in Easton, Pennsylvania. Lee had a poem in *Gargoyle 22/23* and stories in *24* and *30/31.*

Janine Pommy Vega's books include *Poems to Fernando* (City Lights, 1968), *Journal of a Hermit &* (Cherry Valley Editions, 1979), *Morning Passage* (Telephone Books, 1976), *The Bard Owl* (Kulchur Foundation, 1980) and *Tracking the Serpent* (forthcoming from City Lights). Janine had poems in *Gargoyle 11* and *15/16,* and was interviewed in *14.* She lives these days just outside Bearsville, New York.

Dana Weimer recently won an Individual Artist Fellowship from the Arizona Commission on the Arts, and was a Writer-In-Residence for the Writer's Voice. Her work has been published or is forthcoming in *New Laurel Review, Hayden's Ferry Review, ONTHEBUS,* and *Outsider's, a Milkweed anthology.* Dana's first published poem appeared in *Gargoyle 37/38.* She lives in Tempe, AZ.

Valerie Wohlfeld, born in Sacramento, California, in 1956, spent portions of her childhood in American Samoa and Ecuador. She was educated at American University and Sarah Lawrence College and received an M.F.A. from Vermont College in 1983. Her poems have appeared in a number of periodicals, including *The New Yorker, Poetry, Pequod, Agni Review,* and *Western Humanities Review.* Her book, *Thinking the World Visible,* won the Yale Series of Younger Poets Prize in 1993. Valerie had a story in *Gargoyle 30/31.*

Karen Zealand is a counseling therapist in a psychology practice in Cumberland, MD. Karen's poems have appeared in many journals including *Southern Poetry Review, Nightsun, Poet Lore, 5 AM, Snake Nation Review,* and *Hayden's Ferry Review.* She has been awarded a Maryland State Arts Council Individual Artist Award in Poetry.

fiction

Jodi Bloom lives and works in Takoma, DC. Her fiction, poetry, and essays have appeared or are forthcoming in *Atom Mind, The Cherotic (R)evolutionary, The Washington Review, Happy, Potomac Review, Sulphur River Literary Review, Uno Mas, membrane, Caprice,* and *WordWrights!* Her chapbook *Brain Freeze & Other Stories* (Ancient Mariner's Press) was published in Fall '96.

Alison Bundy was born in Texas in 1959 and grew up in Unity, Maine. These days she lives in Providence, Rhode Island. Her books are *A Bad Business* (Lost Roads, 1985) and *Tales of a Good Cook* (paradigm press, 1992). Alison received her M.A. from the graduate writing program at Brown University.

Frank Costello is a lawyer in DC. Saratoga is a race track in Upstate New York. Julie Krone still rides, although injuries have had their effect. All of the other characters are fictious, although each can be found in infinite variations in Saratoga, in August. No horses were injured in the writing of this story.

Donya Currie was born in Atlanta and earned an undergraduate degree in journalism from the University of Florida. She currently is enrolled in the Part-Time Graduate Writing Program at Johns Hopkins University and works as a journalist in Washington, DC.

Lucinda Ebersole has had work published in *Yellow Silk, The Crescent Review, WordWrights!, American Letters & Commentary,* and *CUPS.* Her novel, *Death in Equality,* was recently published by St. Martin's Press. She is co-editor of *Women, Creativity and the Arts* (Continuum). And she has co-edited five pop culture anthologies with Richard Peabody including *Mondo Barbie* and *Mondo James Dean.*

Janice Eidus, two-time O. Henry Prize winner, is the author of the highly-acclaimed novels, *Urban Bliss* and *Faithful Rebecca,* and the short story collections, *Vito Loves Geraldine* and *The Celibacy Club.* Her work has been widely published and anthologized in the U.S. and abroad. Among the many anthologies in which her stories appear are *Mondo Elvis, Mondo James Dean,* and *Growing Up Female.*

Eurydice was born on Lesbos, Greece, and brought up in Alexandria and Athens. She has published two books of poetry, one in Greek. She holds a B.A. in creative writing and Fine Arts from Bard College, a Greek University degree in Minoan Archaeology, an M.A. in creative writing from the University of Colorado at Boulder, is a Ph.D. student in comparative literature at Brown University. Her books are *f/32* (Fiction Collective Two, 1990) and the novella *Scree* (forthcoming from Scribners in 1997). Excerpts from her work-in-progress, *EHMH,* have appeared in a few places including *after yesterday's crash: The Avant-Pop Anthology.*

Lauren Fairbanks is the author of a book of poetry, *Muzzle Thyself,* and a novel, *Sister Carrie,* both published by Dalkey Archive Press. She has degrees from the University of Scranton and the University of Chicago, and studied creative writing with both Gilbert Sorrentino and Richard Stern. She lives in Plano, Texas, with her husband and their baby boy.

Brian Gilmore was born and raised in WDC; Attorney, Neighborhood Legal Services Program. Poet. Writer. Collection, 1993, *elvis presley is alive and well and living in harlem,* Third World Press, Chicago. Poems published in *Warpland, Mondo Elvis, Fast Talk Full Volume,* and *In Search of Color Everywhere.* Essays appeared in *The Nation,* and on NPR. Working on a collection of essays and completing a short story manuscript entitled *Pork.*

Jaimy Gordon's second novel, *She Drove Without Stopping,* appeared in 1990 from Algonquin Books. She is also the author of a novella, *Circumspections from an Equestrian Statue* (Burning Deck), a narrative poem, *The Bend, The Lip, The Kid* (Sun), and the underground classic, *Shamp of the City-Solo* (McPherson & Company). With Peter Bickle she translates from the German, most recently *Lost Weddings,* a novel by Maria Beig (Persea Books, 1990). A chapter from *She Drove Without Stopping* appeared in Gargoyle *20/21,* and Jaimy was interviewed in *22/23.*

Karen Elizabeth Gordon is the author of *The Deluxe Transitive Vampire, The New Well-Tempered Sentence, The Red Shoes and Other Tattered Tales, The Ravenous Muse, PARIS out of hand* and the forthcoming volume from which the excerpts in this issue are taken, *The Dishelved Dictionary* (due from H. Mifflin in August). She divides her time between northern California and Paris.

Cathryn Hankla is the author of a collection of stories, *Learning the Mother Tongue;* a novel, *A Blue Moon in Poorwater;* two volumes of poetry, *Phenomena* and *Afterimages.* She teachers in the writing program at Hollins College in Virginia. Cathyrn had a story in *Gargoyle* 30/31. She also appeared in *Mondo Barbie* and *Mondo Elvis.*

David Haynes is the author of *Right by My Side, Somebody Else's Mama, Heathens, Live at Five,* and the forthcoming *All American Dream Dolls.* His stories have been published in *City Pages, Stiller's Pond, Other Voices* and *Glimmer Train* and recorded for the National Public Radio Series "Selected Shorts." He was selected by *Granta Magazine* as one of the Best of the Young American Novelists.

Cynthia Hendershot was born in New Mexico and now lives in Lubbock, Texas. Her collection of short fiction is *City of Mazes* (Asylum Arts, 1993).

Jamie Holland lives in DC. "Healing" is her first published story.

Hillary Johnson is the author of the novel *Physical Culture*. She has contributed to *The Wild Palms Reader* and *Mondo Marilyn*. St. Martin's Press is publishing her new book, entitled *Dymaxion Lounge*, in the spring of 1997. She lives in Los Angeles.

Dennis Jones is a defense contractor in DC. His fiction has appeared in *Georgetown Review*.

Lawrence Lebofsky after eight years has ditched DC to wander out west and write a novel.

Ben Marcus was born in 1967. He holds degrees from Brown and New York universities. His work has appeared in *Grand Street, Conjunctions, The Iowa Review,* and *The Quarterly,* and he is the recipient of a Pushcart Prize. His book of stories is *the age of wire and string*. He lives in New York City.

Carole Maso is the author of *Ghost Dance, The Art Lover, Ava, The American Woman in the Chinese Hat,* and *Aureole*. She teaches at Brown University.

Laura Mullen is the author of *The Surface*. She is on the faculty in the Creative Writing Program at Colorado State University.

Lance Olsen's many books include the novels *Tonguing the Zeitgeist, Burnt,* and *Time Famine,* the short story collection *Scherzi I Believe,* a book of essays on the future of American fiction *Surfing Tomorrow,* and the first critical study of the godfather of cyberpunk, William Gibson. He is director of Creative Writing at the University of Idaho. For a taste of the future check out his Café Zeitgeist digital retreat (http://www.uidaho.edu/~lolsen).

Leslie Pietrzyk's fiction has appeared in *The Iowa Review, New England Review, Shenandoah, The Crescent Review,* and other journals. She won the 1995 Chris O'Malley Fiction Award from *Madison Review* and her story in *Descant* was selected to receive the 1995 Frank O'Connor Memorial Award for Fiction. She lives in Alexandria, Virginia, and works at the Arlington Chamber of Commerce. Leslie had some reviews in *Gargoyle 32/33*.

Kate Pullinger was born in Canada and has lived and worked in London since 1982. Her first book, a collection of short stories, *Tiny Lies,* was published in 1988, followed by the novels, *When the Monster Dies,* and *Where Does Kissing End?* She edited an anthology of short stories, *Border Lines: Stories of Exile & Home,* a non-fiction compendium on the theme of gambling, *The Gambling Box,* as well as a collection of drawings by writers, *The Writer's Notebook*. She co-wrote the novel based on the film *The Piano* with director Jane Campion and has written for dance, film and television. A new novel, *The Last Time I Saw Jane,* was published in 1996, and the spring of 1997 will see the publication of a new book of short stories, *My Life as a Girl in a Men's Prison*.

Jessie Seigel's dialogue *After the Play* won first prize in a national contest conducted by Grove Press. Her poetry has been featured regularly in *The Boston Jewish Times*. She also collaborated on a translation of the "book" accompanying the compact disc *Napoli, Punto E A Capo,* containing Neapolitan songs sung by Renzo Arbore and the Orchestra Italiana, produced by Electra Entertainment, a division of Warner Communications, a Time Warner Company. Jessie lives in DC and is currently in the Masters Program for Writing at Johns Hopkins University.

Lewis Shiner lives in North Carolina with his wife, Mary Alberts. He is the author of several dozen short stories and four novels, the most recent of which, *Glimpses,* won the World Fantasy Award.

Phil Shöenfelt was born in 1952 in Bradford, England and has lived in London, New York, Morocco and Italy. He currently lives and works in Prague, Czech Republic. He has released several CDs, the most recent of which was *God is the Other Face of the Devil* and has played extensively in the USA and Europe. At present he is playing with the Czech band Southern Cross and will soon be recording a new CD. *Junkie Love* is his first novel and is published by Mat'a Books, Prague, in Czech translation. A bilingual collection of song lyrics and poetry *The Green Hotel* will be published by Mat'a in Spring 1997.

Don Skiles' poems and stories have appeared in a number of magazines, including *Real Fiction, Chelsea, West Branch, Sun & Moon,* and *Between C&D.* He also writes reviews for the *San Francisco Chronicle* and the *American Book Review.* He has published one volume of short fiction, *Miss America and Other Stories* (Marion Boyars, 1982), the title story of which appeared in *Gargoyle 22/23.* Don lives in San Francisco.

Julia Slavin is a former producer for ABC News in New York. She is now raising a family in DC. She has had stories published in *The Crescent Review* and *WordWrights!* and writes the popular internet soap opera *Barnaby Woods* on www.wald.com.

Maya Sonenberg's collection, *Cartographies,* received the Drue Heinz Literature Prize. The title story originally appeared in *Gargoyle 25/26.* More recently, stories have appeared in *American Short Fiction* and the *Santa Monica Review.* She currently lives in Oakland, CA and Seattle, WA where she teaches in the Creative Writing Program at the University of Washington. Thanks to the University of Washington Graduate School Fund, the Oregon State University Center for the Humanities, and the Oregon State University College of Liberal Arts for support during the writing of this story and others in the collection, *Voices from the Blue Hotel.*

Laren Elizabeth Stover received the Ludwig Vogelstein Foundation grant for fiction in 1991. She has been a resident of th Writers Room since 1992 where she completed her first novel, *Pluto, Animal Lover,* published by HarperCollins in 1994. Her short stories have appreared in *The Northwest Review, Bomb,* and *Contents Magazine.* Her "Roy Deutsch poems", the first of which appeared in *Gargoyle,* were set to music by composer Lowell Liebermann for his "Appalachian Liebeslieder", premiered by the New York Festival of Song in 1997.

Debra Riggin Waugh lives in Takoma Park, Maryland. A collection of her short stories— *Homo Neurotica*—is available on cassette. She is also the editor of *Ex-Lover Weird Shit* (Two Out of Three Sisters Press, 1994).

Diane Williams is the author of three short fiction collections: *This Is About the Body, the Mind, the Soul, the World, Time, and Fate,* as well as *Some Sexual Success Stories Plus Other Stories in Which God Might Choose to Appear,* and *The Stupefaction.* She is coeditor of *Story Quarterly* and lives in New York City.

artists & photographers

Annie Adjchavanich is a twenty-nine-year-old fine art and commercial photographer in Washington, DC. A graduate of the Corcoran School of Art she has been working on her own for nearly seven years. Her best known series of photographs, *Biological Men* was made from over three years of work with startlingly convincing female impersonators in the studio. *Boy Marilyn* was a 1996 recent acquisition by The Corcoran Gallery of Art. *Ann as Marilyn* is part of a Museum tour of the United States and Japan called *Elvis & Marilyn 2x Immortal.* She is represented by Hemphill Fine Arts in Washington, DC.

Rikki Ducornet has published a tetralogy of novels based on the four natural elements: *The Stain (earth), Entering Fire (fire), The Fountains of Neptune (water),* and *The Jade Cabinet (air).* She has also illustrated books by Robert Coover and J. L. Borges. Her volume of collected stories, *The Complete Butcher's Tales,* was recently published by Dalkey Archive Press.

Claudine Schafer-Legrand was born and educated in Switzerland, coming to London to study English in her early twenties and never really leaving. She was an artist, a photographer, a lover of language and music, a writer and interviewer, a squatter and a traveler. She died March 1st, 1996. She was 31.

Check It Out!

Robert Bly ⊙ Joseph Brodsky Jorge Luise Borges ⊙ William Matthews ⊙ Marge Piercy Mark Strand ⊙ Jane Hirshfield David Ignatow ⊙ Mona Van Duyn ⊙ Henry Taylor ⊙ Billy Collins ⊙ John Yau ⊙ Diane Wakoski ⊙ William Stafford May Sarton ⊙ Jane Kenyon Jon Stallworthy ⊙ Larry Levis Jean Valentine ⊙ Donald Hall Aleš Debeljak ⊙ Linda Pastan Brooks Haxton ⊙ Charles Baxter ⊙ Henri Cole ⊙ Greg Grummer ⊙ David Biespiel A.V. Christie ⊙ Roland Flint William Meredith ⊙ Boris Xristov ⊙ Paul Zimmer Robert Dana ⊙ Rod Jellema Melissa Green ⊙ Pattiann Rogers ⊙ Timothy Liu ⊙ Tom Sleigh ⊙ Rita Dove ⊙ Michael Collier ⊙ Stanley Plumly Laurie Sheck ⊙ Phillis Levin Michael Burkard ⊙ Lia Purpura

I enclose a check
Please forward my
subscription to:

Name _____

_____

City _____

State, Zip _____

○ 2 issues (1 year): $14
○ 4 issues (2 years): $28
○ 6 issues (3 years): $40

Plum Review
P.O. Box 1347
Philadelphia, PA
19105-1347

The 1997 Mississippi Review Prize

$1000 awarded to the winning story

$500 to the winning poem

Winners and all finalists in fiction and poetry will be published in print and online editions of *The Mississippi Review*.

1997 Jurors
Fiction:
Padgett Powell
Poetry:
Angela Ball

send entries to:
1997 mississippi review prize box 5144, hattiesburg, ms 39406-5144

DEADLINE & ENTRY FEE: Deadline is May 30, 1997. Nonrefundable entry fee is $10 per story, limit two stories per author ($20), or $5 per poem, limit four entries per author ($20). Make check/money order payable to Mississippi Review Prize. No ms returned. Contest open to all US writers except students or employees of USM. Previously published or accepted work ineligible.
FORMAT: Fiction--maximum 6500 words (25 pages), typed, double-spaced. Poetry--each entry a single poem no more than ten typewritten pages. Author's name, address, phone, plus story title and "1997 Mississippi Review Prize Entry" should be on page one of entry. Do not send cover sheet.
ANNOUNCEMENTS: Include SASE for list of winners. Winners will be announced November 1, 1997. The Prize Issue will be available to competitors at a reduced rate ($5). Issue scheduled for late fall 1997. These are complete guidelines. AA/EOE/ADA

" Anything incomprehensible has a sexual significance to many people under 35. **"**

— *Zelda Fitzgerald*

" In <u>Anatomy of Criticism</u>, Northrop Frye suggested that over decades and centuries genres go through seasonal cycles, evolving from romance in their spring to comedy in their summer to tragedy and realism in their fall and then to two things in their winter. First, the forms become ironic; they play against their own characters, their own worlds, their own ideas. 'Oh,' one character says to another, 'wouldn't this be great if it happened in a novel!' Self-reflexive preciosity was a marvel when Laurence Sterne did it in <u>Tristram Shandy</u>, but it has become a mental twitch in our 'postmodernist' age. We see it everywhere as characters wink at the camera, tweak their own antecedents, and invite us to laugh both at the present and the past of the worlds of art. This is bitter, although often funny, but it is becoming tedious indeed. Second, Frye suggested, genres return to myth, to the stories that found worlds, that create the very landscapes within which, later, we may find romance, and then comedy, and tragedy. And modern, or even postmodern, myth, it seems to me, need not be tedious. I point to <u>Finnegans Wake</u>. **"**

— *Eric Rabkin*